FARM STEAM SHOWS USA & CANADA

By
Dana
Close Jennings

Drawing by James Pollock

Photos by the author
unless otherwise credited

GB pb

First edition incorporating: Days of Steam and Glory
first edition © 1968

Library of Congress catalog card number 72-89052
Manufactured in the United States of America
All Rights Reserved
First Edition

Second printing 1974

Copyright © 1972 by
NORTH PLAINS PRESS
ABERDEEN, S. DAK.

Steam was King from soon after the Civil War to the First World War, when food demands stimulated the lighter, faster, more nimble gas tractor. During the glory of steam, the Engine Man was King of the farm community, at least during the four to six weeks' threshing. Mothers fearfully warned their daughters against the blandishments of threshermen, whose very prestigiousness made them all the more alluring to farmers' daughters.

Steam and gas battled for another decade, when weight and honored age gave way to speed the noisome youth.

Farm steam has now traversed its obsolescence and is well into its antiquity. Steam hobbyists are today rescuing mountains of rust from swamps and junkyards and putting them into mint condition. Collecting, restoring and running these gentle giants——some topping 30 tons and 60 years——is the fastest-growing farmers' hobby from Pennsylvania to the Pacific.

You, too, can feel your heart leap to power and neighborliness, sniffing the inimitable steam-smoke-oil perfume, itching to the chaff down your sweaty neck, hearing the old sounds and tasting the dust of days long gone: just go to a Steam Show.

This book is the distillation of the knowledge, skill and experience of many people. Thanks go to Palmer Reinicke, farmer, Winfred, S. D., who provided and checked the engine specifications and other technical matters; to George Klinkner, farmer, Artesian, S. D., who with his son Don braved the icy winds of early March to fire up their Case steam traction engine especially for the photos accompanying the steaming-up section; and for Mr. Klinkner's technical help on that section, thanks; to Prof. Joe Habeger, General Beadle State College, Madison, S. D., and president of the Prairie Historical Club, whose encouragement and technical help were invaluable; and to all the club members and officers all over the nation who so generously provided photographs and information to make this book possible.

Particular thanks are due to all the operators who "held that pose" and "did it again" for pictures, and especially to the engineers who, no matter how it hurt them, "made 'er smoke" for photos.

Real steam buffs will travel half across the continent to enjoy a Steam Show somebody says is good, or just to see a rare engine. Some take pictures and some make recordings of the steam engine's powerful sound.

These Steam Days are the biggest days of the year in many a farm-country county seat, pushing the county fair into oblivion.

Clap on your straw hat and join the Fun Crowd!

We'll take you back to the Glory that was Steam.

This is a more frequent scene these days as old steam threshermen——and new ones, too——all across the land resurrect a nearly-forgotten art.

"The threshers are comin'!"

We kids use to lie in the weeds along the road ditch, wiggling our bare toes in the dirt, watching the steam engine come down the road."

Thus recalls Vern Laustsen, Aberdeen, S. D., publisher of THE DAKOTA FARMER and of this and other such notable books as CATTLE ON A THOUSAND HILLS by the same author. Born on a Dakota farm, and though even now his eldest children are only in college, he remembers Thrashing Day well. (Those of Teutonic stock on the Northern Great Plains will remember it as Trashing Day.)

The huge engine, belching smoke to the skies, pulling the threshing machine and maybe a water wagon and coal tender behind that, made a train immense to little eyes whose horizon had been the dirt road before them.

To the engineer, up at three to stoke the fire and get up 125 to 155 pounds of steam, it was a point of pride to reach the next farm in the threshing ring, get the separator leveled, the engine belted up and ready to go before the hot July or August sun burned the dew off the bundles. The kids heard the whistle rolling over the hills with the crack of dawn and ran to watch and wait among the dewy cuckleburs.

Closer, closer the gigantic apparition lumbered at top speed——2.61 mph——shaking the very earth.

"Finally," Vern smiles, "the excitement got too big. One of us bolted through the horse-weeds higher than our heads yelling, 'Ma! Th' thrashers 'r comin'!'"

As if Ma hadn't been up since three herself, peeling potatoes and picking chickens and baking bread and pies to feed the crew, which might total a dozen or two-score ravenous men, depending on the size of the separator to be "kept up in the collar," as we said of hard-working horse, machine or woman.

Dad was up even before Mom, routing out the boys to do the chores, to fetch the mountains of kindling, cobs and water Mom needed to feed the big black cast-iron range where pots of molasses-rich beans, choked with chunks of fat smoked pork and tangy with mustard, catchup and vinegar, had been simmering for three days "to make 'em good."

"That was the most exciting day of the year, bigger even than Christmas," smiles Vern fondly. "More bustle and noise and action than the little kids could remember. We big kids remembered the last Thrashing Day or two and we knew it was a Fun Day——fun for kids, anyway."

Men still remember Thrashing Day as the greatest day of the year, but the women remember mostly the day of the big work, the big sweat and the big sink full of dirty dishes.

"Thrashin' Day made Christmas Day and all the other days possible. It was the threshing machine that put the grain in the bin that put the money in the bank that filled the Christmas stockings and gave another year's grace on the mortgage," so recalls Vern Laustsen.

As the monster approaches, neighbors converge from all directions, some in wagons, some in buggies, some in rattling/gasping Model Ts, for on Thrashing Day everybody helps everybody. Neighbors "trade work" without quibbling about "I only had 20 acres for your 50." Communities formed threshing rings: one farmer with more capital or credit than the rest would invest $2,000 to $2,500 in a steam engine and separator and go from farm to farm to thresh the wheat, the oats, the barley and rye——rarely flax and clover——for 3 cents to 6 cents a bushel. (An equivalent combine today costs $10,000, farmland costs five times as much and grain prices are about the same today as they were then, as are threshing-combining fees.)

The excitement of a steam engine is more than the smallfry can contain. This little fellow streaks around trying to take it all in at once. You'll feel the same way if you ever get bit by the steam bug.

Neighbors help each other pitch, haul and scoop on Thrashing Day, no favors asked, no records kept. It's your way of life.

The men drive teams and flat-bed bundle wagons with a three-tined bundle fork wedged into the rear standard to pitch the bundles from the shock ("stook" farther north and in Canada) to the wagon, from the wagon into the separator. Those lucky farmers with a grain-tight wagon box are asked to haul the grain to the barn and scoop it through high, tiny granary windows while the hens willingly salvage their misses.

Stout wives bring covered dishes of their respective specialities——"tater" salad or graham cracker pie or pickled pigs' feet——and help Ma cook and serve and "red the table" (that's Wisconsin for "Rid the table of dirty dishes").

Were the house a big one, we've put all the leaves into the big round oaken dining table, set up extra tables and chairs in the parlor and on the porch and (as a last resort) in the Sunday parlor.

When the house can't hold the whole crew, we set planks on sawhorses for tables and benches out under the trees. And the woman who offers paper plates or store-bought bread is snickered at forever.

Feeding the threshers is a point of competitive pride among the women, each striving to set the best table. Her man is sure to have more help than he really needs. The farmer whose wife isn't much of a cook has a time rounding up enough reluctant helpers to keep the big machine up in the collar. And the woman who expects neighbors to bring sacked sandwiches——her man might as well sell out and move the lazy wench to town.

The cast iron pump, just outside the kitchen door, is a busy, noisy place as the men troop in from the field at noon, dust and sweat mortaring chaff to their faces, arms and across the wet backs of their faded blue shirts. More planks set up in the shade carry tin basins or tubs and soap and worn-out towels, saved just for Thrashin' Day to keep axle grease off the good ones. Scorning hot water to cut the chill of the well, the thrashers "dipper" fresh well water out of buckets, sloshing it on their faces, over their necks and behind their ears, rubbing hard, blowing and sputtering through the suds and making a great shower on the grass (a good reason, in the womenfolks' view, for setting the wash-up outdoors), rasping horny hands together to get the worst of the grease off. After all, a fella don't have to get too clean, just to eat, tain't like goin' to church.

The warm smells tantalizing dusty noses are myriad: the aroma of roasting meat and baking pies, the yeasty aura of bread hot in the oven plus the sharp vinegar tang of any pickles, relishes or other spicy stuff the cook might have taken a notion to fix at the last moment.

Just as fine perfume is based on odoriferous musk, so the fragrances of Thrashing Day Dinner play against a background bouquet common to all farmhouses of the day: an exhalation of kerosene for the lamps, soaked into the floors and boiled out by the heat. Second only to the coal oil is the aroma of sour milk which, again, emanates from the woodwork, mingling with wood smoke, some wisps of which escape the cookstove every time someone lifts a lid to poke in another stick. Then there's the essence of honest sweat and the barnyard scents tracked in on boots, plus the perfumes of thousands of feasty family meals.

Such a pungent mix, spelled out on paper, lacks the heart-string yank of the real thing——but to all noses that ever lived it, it was incense bespeaking shelter from the storms of weather and of life, where there was always hot food for the body and warm nutriment for the soul.

These old-time farmhouse smells compounded the cozy balm of home.

Threshing took, besides the engine crew, a separator man, bundle haulers and pitchers, grain, coal and water haulers. Field is now a residential area.

Spikers pitched bundles from shock (sometimes called stook) to 2-HP wagon. This farmer is cheating——he replaced his old iron-tired wooden wagon wheels with auto wheels.

Contents

C. 1

Dedicated

to Dad and Mom
whose lives have spanned
horse & buggy — gas buggy
horse power — horsepower
ox — jet
cookwood — atomic fuel
Great American Desert — men on the moon
steam traction engine — steam-turbine tractor!

HOW STEAM SHOWS START: Farmers and retired farmers around Madison, S. D., decided they'd like to have a steam threshing bee but they didn't have an engine. They borrowed Adolph Rude and his 40-HP Case steam traction engine from Flandreau, S. D., and staged a one-engine show in 1963, their first annual Steam Threshing Jamboree. That was the little beginning of one of many marvelous success stories related in this volume. "I could have bought 'er for $500 three years ago," Rude ruefully told me in 1963. "But I thought the price was too high. So I waited for the price to go down. The next year it was a thousand bucks. I finally got 'er for $1,500, the price of 'er when she was new 60 years ago."

Introduction

If your nerves have not tingled to the smell of steam and hot cylinder oil——if your blood has not raced with the rhythmic chuff-chuff of a steam traction engine under load——you have not fully lived. But cheers!

You yet may live.

These nearly-forgotten sensual delights can now be yours at any of the many steam threshing jamborees up and down our land where old settlers meet, old threshermen thresh, and the shout still echoes across the land:

"Hold Your Horses!"

...and the steam whistle splits the dewy dawn.

Each summer, even in these space-age times of ours, old-time steam threshing bees attract increasing thousands of spectators. Old-timers thrill again to throbbing steel under their feet——to the bite and rustle of the grain as they cut the bundle-bands and hand-feed an ancient threshing machine. Youngsters thrill to purposeful uproar, seeing how their grandfathers worked and lived. Grandmothers brag to their daughters-in-law of the great threshing-day feast they prepared over the roaring, smoking, cob-burning range in the stifling oil-lit kitchen.

A century ago our forefathers ate by the sweat of mule and man and horse. Then steam left the rails and marched across the fields; the first relief human and bestial muscles had gotten since man first poked seed into stubborn soil. Steam sparked and powered the Agricultural Revolution for more than half a century until the clanking, stinking gas engine displaced it.

The Thrasherman's Dinner was always the same yet different: huge beef-roasts done brown plumb to the bone; platters of fried chickens, crisp and golden, that had trumpeted up this very dawn; snowy mashed potato mountains cratering lakes of home-churned butter without any artificial color in it, and more bowls of the same golden stuff heaping around; boats of rich brown beef and chicken-giblet gravy; platters of home-baked bread, still hot, and of steaming home-smoked ham; great brown earthenware crocks of much-baked beans lumpy with real pork.

Then there were all the trimmin's: home-made pickles——watermelon, dill, mustard, onion, tomato; home-made fruit jams and jellies of wild plums, cherries, gooseberries, elderberries, grapes, whatever the woods and fields afforded. Fresh green onions and "reddishes" and leaf lettuce pulled from the garden by the door while the dew was still on them, along with tomatoes picked this very morn and kept cool in wooden tubs of chill well water or lowered into the springhouse, were the farm lucky enough to have such; deviled eggs picked yesterday and still warm from the stove; huge blue granite pots of brawny coffee; cream thick enough to cut.

And it's a lazy woman who doesn't offer for dessert apple, raisin, pumpkin, peach, cherry and mince pie, all hot. If she has a bit of humor in her, she'll put out at least one vinegar pie.

"Everything on the table come from our own place," invariably brags Dad, "'cept th' coffee, sugar, salt 'n pepper——'n Ma's eggs bought them!"

Dad, host, wastes no foolishness on a roast-carving ceremony. Hungry thrashers can't sit still for frills. The wise cook plops the roasts on the table torn to chunks ready to pile into, swimming in their juices in the big platter her granma brought over from the Old Country. Dad's job is mostly to keep things running——to show the separator man where he wants the strawpile, to show the grain haulers which bins to scoop into and to make sure there's hay and oats and water for all the neighbors' horses. He takes his turn pitching bundles, just to prove he isn't trying to get out of work, then scurries about other errands relative to supplying the engine with 2,000 or so gallons of soft water it will puff away today, plus the 1,500 or more pounds of coal.

Occasionally he stops long enough to peer up at the lordly separatorman, high atop his mechanical kingdom, sceptered with a long-spouted pump oil can, to ask, "How's she turnin' out, Emil?" and to grin at Emil's estimate of "a good thirty bushel."

One of the few remaining steam rings in the Red River Valley is on the S. A. Roen farm, 2½ miles from Comstock, Minn., along the Red River. Photo taken August, 1946.

"Dig in, boys. We ain't elegant," says Dad.

"Root, hog, or die," someone says ritually, licking his fork and spearing another drumstick.

"Fingers wuz made before forks," another inevitably says, tearing at a gold-dripping second joint.

Then there's not much sound for the first round except the clank of eatin' tools on thick china, earnest chomping, slurping tasty fingers and the murmured "pass the biscuits, Sam," and "say, Jake, chase some chicken up to this end, will you?" and "Oscar, slip the brakes on that-there roast beef."

After appetite's sharp edge dulls against seconds, the pace relaxes and conversation picks up.

"Feelin' better ev'ry minnit!"

"Man, is it hot!"

"You don't need a fire (this to the engineer) t'day. Jest open th' firebox door and let the wind blow through them tubes."

"By gum, it's so dry we hafta soak th' hogs over night before they'll hold swill."

"You think it's dry here? Got a letter frum m' sister in Kansas 'n th' stamp wuz **pinned** on!"

"You can count on a steam enjine. Yon Yonsen couldn't even git his gas tractor started. His missus is feedin' th' hull durn crew 'n not a bundle thrashed yit."

Someone is sure to recall the hapless neighbor's unfortunate wife in a Catholic community who, expecting threshers on Thursday, stocked up on beef roasts. That new-fangled gas tractor contraption stripped its bull gear, delayed the crew a day. She had to throw out all that good beef and buy fish.

After seconds, the women, damp from the cookstove's blast (belying the prissy dictum that a horse sweats, a man perspires but a woman only glows), pressed thirds upon the men: "Here, Hiram, have some more taters 'n giblet gravy. More chicken? Lan' sakes, Ole, you et like a bird."

"Ya, yoost a peck at a time," agrees Ole.

"Et so much makes him poor t' carry it," volunteers his best friend.

"I've got another pie in the kitchen," says Ma. "I'll cut it if anybody wants some."

This is a risky maneuver, especially if she's so unfortunate as to say it backwards: "I won't cut it if nobody don't want none." She thereby leaves herself wide open to behind-the-barn accusations of not wanting to put out more pie, and the tale will inevitably be told of the woman who, by this dodge, made one pie last all summer.

The sandwich stand you find at threshing shows falls far short of Mom's old-time thresher dinners, the Old-Timers assure you.

A return-flue engine, web stacker and Gay 90's-type bike mark this photo as a real oldy.

Old steel-wheel Hart-Parr tractor denotes early replacement of teams on bundle wagons ("Tractors ain't burnin' up hay while they're settin' still!") soon after they replaced the steamer on the belt.

As the sun sank, bundles began to soak up atmospheric moisture and get too tough to thresh. Farmers had to quit and do chores anyway.

Picture is unidentified.

Boys big enough work with the men——scampering off to fetch a
wrench, fill the burlap-soaked water jug, minding the water or the
horses or the fire, breaking coal, even driving teams and pitching
bundles. By virtue of this apprenticeship they get to eat with the
men. The women and girls eat after the men but their pain is not
too extreme; they've been tasting and snitching all morning. The vast
reservoir of human misery lies in the tummies of the smallfry, who in
this era before babysitters are ordered only to "keep out from under
foot, now," and must wait for second table.

Following dinner there's a brief pause for rest, neighborin' and slurping toothpicks. (On the farm, even today, you eat dinner at noon.
Supper comes in the cool of early dark, after chores. Lunch is that
little snack of meat sandwiches, pie and coffee the women fetch to
the field in mid-morning and mid-afternoon to pry your belt buckle
loose from your backbone and to take the rubber out of your knees
[lunch is not seen so much any more, now that the farmer is reduced to manager-machine operator]).

It took two wagons and four men pitching together to keep a big steam outfit up "in the collar."

As one child of these sweaty days recalls, "My folks raised and edu-
cated six kids on 160 acres, but I was 22½ years old before I knew
Grace ended with just 'Amen' instead of with 'Amen-hitch-up-boys!'!"

One such meal a year was the average farm wife's obligation, beside
helping all those neighbor women who helped her, for the average
farm was threshed in a day, barring breakdown. Such a crew could
clean up two little farms in a can-see-to can't-see day. It was the rare
farm that had enough grain to keep the separator busy a second day.
Of course, the big western wheat ranches owned their own equipment,
hired their own crews.

Come choretime, the neighbors rattle home to milk their own cows
by lanternlight, since you can't thrash after the straw toughens with
evening moisture anyway. The engineman, who must be belted up
again in the morning on another farm as soon as the dew is off, rolls
in a blanket under the water wagon, sung to sleep by the engine's
soft sighing to itself as little wisps of smoke and fugitive steam escape
into the warm night. If he has some crew of his own, they sleep in
the bright golden strawpile or in the hay loft over bins full of yellow
grain promising another year's grace against "The Mor'gije." The pasture is
full of tired horses. The beds are full of exhausted men, women and
children. The hogpen is full of fat swine full of the most gorgeous heap of
garbage within living pig memory.

*Lining up the belt separated the men from the boys when it came to
running a steam engine. You couldn't have the wind blowing chaff
back on you so you tried to set windstacker downwind. When wind
switched, you had to change the set to another direction. When you
had to thresh in a strong crosswind, the engine might have to be two
feet out of line to keep the 150-foot belt on. The belt looks dangerous, but I never heard of anybody tangling with it.*

16

"We buy junk, sell antiques"

That's a sign in the Kissin' Cousin Candy store between Madison, S. D., and Prairie Village.

Just when does a hunk of obsolete junk become a valuable classic?

Apparently, with steam engines, this subtle but important psychological change occurred during WW. II. Junked engines became valuable. In the '40's old-time threshermen began to rescue them from swamps and junkpiles and lovingly to restore them. Perhaps so many got broken up during wartime scrap drives, people were shocked into realizing here was a precious bit of our recent past that would soon be irrevocably lost if Somebody Didn't Do Something.

Besides that, once a steam man, always a steam man. There's another subtle difference between playing around with an old-fashioned, obsolete machine——and keeping alive an ancient and noble skill.

Thus steam threshing was reborn as individual farmers, just for nostalgic kicks, fired up their old engines, invited the neighbors to help, and were amazed at the crowd of city people and reporters attracted by the smoke and din.

Unidentified

Good old Yankee enterprise suggested charging a dollar admission.

AMERICAN DINOSAURS

It may come as a surprise to many, that the traction engines seen here today are very popular in England. The English have attached the most appropriate name "Dinosaurs" to their tractors. They do not have the machines work, as in this country, but enter them in "Rallies." Here they are displayed in the Concourse d'Elegance for judging, slalom races around oil drums, tug of war and other playful events. It is very much a sporting and dress-up affair, as contrasted with American Thresherees which are work shows. Except for the parades where the tractors can strut their stuff, it's a big day of work for the American "Dinosaurs."

—*From Rock River Thresheree Assn. program book.*

There's a show wherever you go

Up and down and across America you'll find these steam shows, threshing bees, etc., going on just about every day from May to October with an astonishing array of ancient equipment, all of it working like new. You'll find clubs from New York to California, rescuing and rejuvenating not only steam engines but early gas tractors, barrel engines, cars, farm implements, airplanes and early-day home and farm gadgetry.

You could leave home in May and cross the country clear into Fall and hit a steam show somewhere in every area. In many farm counties the annual steam threshing bee outdraws the county fair and becomes the biggest event——in terms of participants, spectators and tonnage of equipment——of the year.

Big daily feature of every show you find will be the parade. All machines have been restored to working order, many repainted in original reds, greens and gold.

*Kings

*Sycamore

New Lenox *

*Pinckneyville

Illinois

THE AMERICAN THRESHERMAN ASSOCIATION
Pinckneyville, Ill.
3rd weekend in August

"We are especially proud of our 18-HP Peerless steam engine and a 12-bottom John Deere steam engine plow that we plow with each year," says George F. Bahre, secretary-treasurer. "We are very proud of the fact that we are known as the 'action show of the midwest.' All machinery is in action daily.

"We sponsor a large and popular tractor-pulling contest, and one of the largest antique auto shows in the country. Our latest acquisition is a 350-HP Hamilton-Corliss steam engine from a flour mill."

Pointing out that since the pre-WWI Winnipeg tractor demonstrations, farmers have not been able to see the tractor's primary function—its pulling power—measured, the ATA fills this gap with its strictly-conducted tractor-pulling demonstration.

Fifteen farmers and businessmen got together in 1959 at Brownstown, Ill., and decided to stage a steam power show "for the enjoyment, entertainment and education of anyone who wished to take part."

The American Thresherman Association show was held at Highland, Ill., in 1960 and '61, then moved to Pinckneyville, Ill., to the grove-shaded, century-old fairgrounds. The 4-day show draws an average of 18,000 spectators.

Honorary chairman is D. R. Bartimus, Beecher City, Ill. President is Paul Wagner, Willisville, Ill.

1880 Sterling hand-fed, web-stacked separator. Emil Steinheimer, owner.

Double-cylinder Keck-Gonnerman on a veneering machine.

Maybe We Gave Up Too Quick on the Steam Engine

Steam engine development was just getting started when gas took over. Steam may yet have as glorious a future as its past, opines Amos Rixmann, past president ATA, Oklahoma City. Writing in the 1962 ATA program book, he says of the steam engine:

Everett Pyle demonstrates shingle mill. Photos by Kennedy Studio

"Never developed to the fullest extent, it could well have been the sole, or nearly sole, power used today! . . . .Yet the potential of the reciprocating steam engine design has never been developed beyond its infancy! For example, there is a new design 3-cyl. steam engine under test with only 267 cu. in. displacement, yet it develops 300 HP at only 1,000 RPM! . . . developed the same number of horsepower-hours per gallon of fuel as the best diesels of today. The future of newer and small atomic power plants may yet see our forgotten age of steam return in a new dress.

"The versatility and performance of steam has not yet been duplicated in industry or transportation. So it may well be that this monster which can stand silent, but ready to put forth full power in an instant in either direction, may return to serve us far better than we have yet been served."

Keck-Gonnerman 20-HP threshing.

Dee Quick 20-HP Keck-Gonnerman engine on sawmill.

36x62 Belle-ville separa-tor. Ollie Kneppe, owner.

20-HP Jum-bo on a 36x62 Belle-ville separa-tor.

NORTH CENTRAL ILLINOIS STEAM POWER SHOW
at the King farm
Kings, Ill.
2nd weekend in August
(Hedtke's Steam Power & Horse Power Threshing Show)

12-horse Case sweep was built in 1889, is fully restored in its original colors. Threshes with hand-fed Case Agitator, equipped with slat stacker and bagger.

You'll see things you maybe thought didn't exist any more: like threshing with an 1889 Case 12-horse sweep and Agitator thresher, horse plowing, etc. The sweep is fully restored and is thought to be the only one refurbished in its original colors.

Here you can see more than 130 pieces of old farm equipment. Eight draft teams demonstrate horse-farming operations. You'll see grain threshed by steam power, too, and a 65-piece parade each of the four days. Also demonstrated are the largest Case threshing outfit in existence

and the largest Avery gas threshing outfit ever built.

In daily operation are a sawmill, shingle mill, corn mill, baler and Baker fans. Here are shade, plenty of parking, floodlighted grounds. Meals are served continuously and there's entertainment every evening.

George Hedtke, Davis Junction, Ill., held his first steam threshing show in 1957. As his collection grew, so did popular interest. He joined another group the following year and, due to mounting interest in Ogle County, he formed a new corporation with Emil Svanda and J. Floyd King—the North Central Illinois Steam Power Show, Inc.

"Our aim is to promote and sponsor a steam and horse power threshing show annually and to preserve agricultural history and heritage for future generations and to provide ancient demonstrations for your entertainment and education."

Kings is 20 miles southwest of Rockford, Ill., and 80 miles west of Chicago on Highway 64.

Threshing with 1911 32–110 Case and 42x70 Avery Yellow Fellow.

This you don't see much any more: 5-horse team on a 2-bottom sulky plow.

Plowing with the 1911 32–110 Case.

You'll also see a sawmill sawing at the King farm.

50-HP Case; right, 110-HP Case.

25

NORTHERN ILLINOIS STEAM POWER CLUB
Taylor Marshall Farm
Sycamore, Ill.
2nd weekend in August

Northern Illinois Steam Power Club Photos

Club members bind and shock 30 to 40 acres of oats to feed the several threshing rigs during the 4-day show.

30—90 Russell pulling 8-bottom John Deere plow. Engine owners are LeRoy Levine and Chuck Raymond, DeKalb, Ill. Plow is owned by Ed Schmidgell, Tiskilwa, Ill.

In 1954, Chuck and Roy Levine bought a 24-HP Greyhound Banting steam engine. They ran it in the DeKalb centennial parade two years later, which set a lot of steam nerves to itching and resulted in the club's formation the following February. Rupert Jordan, who has always been interested in steam power, was elected president.

The show is held Thursday through Sunday of the second weekend each August, 50 miles west of Chicago.

Demonstrations include, besides threshing, the Flink fan, designed and built for testing engines by Gene Flink, Sycamore, especially for the club. They bale straw with a stationary wire-tie baler and a new modern baler. A sawmill goes full tilt. Hobbies and other steam and gas equipment are displayed and operated. Sunday features outdoor church services with sacred music.

Some of the equipment includes a 90-year-old Westinghouse portable steam engine, 1872 Westinghouse thresher, 1900 stationary sandwich baler with egg-shaped gears, a McCormick shocking machine, bullpower treadmill, potato marker, 13 steam traction engines and more gas tractors and engines than you can count.

Showing growth each year, the show features steam threshing, sawing, plowing, grinding, well drilling, shelling, a daily parade, contests, teeter-totter and ladies' hobby fair and antique show. The 220-plus members also stage an annual picnic and Christmas party.

Equipment includes nine steamers, over 25 gas tractors, many small engines, nearly 30 antique cars, five threshers, sawmill, fans, teeter-totter, well drill and much horse-drawn equipment.

The Will County Threshermen is an outgrowth of the Manhattan Threshers Show started by Ray Kestel and son Kenneth with the help of neighbors.

After three years the Will County Threshermen's Association organized February 15, 1966, electing Ray Kestel president, Harlan Nicholson, vice-president, Herman Christiansen, secretary and Gary Fellows, treasurer.

GO tractor was made by General Ordnance, features friction drive. This is a 1919 14—28. Only one other is known to exist.

WILL COUNTY THRESHERMEN'S ASSOCIATION
Francis 4-H Field
New Lenox, Ill.
Th-Sun, First week in August

"Very rare" 1909 International 1-cylinder owned by Ariel Lee, Morris, Ill.

1925 Rumely 20—40 Oil-Pull balanced on teetertotter by Gordon Ferguson, Morris, Ill.

Ray Kestel's 1929 Keck No. 1868 19—65 HP. Only 4 or 5 were made after this one, Kestel believes.

*Ft. Wayne

*Indianapolis

Indiana

Crowds at the Old Time show are attracted to 40-HP Case owned by Eiffel Plaster, Huntington, Ind.——Photo courtesy Jim Whitbey

The steamer with the fringe on top is a 1913 M. Rumely 20-HP, 10x10¼, 12 tons, Gould balance valve. Cost new about $2,000.——Whitbey

"They're a different-looking engine without the canopy," enginemen tell you, and you have to agree. Ralph Lindsay, Los Angeles, owns this 50-HP Case pulling a 36-60 Minneapolis separator in the Old Time parade.——Leo Clark Photo

1915 18-HP Advance-Rumely owned by Jim Whitbey pulling 8-bottom plow.——Photo by Earnest Hoffer, Toledo, Ohio

THE OLD TIME THRESHERS AND SAW MILL OPERATORS ASS'N., INC. FT. WAYNE, IND.

This Indiana group started in 1951, reports Mrs. J. H. Whitbey, Ft. Wayne, Ind., when her husband, a retired railroad engineer, bought a 1913 Rumely 20-HP steam traction engine and a Baker threshing machine and put them into running order. He and F. W. Bloom, Churubusco, Ind., who had a 5-HP working model steam engine and threshing machine he'd made, put on a demonstration in Whitbey's wheat field along the road.

Jay Gould, noted farm director, WOWO, Ft. Wayne, announced it and, much to the Whitbey-Bloom surprise, produced a throng.

The third show brought 12 big engines, some small ones, four threshing machines, sawmill, Prony brake. "The show has grown now to include everything——not only 20 large steam engines and models, large and small, but Baker fans, gas engines, tractors, antique cars and farm machinery, steam plowing, veneer machine, teeter-totter, incline, threshing, corn husking and corn shelling," reports Mrs. Whitbey.

There's always plenty going on at Old Time. Typical scene shows two threshers.-Leo R. Clark Photo

29

Left: Game of steam chicken. Jack Egbert, Botkins, O., shows his hill-climbing skill with his 12-HP Frick. Both engines had to back down.—Clark

Hill-climbing takes a knowledgeable engineer like Woodmansee, too. Explains Whitbey, "The engineer must keep his engine straight so it won't go sideways. He must give his engine the right amount of steam so she won't r'ar up." 12-HP Case.—Old Time Photo

It takes rare skill to balance a steam engine on the teetertotter bearing on a log. Explains Whitbey, "The difficulty is the swinging of water in the boiler and the old, worn gearing. The gears on these old engines never was too tight." This is his 1915 18-HP Advance-Rumely 9½x10¼ with Marsh valve gear. Engineer is Harry Woodmansee, Dowling, Mich.—News-Sentinel

Right: Advance-Rumely just plays with modern tractor plow. Charles Barker & Wickie Jones, Lexington, Ky., at the controls.—Clay

Even gas gets in. This is Dean and Shey Bonnell's 35–70 Minneapolis. Bell was not original equipment.—Clark

Ken Lewis and his 20-HP Nichols & Shepard from Jackson, Mich.—OT

Jim Whitbey's 20-HP M. Rumely, 1913, with 10-inch bore and 10¼-inch stroke and a Gould balanced valve.—Hoffer

Very rare De June 12-HP was built between 1850 and 1870. Operates at 100 pounds.—OT

This groundhog thresher attached to fanning mill and straw walker was built in the 19th century.—OT

Jim and Mrs. Whitbey started it all with his 1913 M. Rumely. Granddaughter Dana Jo Clark is all grown up now. —OT

A Mr. Baker, Butler, Ind., brought his matched mules on the water wagon. —OT

LeRoy Blaker's 24-HP Port Huron Longfellow shows off on the Prony brake. —OT

Frank Miller pulls the Case No. 25 with his 80-HP Case. —OT

Rolland Maxwell with his Robert L. George steam engine and hand-fed web-stacked Ellis Keystone separator. —OT

Jim's proud of this Gaar-Scott Rumely double-cylinder 25-HP 1916 engine. Works at 175 pounds; 7x11 bore and stroke. Stevenson valve gear. With its 9/16 boiler plate and 6-inch gearing, it weighs about 18 tons.—OT

1870 Case No. 25 8-HP pumped water originally for Angola, Ind. Ted and Earl Brindle, LaOtto, Ind.—OT

R. W. Lindsay's 1919 50-HP Case flexes its 9x10 muscles on one of 4 Baker fans.—OT

Double-cylinder Napoleon No. 112, 16-HP, was built in Napoleon, O. Scene near Hamler, O., 1910.—OT

Case 60-HP 1911 with early 1900 tiller. Arthur Lucas, Clermont, Ind., owner.——Photo supplied by John J. Menchhofer, Indianapolis, Ind.

THE PIONEER ENGINEER CLUB OF INDIANA
Indianapolis
August

This was organized in 1948 with five men and one steam engine, a 50-HP Case. "Now our membership amounts to about 500 paid-up members from every state in the union including Hawaii and Alaska and Canada, France and England," reports John J. Menchhofer, sec.-treas., Indianapolis, Ind.

Today, he says, "We have about 25 large engines such as the New Huber, Case, Advance Rumely, Keck Gonnerman, Russell, Peerless, Minneapolis, Baker, Nichols & Sheppard. We have an 1876 wooden hand-fed Farquar separator, hand-sacked and web-stacked." Members own such gems as a 1900 wooden Case 36-inch separator, all kinds and makes of stationary gasoline engines, all kinds of model engines, separators and sawmills.

"We exhibit an old steam peanut and popcorn machine and an old hurdy-gurdy hand organ. Every year we have a 3-day show in August."

5-HP model Case engine operated matching sawmill at the Pioneer Engineers show.——Menchhofer

Model Case cranks out 5 HP, big Case, 50. The 1924 steamer is owned by Dr. Russell Holmes, Louisville, Ky.——Menchhofer.

John J. Menchhofer, secretary-treasurer, Pioneer Engineers Club, Indianapolis, poses by a 1925 18-HP New Huber return flue owned by Roy Tempest, North Vernon, Ind.——Menchhofer

Greatest Steam Show on Earth

MIDWEST OLD SETTLERS & THRESHERS ASSOCIATION, INC.

McMillan Park
Mt. Pleasant, Iowa

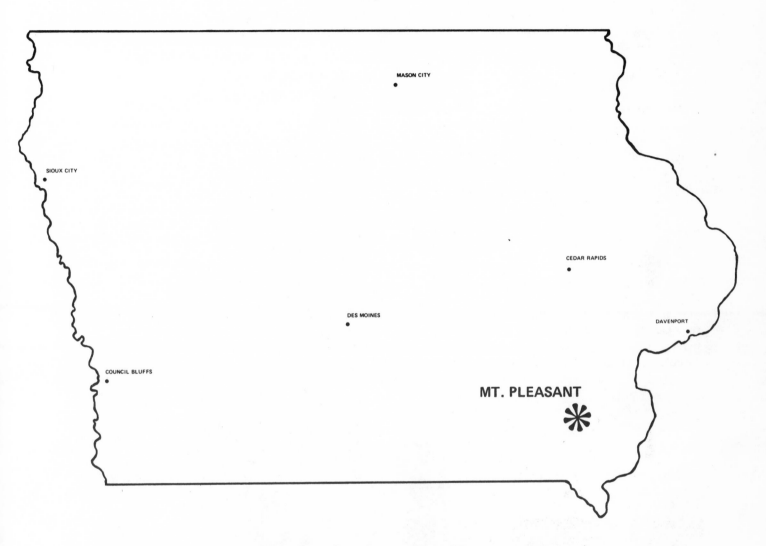

MASON CITY

SIOUX CITY

CEDAR RAPIDS

DES MOINES

DAVENPORT

COUNCIL BLUFFS

MT. PLEASANT

Open Memorial Day through Labor Day
Big Show starts Thursday before each Labor Day,
runs through Labor Day

When nearly a quarter-million people from practically every state and many nations visit a little farmers' town of 9,000 during five Fall days, you've got something.

You've got THE GREATEST STEAM SHOW ON EARTH. Here is the biggest conglomeration of ancient steam traction engines, early gas tractors, classic automobiles, old-time steam trains and pioneer artifacts you'll find anywhere.

And they're all operating—all but one: The Sheriff (or was it the Revenooers) discombobulated the old copper still that used to make a mighty high-octane White Lightnin'. More about this later.

As you approach Mt. Pleasant in southeastern Iowa on a show day, you'll think the whole world is afire by the smoke billowing across town. You won't have to ask where McMillan Park is at. Just head upwind and you'll find it on the south edge of town.

Ever since I'd been interested in steam shows, I'd heard about Mt. Pleasant as the biggest and best. As I worked my way East from show to show, the closer I got the more I heard about it, the louder the praise.

I found out people weren't woofing.

But when you get there, remember where you park your car. I was so excited by the spectacle (and I've been to more steam shows than most), I dashed away like a kid turned loose from school, plumb forgetting where I parked. Took me an hour to find my bolt-bucket. And

Russell 12-HP 1914 steam engine with 7½-inch bore x 10-inch stroke, running at 230 RPM and 100 pounds, drives ancient hand-fed, web-stacked "chaff piler." Owned by Ray H. Ernst, Wayland, Ia.––A. M. Wettach photo

Wood 1914. 22 HP @ 250 RPM, 150 pound pressure. Ted Cress, Wolcott, Ia.--AMW

it was smack-dab in the shadow of the railroad water tower that I could have seen from anywhere on the grounds if I'd but noticed.

Where to start taking in the sights is your big problem. This is a 1,001-ring circus with everything going on all at once: steam threshing, steam sawing, threshing with horse sweep power, two genuine narrow-gauge steam locomotives, an early-day village with a rootin'-tootin' saloon complete with blue-gartered dancin' gals and the best sweet cider this side of Mt. Olympus and a church that really works.

With just a little effort, you can get caught in the surprise holdup that occurs every afternoon precisely at 3:30 when the depot gets robbed by a pack of pistol-packin' varmints. The Sheriff never gets there in time except to see that they went thataway and to fire one scattergun load after 'em to make sure they don't come thisaway.

He's a pretty efficient sheriff. I hadn't been in town half an hour before he threw me in jail with a stiff and a black bachelor spider. And I hadn't done nothin' hardly.

Every morning's show starts with invocation. Then there's a songfest in the schoolhouse, followed by Monday Morning On the Farm where you see the wash washed by elbow-grease and handmade soap while somebody makes more lye soap in the lard kittle. Visit the schoolhouse and study Grandma's lessons. Sing hymns in church to the melodies of a foot-pumped reed organ.

The Village Band plays at The Bandstand, drowning out the steam whistles. Old-Time Fiddlers fiddle, checker tournaments are won and lost, folks sing folksongs and watch Chautauqua Chalk Talks.

Eat a whoppin' threshermen's dinner in one of the nine chow tents operated by local churches. You can diet at home. The Cavalcade of Power chugs past the grandstand with more steam and gas engines than you thought possible (over 100 of each).

Note power steering detail.

Let's Just Walk Around, First

Opposite page: One of the biggest engines at Mt. Pleasant is 1913 Case 110-HP one-cylinder simple (left) that plowed Dakota wheatland with 14 14-inch bottoms. Drivers are 3 feet wide, 7 feet high. 12x12 cylinder, Woolfe valve gears drove unit 2½ MPH @ 250 RPM and 160 pounds. J. J. Hengtgen, La Motte, Ia.—AMW

Below: Double your trouble with identical twin 18-HP Averys, or is it Averies? Cast-iron bulldog trademark on smokebox cover growls TEETH TALK.—AMW

Above: Biggest engine on the grounds is the 1913 Avery 40-120 HP, the largest the company ever made. Designated a locomotive undermount type, it weighs 25 tons all dried out. C. R. Willits & Son, Mt. Pleasant, brought it from Oklahoma where it powered a sawmill. A double simple with Springer valve gear and 7x10 cylinders, its two gears give it 1¾ and 2½ MPH at 250 RPM and 200 pounds WP.

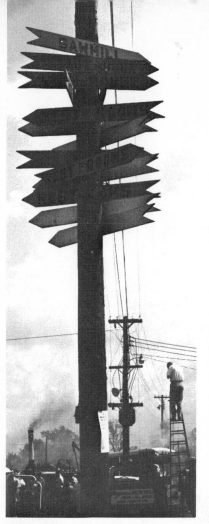

No need to get lost. Just watch world's busiest signpole:
sawmill
train
rest rooms
cars

Lessee, now, where's the———?

Did you ever see so many steam engines?

Model merry-go-round really goes, entrances all ages.

Happy little face tells big, happy story.——AMW

Below: Better get there early if you're camping. Old Settlers buy another farm every year to make room, but still the 1,200 plus campers overfill the spaces. At last count, 95 private planes checked in at the Mt. Pleasant airport, too.——Old Settlers

Drop in at Headquarters tent and buy a membership and watch the hard-working ladies at work keeping records, relaying messages, paging——"Will the owner of a '69 blue Spitball Eight please go there." Note the REACT boys on the two-way citizens band radio, and the sheriff and his pals helping children find their frightened, lost parents. When your feet get tired, hop on the Ground Train guaranteed not to hop the track.

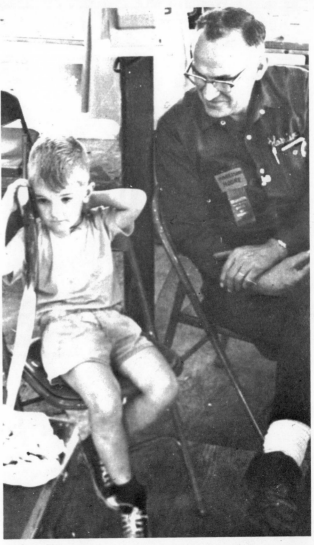

Watch sorghum molasses being made. Leaves are carefully stripped from stalks by hand; stalks are crushed; greenish watery syrup is boiled down over wood fire to thicken brown savory molasses. Ten gallons juice make one gallon goodies. Old Settlers recipe is a carefully-guarded secret.

Sweetness & Smoke

At 5 PM you can attend vespers in the church (worship services Sunday morning).

You'll find the Salem Kitchen Band in the schoolhouse after supper, and there's a real old-time traveling tent show (the only one left) every night. Watch a pageant of pioneer life—"We Didn't Make it Easy" by Mrs. Helen Virden, Mt. Pleasant. There's an all-day cooking school in the Ladies Auxiliary tent.

You'll see golden wedding observances. Memorial services. The Gaytones, National Queens of Harmony. Spell down a line of young whippersnappers. Hear the Beauty Parlor Quartet (ladies' barbershop). School bands. Drill team. Antique sale. Horseshoe match. Gospel team. Dixieland showboat. Pioneer newspaper shop. Western music. Square dancing.

Take 14 or 16 hours to sort of case the joint and get an idea what's here. Then spend the other five days zeroing-in on the activities that entrance you the most.

Old Settlers and Threshers isn't the oldest steam show, but nobody argues—it's the biggest and best.

Three Old Mills Working for You

You can watch corn meal and wheat flour being ground by steam power at Old Settlers for your cornpone and biscuits—and you can watch the 'lasses being boiled to go on 'em—and you can buy the meal, the flour and the sweetnin' in the Country Store right there on the grounds. The burr mill came from Argyle, Iowa, where it was used from about 1890 to 1900. Lyle Shellabarger restored the mill. Meal was a staple for pioneer folks, and some kind of sweetening a must. Most settlers had a sorghum cane patch, called sugarbush, near their cabins, or marked bee trees for their very own honey. The "Honey War" was fought over bee trees along the Des Moines River. Old "receipts" for filtering, clarifying and storing sorghum are guarded like national secrets. It's a matter of taste and skill whether your molasses comes out like blackstrap or a clear, thinner amber delight. Some sorghum-makers judge the syrup's readiness by the bubbles in the bottom of the pan—whether they're dime or dollar size, or fifteen cents. Powering the corn mill is an 1885 Nichols & Shepard 6-HP operating at 85 lb. WP with single simple 6x9 cylinder. Owner is Ray H. Ernst. Bill Sater, left, Old Settlers president, is manning the mill.

Pick up free shingles from the shingle mill, handy for whoppin' the kids.—AMW

Happiness is a

Old Settlers feature one of the few steam merry-go-rounds left: a Herschell-Spillman, made in the '80s in Tonawanda, N. Y., an 8-HP twin-cylinder simple with upright boiler. Everybody's forgotten bore, stroke and all those vital statistics.

You have to have a classical education to set 'er up because the 365 pieces are coded in Roman numerals—and owner-operator Guy C. Miller, Ames, Iowa, does very well.

A military bandorgan makes music by air-and-vacuum through a punched paper roll like a player piano's.

happiness IS a steam merry-go-round!

. . .and the chance to get out . . . and get under . . . and fix the cable drive!

Steam Merry-Go-Round

. . . and riding the ponies. . .

. . . and listening to the bandorgan. . .

We don't need to worry about the breed dying out as long as sharp youngsters like these are learning the business with their huge enthusiasm.

You Meet the Most

If you're young, tired and charming you can always bum a ride.

Young Miss Hoopskirt gives Old Settlers the ol' thumbs-up!

Sister-sister outfits are always fun.

So are mother-daughter costumes.

Wandering hostesses delight the eye.

Woops! my dear.

nteresting People

President Bill Sater keeps in touch with his far-ranging chairman by walking-talking radio.

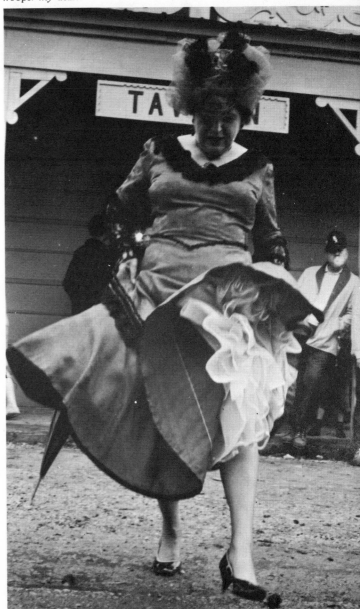

Step
Right
Up
Folks...

Ol' Doc Mots will cure you of everything you got and lots you ain't. His nimble assistant, Honeylips Hult, barks a clutch of porkypine eggs, in case if you're all outta cuckleburrs at home.

50

Moviemaker borrows REA cherry picker. I was stuck up there in that thing myself during the wedding, is howcome no wedding pictures.

Get hot fried bread made by real live Fox and Sac Indians from Tama.

Even the dogs are fascinated by it all.

Ye Midwest Threshers Fife & Drum Corps hugely entertain huge crowds.

Art Meads lives in Illinois.

Four drums don't drown out Tom Scepter's one fife. He's from Marengo, Ia.

Bill Kines, Richland, Ia., plays a century-old drum that fought in the Civil War.

Pop Parrell comes from Kahoka, Mo. All the boys were well past their three and ten.

Bill Lutz, Monmouth, Ill.

52

Antiques

Drop in on the Old Fiddlers.

Above: There's a whole building full of old antiques, and some young folks, too!

Left: You might even be lucky enough to run across this 1869 fan. No, it's not electric. It's driven by a candle in its base! A curious 2-cylinder heat engine has one cylinder working inside another. Don't ask me how.

Below: When your feet give out, there's a durable bench hewn from a single largish log.

Make *Hot air*
H.P.   Built *1869*
Owner *Geo Perton*
Address *Belle Plain*

Enjoy the Singing Zither played by Willie Dietrich, Amana Colonies.

Said to be the only car to make it to the top of Pike's Peak, this fire-engine-pink '06 Brush 1-cylinder runabout has up-to-date features like tubular front axle, brass carbide headlights, coil suspension. Owner D. C. Wilson, Mt. Pleasant.––AMW

See Gas Buggies from '03 to '33

One entire building at Old Settlers is jammed full of classic cars.–OS

Mail order '08 Sears and Roebuck. Better hurry or they'll be out of stock.

Steamsteamsteamsteamsteamsteamsteamsteam

Ancestor of the steam traction engine: the portable steam engine, hauled by team from belt job to belt job on the farm. Data on this one are unavailable, but it is fairly advanced, having iron wheels instead of wooden. This is one of more than 100 steam engines you'll see at Old Settlers and Threshers.—AMW

A 100-HP "Jumbo" built in Belleville, Ill., before 1870. These engines were used for threshing, sawing, pumping, grinding, shredding. Owned by Milford Reese, Franklin, Ill., it was one of the first engines shown at Old Settlers and Threshers—in 1950.——AMW

An early self-propelled, this 6-HP Nichols & Shepard was built in 1885. Single 6x9 cylinder had Link valving, operated at 250 RPM, 85 pounds. Ray H. Ernst, Wayland, Ia., owner.—— AMW

Right: 6-HP Case of unknown vintage, 1-cylinder 125 pounds, 250 RMP.——AMW

1878 Blumentritt was built in Minnesota and is said to be the only one left. This was the first traction engine built west of the Mississippi. Either it's a front-wheel-drive, rear-wheel steer, or else the steering wheel points the wrong way. Generated 12 HP at 200 RPM, 85 PSI, went 2 MPH. Double simple cylinder. Orrin Krogstead, Osage, Ia.——AMW

"The Hawkeye Express"—16-HP New Huber.

16-HP Gaar-Scott, owned and driven by Everett Holtcamp, Winfield, Ia.

Rumely 2-cylinder, 1903. Roy and Tom Trout, Donds, Ia.

16-HP Garr-Scott. Neil McClure & Son, Colchester, Ill.

Case 1908 15-45, 125 pounds WP. Art Hudachek, West Liberty, Ia.

Colean 18-HP 2-cylinder No. 322. Milo W. Mathews, Mt. Union, Ia.

Ray Ernst had this 1914 Russell sitting around. Sometimes he'd save a patch of grain from the combine, bind it and shock it like in the old days and have a little neighborhood gathering to fire up the old pot and do a bit of threshing. That's how come he was one of the Old Settlers founders.—AMW

Identical Russel: A 1914 12 HP with 7½x10 single simple cylinders operating at 230 RPM and 100-125 pounds. Top as originally owned by Ray Ernst and bottom (note ladders, governors, whistles and toolboxes) as presently owned by Fricke Bros., Mt. Union, Ia.––AMW

Fricke Bros.' 1925 Russell 25-HP makes 2½ MPH at 250 RPM and 150 pounds.––AMW

Kicking up the dust, Neil McClure and Son's 1910 Garr-Scott shows off its single simple cylinder with Link valving; 250 RPM at 100 pounds gave it 16 HP at 2½ MPH. Like all boilers on the grounds, it is state-inspected for safety.––AMW

Dave Schantz, Washington, Ia., owns 1928 Minneapolis 20-HP, 150 pounds.––OS

Aultman-Taylor 18-HP was built in 1916 with single simple cylinder, Woolfe valve 250 RPM, 100 pounds. Milo W. Mathews, Mt. Union, Ia., belongs to her.––AMW

Testing horsepower on the Prony brake. Named for its inventor, the Baron de Prony (1755-1839), the brake consists of a heavy flywheel braked by a band of wooden blocks which can be tightened to increase friction. The drag on the blocks is measured by a scale which, calculated by the speed, gives the horsepower output.--AMW

Prony & Baker

Baker fan's four flat plates create air resistance, thus A. D. Baker invented it for loading his engines during the runin. Not a dynamometer. Advance-Rumely doing her stuff.

That's Susie Kreutner, 13, who assists W. J. Coonrod on his hybrid Coonrod Special. Daughter of Albert, Mt. Pleasant implement dealer, she says of engines, "I guess I like them 'cause I've always been around 'em." She doesn't think she'll be a steam engineer when she grows up, though—more likely a schoolteacher.

Susie at the throttle.

Susie and Coonrod Special.

Nor gloom of night nor rain nor depth of mud can stop steamshowgoers from their many rounds.

Would you believe there's so many engines left?

A hundred engines do pollute the air.

63

Carrying on the tradition, young Wendell Shellabarger, Mt. Pleasant, takes proud care of his 1917 Happy Farmer 12-24 tractor.—AMW

Avery 1920 8-16. Made in Peoria, Ill.—AMW

Art Hubachek, West Liberty, Ia. plowing with his 1917 2-cylinder 2-speed Titan, chuggety chugging at 300 RPM—AMW

4-engine Paul Gorrell Special, Burlington, Iowa, carries 4 engines aboard: an Ellis 3-HP, Monitor 7-HP, a 15-HP Master Workman and one unspecified. The Master Workman propels it on the road at 15 MPH.

Eli 1896 owned by Shellabargers, Mt. Pleasant.

The only one left in the world, this 1914 LaCrosse 7-14 HP 2-cylinder rein-drive tractor steered like a horse. During the Cavalcade of Power the driver stops, starts, reverses, circles and does figure-8's using just the reins. Pulling the lines back all the way reverses the tractor; half-way stops; releasing them makes her go forward at a larrupin' 1½ MPH. Has friction drive. Pulled implements of 1-plow category. Owned by Shellabarger Brothers, Mt. Pleasant, it's driven by Dwight Shellabarger. Note 4-wheel-steer buggy.

One Left—LaCrosse Rein-Drive

Teamster's-eye view.

Kinda complex control giblets.

No End of Models

Kids of all ages are fascinated by true-to-life model steam engines that burn real coal, make real steam.—AMW

Railroad engineer C. M. Phillips built ¼-scale Case 65-HP. Although he lives in Kansas City, he is a past director of the Association.——AMW

Otto Zwicki, Ainsworth, Ia., likes whistles. So he put a potful of them on 5-HP model he built in 1957. Operated by son Don.

Miniature sawmill rips boards from 3-foot logs. Tender as well as engine and mill are accurate scale models built by Ted Dietrick. Clayton Parsons (operator), New London, Ia.--AMW

Above: Ralph Potter, Clifton Hill, Mo., owns 4-HP model of Avery under-mounted. Right: Ralph Shelburne, Zionsville, Ind., owns "2 to 3-HP" gas model that looks like it might have been patterned after an Aultman-Taylor.

The fascination of a live-steam model keeps fellas out of mischief.——AMW

Jacob E. Lowen, Meade, Kan., and his 1/5 scale model of a 16-HP 1902-4 16-HP Nichols & Shepard.——AMW

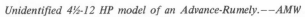

Unidentified 4½-12 HP model of an Advance-Rumely.——AMW

An absorbing hobby.--AMW

Gerald Carruthers, Lenox, Ia., teaches the young at Midwest Old Settlers and Threshers Reunion.--OS

Wendell Turner (left), Oakland, Iowa, built free-lance engine developing 3½ to 4 HP. Took him five months in 1959.

Lester Roos, Geneseo, Ill., pulls himself and supply of bottle gas with his Avery.--AMW

A Whole Tent Full of Working Live-Steam Models

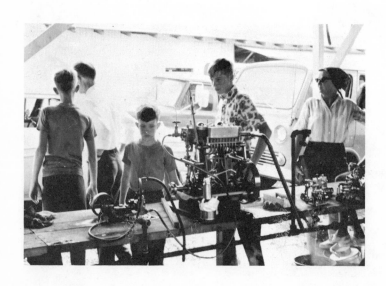

Let's Visit the Village

Old Settlers re-created an authentic early-day village where everything works. It isn't just for show. Bring your camera. And your kids.

Shave & haircut anybody? Village barber shop has extensive collection of old straight razors & personal shaving mugs. Baths have gone up to 20 cents (inflation!) and soap is 5 cents extra.

Hold a rendezvous with yesterday at the general store, where you will find century old items; just as it was when it was the hub of activity in Mt. Pleasant years ago.

Village bank sells only the very highest-quality U. S. money——and at wholesale, too! Better lay in a few thousand bills before they go down again.

See red iron take the shape the blacksmith wills at his hand-powered forge.—OS

Attend class in the village school, catch up on your 3 Rs. Next year they'll teach 4 Rs: readin, ritin, rithmetic & riots. You may also catch an old-time literary debate such as shown here, a temperance lecture or a hot discussion on whether to give (I'm agin it) women the vote.—OS

Village Model T fire truck really goes but doesn't often get to—thank goodness.—OS

Pioneer log cabin is authentically furnished.—OS

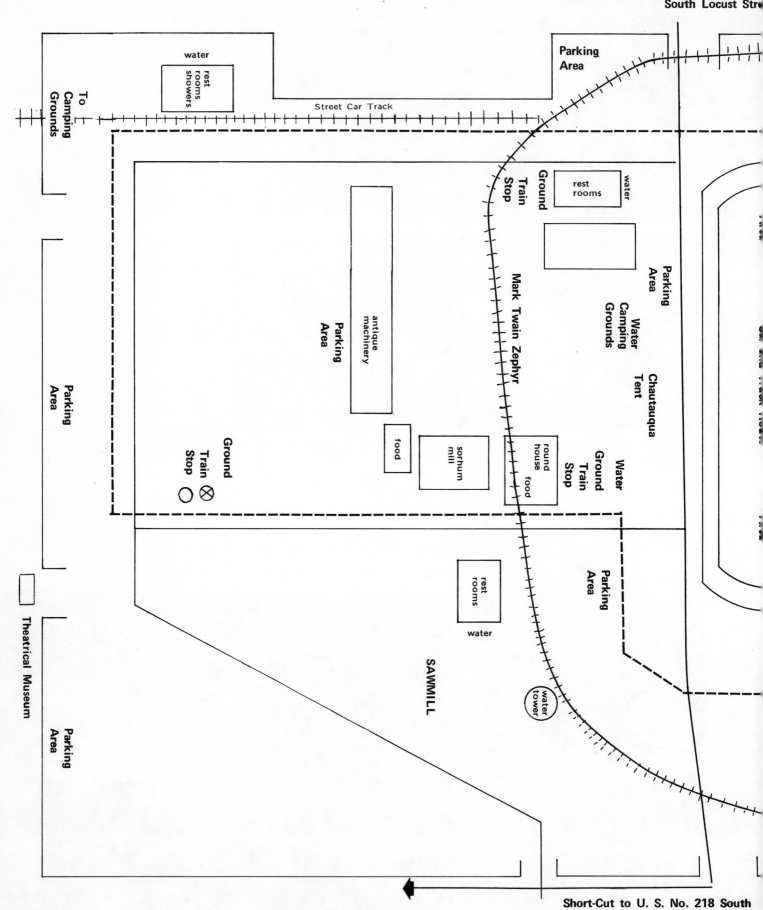

To. U. S. No. 218 North-South and
South Locust Str

Parking
Area

water
rest rooms showers

To
Camping
Grounds

Street Car Track

Train Stop

Ground

rest rooms
water

Parking
Area

Parking
Area

Water Camping Grounds

antique machinery

Parking
Area

Chautauqua Tent

Mark Twain Zephyr

food

sorhum mill

round house
food

Water

Ground
Train Stop

Ground
Train Stop ⊗ ◯

Parking
Area

Parking
Area

Theatrical Museum

rest rooms

water

SAWMILL

Parking
Area

water tower

Short-Cut to U. S. No. 218 South

MAP OF MC MILLAN PARK – MOUNT PLEASANT, IOWA
HOME OF OLD THRESHERS REUNION

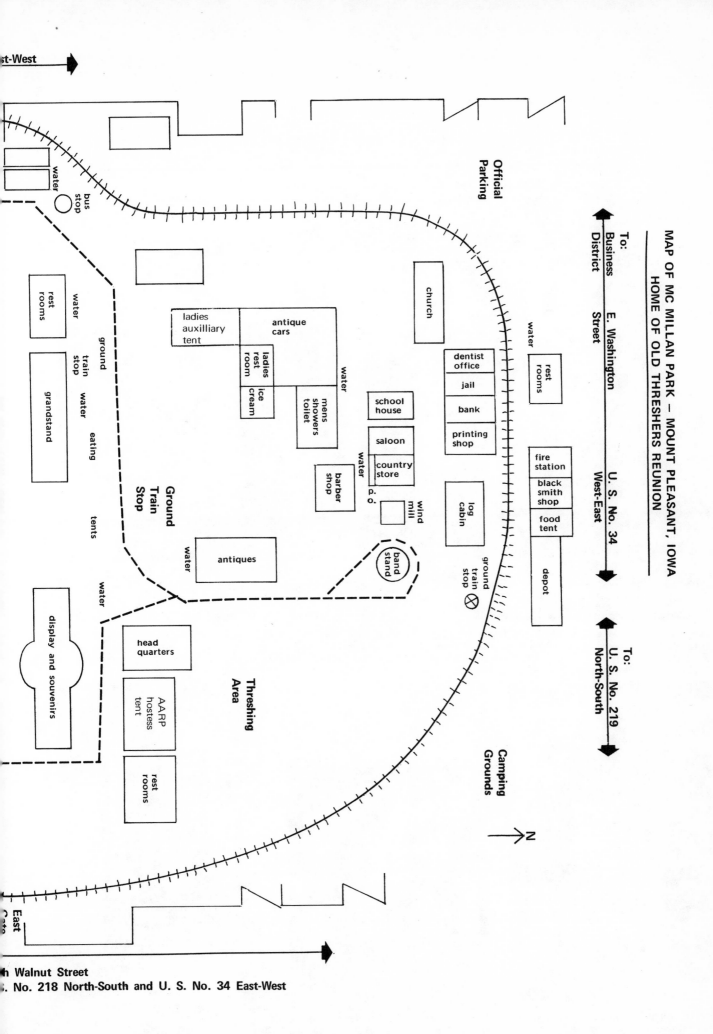

To:
Business
District

E. Washington
Street

U. S. No. 34
West-East

To:
U. S. No. 219
North-South

N

Official Parking

water

bus stop

water

rest rooms

water

ground train stop

grandstand

eating tents

water

water

Ground Train Stop

antiques

display and souvenirs

head quarters

AARP hostess tent

rest rooms

Threshing Area

ladies auxilliary tent

antique cars

ladies rest room

ice cream

mens showers toilet

water

school house

saloon

country store

p. o.

barber shop

water

wind mill

band stand

church

dentist office

jail

bank

printing shop

log cabin

ground train stop

water

rest rooms

fire station

black smith shop

food tent

depot

Camping Grounds

st-West

East

Walnut Street

No. 218 North-South and U. S. No. 34 East-West

Store Full of Goodies

They sell more sunbonnets in the General Store than anyplace else on earth. Here you see horsecollars, yard goods, old-time hard rubber penny combs (29 cents). You can buy stone-ground flour, corn meal and sorghum molasses made right on the ground. Right out of the barrel come nickel pickles, 15 cent cheese cut from a huge wheel, assorted hardware. Like the new-type magic iron the young lady offers you: you don't have to plug it in or anything. Just fill the tank with gasoline, light the generator and run like blazes.

At the good old General Store you can buy sunbonnets, horsecollars and/or dill pickles.

New-type magic iron that you don't have to plug in or anything: you just fill the tank with gasoline, light the generator, and hope it doesn't blow up.

Cheese, please!

"The Sheriff went thataway," the barkeep tells the Vulture Gulch gang who makes a surprise raid on the town every day precisely at 3:30.--OS

Great Depot Robbery & Kidnapping

Bad Bill Bolt grabs the depot's moneybags while Sure-Shot Sylvester keeps 'em covered.

Ruthie gets ruthlessly kidnapped. Seemed to me she helped a lot. Below: Them varmints made a breakneck getaway, pausing only long enough to rob the bank, too, because the sheriff might show up any day now.

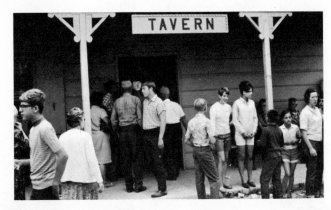

There's a Tavern in the Town

THERE'S A TAVERN IN THE TOWN where no one sets 'im down 'cuz there ain't no stools 'cept one for the pianner-player and he's already settin' on it.

Livin' it up in the Blue Garter saloon on a diet of sweet cider.

Pianna-player hams it up a little with charmin'-type dancin' girl.

Garters are for snitchin'. Sometimes a girl gets carried away by it all and tosses her garter into the crowd. More people trampled.

Garters

You'll even see the Charleston.

Come on, now girls--you can't all dance on the piano! Can you?

The Ballad
of
Mt. Pleasant
Gaol

Miss Kitty got me into trouble. She introduced me to the Sheriff. Soon's he got through arresting this desperado he caught selling pre-wired electric corn cobs, he graciously threw me in jail with a stiff on the bunk and a thunder mug under it and a black bachelor spider over it on a charge of shootin' people. An unidentified flatland tourist snapped the Polaroid of me in durance vile. Last picture is a prisoner's eye-view of the great big wide wonderful world.

Monday Morning on the Farm

In and around the Antique Building you see lye soap made in the lard kettle that also boiled the family wash, other early farm home activities——all performed by Henry County ladies.

Another hand-cranked labor-saver: a wooden-geared kraut cutter!

The housewife has hardly anything to do any more, what with all them new-timey gadgets like this labor-eliminating iron. You just shovel it full of hot coals, but don't get your nose too near the chimney!

A real wife-saving washing machine——as long as sonny turns the crank!

Woman's Work got Done

The incredible industry required of men as well as of women when everything the family used, practically, had to be grown, dug, carved or made right on the place . . . when the nearest thing to a labor-saver was a crank . . . when there was no electricity to mix and clean and wash . . . makes the muscles of the mind ache just to try to comprehend the labor. Not only did Mom have to make the clothes—but weave the cloth, spin the yarn, card the wool, help tend the sheep. These labors—these nearly-lost skills— you will see employed in the Antique Machinery building.—— Spinning photo courtesy Old Settlers.

You'll see a whole kitchen set up and going—including a coffee mill.

Rockin' chair's got her—but she can still produce for the family with stone churn and wooden dasher.

Our ancestors had little time for fun, so they made a pleasure of their work. Remember Aunt Dinah's quilting party?—OS

Nearly-blind rugmaker K. M. Dearinger, Burlington, Ia., sells his wares at the Show.

Wagon works side of the blacksmith shop.

See brooms made by hand: see three-color handles come out of one paint-pot!

Star of the Antique Machinery building is this 125-HP Corliss double-action standard non-condensing engine. Built in 1903 by the Murray Iron Works, it produced all the power for the Iowa Malleable Iron Co., Fairfield, for 54 years with only two half-days of downtime. She makes 78 RPM at 80 to 125 pounds steam pressure. The 14-inch piston makes a 36-inch stroke. The 10-foot flywheel with a 22-inch face weighs 5 tons. Steam line is 3-inch and exhaust 6-inch. Plans are being considered to belt the old jewel to a generator to supply the entire building. Meanwhile she gently idles over with hardly a whisper of sound.

"We Didn't Make it Easy"

Old Settlers are proud of their replica of Cyrus McCormick's 1837 reaper, the first improvement over the cradle. Drawn by one horse, the wooden bull wheel transmitted power to reel and saw-tooth sickle. A man (or woman) walked along beside with a wooden rake and pulled sheaf-size bunches of grain onto the ground, which other men and women then hand-tied with bands twisted from a handful of straw, and shocked. Whereas a man with a cradle could cut an acre a day, two men with the reaper could lay down 7 acres.

Next big harvesting improvement was the self-rake reaper which deposited bunches of cut grain on the stubble, to be hand-tied with straw. After this came the short-lived wire-tie binder, followed by the twine-tie that reigned supreme from the '70s into the '30s. It is still used in some dairy areas where farmers like to thresh so they can pile or barn the straw for bedding.—AMW

The Groundhog

First after the flail and threshing-floor came the Groundhog Thresher. This one was built in 1831. It doesn't look like much—just a spiked cylinder cranked by hand (its name comes from the dark maw into which the stalks were fed—like a groundhog's hole)—but it was a tremendous improvement. To the Groundhog somebody belted a treadmill worked by a dog, goat or sheep—then a larger one worked by horse—then sweep power. Somebody else attached the fanning mill and the threshing machine was born. Latest threshing machines made used spiked cylinder. Combines use either that or the rub-bar cylinder.—AMW

Other displays of early equipment include a row of one-horse walking cultivators hung on the wall in chronological order. They scratched only half a row at a time.

Old copper whisky still is the only exhibit in the show that won't work. Sorry about that, Fellas. Maybe some dark night———

Wooden-frame rope-check planter was sold new in Mt. Pleasant in 1877. Knots in the rope tripped the planting mechanism, placing corn hills in a checkerboard pattern that could be cross-cultivated (N&S, E&W) for close weed control. The rope check didn't work very well and was replaced with the modern check wire coiled at lower left. Note knots in wire that trip the planter every four feet.——AMW

Rare, well-preserved 32x50 Case hand-fed web-stacked thresher and 12-horse sweep were built in 1880 and used on the farm of John Benischek, an Austrian immigrant. The unit was acquired by Old Settlers from his grandsons Leonard and Herman who still farm the Old Home Place near Oxford Junction, Iowa.

Driver stood on center platform. Light whip was sufficient to inspire team's enthusiasm. Terrific strain on mechanism can be judged from heavy stakes, chains, broken wheel. Crowd's interest was evidenced by their doggedly maintaining their places around the rope barrier for over an hour while repairs were made. They weren't about to give up their vantage point, even from the 13th row back.

Power to Feed Mankind at Last

U. S. patent was issued in 1837, 50 years after Scotsman Meickel invented the groundhog, on a "combination thresher" mating the fanning mill to the groundhog. One-horse treadmills and sweeps powered them. Threshers got bigger and so did sweeps until they employed 12 or 14 horses.

Here at last was power to produce plenty and to sell. Always before a farm family's production was limited by the grain they could reap and thresh. Here began the era of food a-plenty. This outfit with a 12-man crew could thresh maybe 500 bushels a day, compared to the 10,000 one man on a modern combine, and another on the truck, can bin today.

"Dirtiest Job on the Farm"

Hand-feeding the old wooden separators was considered the dirtiest job there was as this Old Settlers scene suggests.

Bigger and bigger threshers were built——and bought——to use the power of big plowing engines. Case woodburner, photographed in 1940, was one of the last steamers to run the threshing rings in SE Iowa.——AMW

Stacking the stack helped preserve straw for feed and bedding (above). I've never seen it done but I've been told—and its easy to believe—working under that blast of straw, chaff, dirt and cuckleburrs from the windstacker was the worst job of all. Let's face it—all farm jobs are dusty—except fighting mud and snow. Late in the threshing years, farmers just burned their strawpiles, wasting all the potential humus and reserve feed. Now the trend is back to utilizing straw, even baling it for bedding. Ten farmers cooperatively owned this rig, above, called a "company machine," near Montrose, Ia., in 1925.—AMW

Steam engines didn't eliminate all the work. Flues had to be cleaned several times a day––a hard, dirty job. And there was plenty else to do around an engine, too.––AMW

Pitching to the old stationary balers––especially from a moldy stack was also considered one of the dirtiest jobs there was.––AMW

Early gas tractors were 12- to 20-ton monsters like the 1920 Twin City (above), heavy as steam engines. Its 4-cylinder 7¼x9 engine at 500 RPM gave it two speeds: slow and stop. Farmers wanted a lighter, cheaper tractor, small and nimble enough for light work, powerful enough to plow and belt a thresher. One attempt to cash in on the farmers' revolt against Iron Mountain was the 1917 IHC Titan, left, restored by Art Hudachek, 2 cylinder, rated 10-20 HP. Another was the Huber, below.—AMW

How Come?
History of Old Settlers

When the Black Hawk Purchase was opened to settlers June 1, 1833, the pioneers brought farming implements and methods that Jesus and Joseph could have used without a question. Some of the settlers knew that an iron share on a wooden plow poisoned the soil.

By 1900, the man on the land was sure that farm mechanization had gone as far as it could ever. After all, he had a steel plow he could ride. His neighbor had a steam engine that would do the work of fifty horses. He'd heard tell of gas tractor contraptions, but obviously they'd never amount to nothin'. So tell me one more farm machine that's left to invent!

The steam engine's short, glorious reign was soon challenged, and sooner put down, by that stinking, clanking contraption of equal tonnage, the gas engine that required no fireman, no coal-hauler, no water wagon. Took only 20 minutes to start, sometimes, instead of the hour or more to get steam up. One by one the old steamers retired to the woodlot to rust away as lusty trees grew between their iron toes. Came WWII and its appetite for scrap iron, and many of them went piecably to war.

But a few cantankerous farmers held out, even hiding the rusty old monsters in the barn, away from the pryings of scrap scouts. Shaken by so narrow an escape, some of these farmers after WWII began oiling up the old brutes and asking around if the neighbors wouldn't like to come over and pitch a bundle, just for old times' sake. Neighbors, it turned out, would like to very much.

Some of these lived in Henry County, of which Mt. Pleasant is the governmental seat. Ray H. Ernst, Wayland, Milo Mathews, Mt. Union, Bob Willits and H. E. Elgar, Mt. Pleasant and Roy Vorhies, Lockridge, were among them. Ernst heard there were others. He suggested a bunch of them go to one of those new-fangled "steam shows" he'd heard about, and in 1949 they attended the Zehr Threshers Reunion at Pontiac, Ill. They decided they could, by putting their heads and their machines together, stage a better one.

Many meetings later was born the Midwest Old Settlers and Threshers Reunion Assn., Inc., "with considerable misgivings," according to reports. The fellows elected Ernst their president. Ernst was born on a Henry County farm in 1890 and had operated threshing rings there and in Dakota for nearly 50 years. He began collecting old engines, separators and whistles.

Mt. Pleasant business and civic leaders lent their support—moral, physical and financial. The 2-day show of 1950 boasted 15 steamers and 8 separators. Despite a rainy morning, several thousand folks showed up. They went away with the daylight, and next day they were back with friends and relations from 14 states.

The directors issued a statement of gratitude: "The Association is proud of the fact that the reunion demonstrated beyond any question that the spirit of our colonial fathers still lives in the hearts and minds of our present-day generation, and they still enjoy a clean, wholesome gathering of an educational and historic nature such as ours; the Association hopes always to keep the gatherings like this, where we can meet and harvest the golden memories of yester-year and pause in our daily tasks for a day or two each year to visit and relax, but always with a thought in so doing to improve the future harvests of good fellowship and good citizenship."

They banned sideshows, con games, carnivals, any commercialism and advertising aside from the necessary sale of food and soft drinks to keep the folks from starving themselves out of the park. THE PALIMPSEST, Iowa's historical monthly, termed what followed "one of Iowa's most spectacular success stories."

Next year, a third day produced still greater crowds. Added were the Midwest Fife & Drum Corps and an old fiddlers contest, besides a square dance. That year it was reported, "It is almost unbelievable the number of fine old heirlooms and family keepsakes there are in the homes of Southeast Iowa that have been handed down from generation to generation."

Building on their success, the directors named 4 days for the '52 show. Added were some antique autos plus events especially attractive to the ladies. Four church groups set up tents in which to serve threshermen's dinners like creamed chicken, meat loaf, roast beef, ham, mashed potatoes and gravy, creamed corn, sliced tomatoes, baked beans, applesauce, coleslaw, wieners, beefburgers, potato salad, pie, ice cream and, of course, boatloads of hearty, heady coffee.

Why all this happy whoop-te-do about the hardest, hottest, dustiest work on the farm that everybody was glad to see pass away? Actually, nobody wept to see the one-man combine replace the threshing machine and its crew—especially the women, relieved of the gargantuan annual labors of feeding the crew. Still—there was SOMETHING about steam engines and neighbors helping neighbors that was precious—best expressed by Dan B. Murphy in 1952:

"Of all the jobs I can remember on the farm, the old threshing ring cooks up the most pleasant batch of memories. Just thinking about the kind of meals Mom and Aunt Lizzie and Mrs. Bashore cooked makes my mouth water, a good 20 years later. . . .

"You remember that it was work, harvesting with pitchforks and horses. Nobody envied the man who went into the barn and mowed back the hay, nor does anyone today particularly seek to go back to pitching bundles and scooping oats.

But we did the hard job the easy way, by trading help and having fun while we worked.

"That's why so many of us have these good memories, and it's no doubt a big reason for the huge success of the Old Settlers and Threshers Reunion . . . It's fun. A lot more fun than the 'combine association' will have 50 years from now."

Even though we sweated and cursed and worked beyond our endurance and felt no affection for the work nor the machines at the time—and the women glowed over their furnace-hot wood-burning ranges and no doubt grumbled just a little—although we were glad to see the combines replace the crews—although the women-folk are glad they don't have to work that hard any more—still, we love to work and sweat and cuss, and the ladies vie with each other to help out in the church chow-tents, now that we don't HAVE to do it any more; we just do it for fun.

It was all good fun, the 1951 show was, for everybody but the directors, who faced a monumental deficit. They passed a bunch of hats around town and loyal Mt. Pleasanters bailed them out. Undaunted, the directors set four days for the '53 show.

Bigger and better with bigger and more engines, the fourth Reunion established miniature models, running on real live steam, as another attractant. Seats were added for the Prony brake contest. A record 18,000 people turned out the last day, swelling the year's total to 60,000.

Then Came Old Maria No. 6

A cabbage-stack narrow-gauge logging engine, an 1891 wood-burning Baldwin locomotive, was rescued in 1960 from the South Carolina backwoods. Volunteers built a mile of track, the only

A float depicts pioneer women.

operating 36-inch narrow-gauge in the Midwest. Running gears were imported from California and Pennsylvania. Hardy local souls handbuilt four bright yellow authentic passenger coaches and a caboose to run on them. A signal tower was hauled in from Washington, and a genuine CB&Q depot transported to trackside.

MT. PLEASANT NEWS attempted to analyze the attractions with a list of six Old Settlers delights: steam threshing, operators' reunion, antique cars, railroad, antiques, threshermen's meals. That's why Old Settlers is the biggest steam show on earth.

Noting the frentic scramble for parts to restore their rusting hulks, hulks for which the hobbyists may have paid more than the original owners paid for the spanking-new engines 50 years ago, hand-making parts when they can't find any, POPULAR MECHANICS (Sept. '58) commented, "Steam-engine fans don't make sense, and are proud of it . . ."

And Evelyn Birkby wrote in Kitchen-Klatter Magazine, November, 1963, "Across the country threshers' reunions are springing up. For, pray tell, what USE is such a hobby if it is not SHARED . . .?"

The New Thing for the '63 show was the Chautauqua—the re-incarnation of the week-long event that annually brought entertainment, education and culture to 40 million Americans and Canadians from its inception at Lake Chautauqua, N. Y., in 1910, to its movie-motivated demise in the '30s. Bands, singers, dramatists, lecturers, Swiss bell ringers, cooking schools, W. Jennings Bryan and Russel N. Conwell's "Acres of Diamonds" were rural America's cultural fare for those 20+ years.

Attendance passed the 200,000 mark in 1965.

The 1966 New Thing was a 60-year pageant of automobiles. Said the KEOKUK GATE CITY, "It is one thing to see a car of 1902 vintage shined and polished in a museum, but it is quite another to see a 1902 Olds driving along a dirt track . . ."

PALIMPSEST reports the 1964 show had 47 engines in operation, only 34 of which were owned by Iowans. One came from Livonia, Mich., and another from Oklahoma City. And if you've ever moved a 12-foot-wide 23 tons from Oklahoma to Iowa, you've got a notion of the immensity of the task—and of the expense—just to show some folks (incidentally, including your-self) a good time. Models came from Kansas and Wisconsin as well as adjoining states.

The famous Mark Twain Zephyr streamlined passenger train, including engine Injun Joe, was purchased from the Chicago, Boston & Quincy RR Co. by E. A. Hayes and given to the Association. It's parked on the grounds to be restored eventually. Way-off plans are to serve the famous Mark Twain meals in it—someday.

A 1923 Shay logging locomotive came from California in 1966 to join Ol' Maria in hauling you around the narrow-gauge track.

To stage a spectacle of such immensity requires, as you can guess, an incalculable amount of work. And it's all done by volunteers under the inspiration of Old Settlers' second (since 1955) president, William O. Sater. Bill's a blacksmith by trade and is responsible for the magnificent display of 19th-century blacksmith tools and the going shop at the show.

It takes more than 300 volunteers just to man the machines, take tickets, direct traffic, care for the livestock, answer visiting journalists and pick up the paper cups. I don't know if this figure includes the scores of ladies in the church tents who prepare, cook and serve those mountainous threshers' dinners, and their husbands who work long hours "pearl diving" as they grinningly refer to dishwashing.

The only paid employee is Secretary Herbert Hult, who works full time according to the record and more than full time off the record, I suspect. This is, of course, a non-profit, non-commerical corporation.

Hult pays high tribute to the Ladies Auxiliary—mostly wives of engineers who first got together in 1953 to see how they could help the Reunion. They decided to take the responsibility of entertaining the wives of visiting steam engineers. In their first years the ladies sponsored a tea table and exhibits of fancy work for viewing and for sale and in 1955 turned a whopping profit of $12 to help the show along. These days their cash contribution ranges from $500 up. They have also upgraded restroom facilities, and financed programming for the afternoons in the Auxiliary tent: music, drama, cooking schools, crafts, demonstrations of flower arranging. They published an "Old Thresher's Cook Book" which tells today's apartment bride how to roast beef for 30 men.

Says Hult, "The Ladies Auxiliary, especially in those early, struggling years, had a large part in the preserving and presenting a part of our early

American Heritage. They like the organization, they believe in the 'nostalgia' theme of the enterprise and that its future success lies in their desire to give young Americans a glimpse of the era of steam power; to let them touch and see their heritage in motion."

Hundreds of families save their vacations for Labor Day's long weekend and spend five 18-hour days working for Old Settlers far harder than they ever work for their living. And think of the astounding labor that must precede each show to get the engines hauled out, the tents set up, machinery dispersed, etc. By the time you read this, volunteers may have finished building an opera house and a standard-gauge track and put an electric trolley into operation. If bigger crowds every year and constant repeaters don't spell "enjoyment," let's read what folks say:

Martha Crane Caris, of Chicago's WLS: "I come home each year to attend the Reunion. They always have a spot waiting for me in the church tent. I serve the mashed potatoes. I wouldn't miss it for anything."

Leland Ries, Murray, Ia., engineer: "I've been coming to the Reunion for 12 years and think it is the best in the world."

Arthur Tipton, Stockton, Ill., who had operated 15 different engines in his career: "I think the show here is just great. I enjoy meeting many old friends."

Mrs. John F. Myers, Wankee: "Just wonderful. We drove 190 miles."

Mrs. John Meyer, Milford, Neb.: "Everything here is beautiful. I like all of it and am enjoying the show so much."

Visitors are asked to turn in cards with comments pro and con and suggestions for improvements. The bulk of the cards echo: "Liked—hospitality—atmosphere—everyone's happy—darn good show—perfect—etc."

Clementine Paddleford, THIS .WEEK food editor, praised "the way the hometown people dig in to do the job." Richard Howland, Curator, Smithsonian Institution, liked "your amiable hospitality."

When asked to list first, second and third choice of exhibits one visitor said, "My first choice is everything." Another: "If it was any better I couldn't stand it." There was one complaint: "The show don't run long enough."

The nearest thing to commercialism is the antique sale where you can buy a gout chair, 1700 German kraut cutter, Model T tire lock, horizontal ice cream freezer and such.

Commented one guest speaker, ". . . the youth I talk to on the ground seem surprised at how it swings. Who would expect so much life in a festival of remembrance?" And another said attending Old Settlers and Threshers Reunion ". . is like a trip to the attic to meet yourself." And you'll meet a lot of old friends already there.

LAUGH WITH TOBY TOLLIVER 2, TOO

You see living history in its most entertaining form every night at Old Settlers. For there, in the Chautauqua Tent, performs the last survivor of the more than 400 traveling tent shows that 40 years ago set up for one-week stands in the little towns across America.

It was the late Neil Schaffner who immortalized the Toby and Susie characters. Soon after WWI Schaffner founded his own traveling troupe, the Schaffner players. He soon found audiences loved best Toby T. Tolliver, the red-headed, unlettered but shrewd and kindly rustic, and his equally be-freckled and rustic sweetie. When the Schaffners retired in 1965, his protege, young Jimmy Davis, took over as Toby T. Tolliver II, and his beautiful young wife, Juanita, stars in the show. Jimmy and Juanita carry on the Schaffner players, making the Iowa tent circuit every summer with a troupe of seasoned old professionals and starry-eyed college drama students.

If you like belly-laughs from toes to nose, you'll love Toby in his red wig and freckles.

98

At 8 p.m. any evening during the Reunion you can sit on soft pine chairs in the much-traveled tent and guffaw from your toes up at the antics and ad-libbing of Toby as he outwits some city slicker. In the same program you'll enjoy everything from vaudeville to Shakespeare, dixieland to classics. Nor need you hesitate to take Mom and the kids. There's not an off-color line in a full season on Jimmy's stage, proving once more you don't have to talk dirty to pack 'em in.

As Toby II frequently points out, far more people were influenced culturally by the traveling tent shows than by the "legitimate" theater which stuck to New York and other big cities. Before superhighways, radio, TV and the movies, traveling tent shows were the only boughten entertainment rural people had. Today people are so tired of the canned stuff on the screen, they find real live actors a refreshing boost to morale.

Toby (that's how I think of Mr. Davis, and address him as such, and he responds) presents two plays a night along with song, dance, juggling and musical numbers. Every member of the 15 or so in the troupe displays an amazing assortment of talents, playing several different dramatic roles each evening, playing a bewildering variety of musical instruments and entertaining with between-the-acts specialties. Considering that the company will present 10 to 14 different plays a week, and every member has multiple roles, think of the staggering memorizing job for everybody. I guess that's why it's called repertoire theater—every player has to have a huge repertory of acts and parts.

Toby II terms his surviving art form "folk theater" because the performers write most of their own plays, or update old ones.

A big share of today's TV and movie stars got their start on the tentboards. Some of them are proud of it while others prefer you didn't mention it.

The night I was there I saw some of the finest theater ever.

It was raining. Toby had just bought a brand-new tent that leaked worse than the old one. "Looks like a hardly-able outfit," he said in

Toby loves Suzy and so will you.

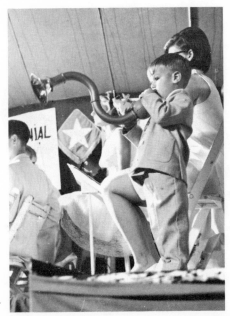

Jimmy and Juanita's son Brant stars in their Dixieland Band.

Tom Sawyer and Huckleberry Finn whitewash Aunt Polly's fence.

momentary gloom. The tent was packed. People squirmed on their wet soft pine chairs (Toby makes a Big Thing of those soft pine folding chairs—pointing out he doesn't ask his customers to sit on hard pine ones) and pulled newspapers over their heads to slow the drip and giggled and stayed. Actors shifted their positions on stage to move from under a large drip to a smaller one and Toby ad-libbed, "Wotsa matter—aintcha got enuf sense t' git outta th' rain?" stopping the show with laughter not only from the audience but from the cast.

The stage was so wet there was some question that the dancers could get through their routines without breaking their painted necks. More than one make-up was smeared by the drip.

A highlight of the evening's program was a violin solo by a concert violinist who, with his wife and children, had joined the troupe for summer kicks. The closing scene of a slapstick comedy was one of the most beautiful, moving bits of drama I have ever seen, with the violinist, guarding his rare old instrument from the rain as best he could, played a haunting gypsy lovesong which moved the audience, belly-laughing at Toby and Suzy moments ago, to tears.

As one person remarked to me, "Who would expect to hear—in a slapstick comedy in a leaking tent on a wet stage in front of an audience of farmers—a concert violinist playing classical music?"

Who, indeed?

Any summer you catch the Schaffner Players touring Iowa in their tent (they have a new, waterproof one now), by all means stop and treat your family to the last surviving bit of folk theater. It will remain a favorite highlight in your treasury of happy family memories.

Cavalcade of Power

Twice a day, everything on wheels lines up on the race track and parades past the grandstand while the announcer reads off the data. Steam engineers, whether lost in the cavernous cab of a 20-ton job or squatting, chin on knees, atop a 50-pound model, salute with a toot. Gas operators just wave and grin.

In The Cavalcade of Power you can see nearly every kind of farm power from the horse through many generations of steam engines and gas engines from the '80s into the '30s.

On this and the following pages you see just a few samples.

Unidentified.

1909 16-HP Gaar-Scott. Neal McClure, Colchester, Ill.

Wood Brothers 22-HP, 150 pound WP, and model. Big engine is owned by Helen Wood, Des Moines, daughter of F. J. Wood, builder.—AMW

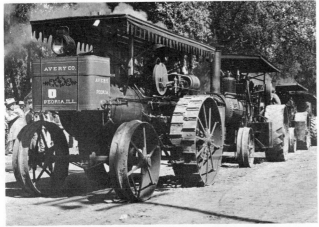

Parade line-up, led by 1913 return-flue 20-HP Avery. Bill Sater, owner.—AMW

1923 Keck-Gonnerman 19 HP, 1-cylinder, built in Mt. Union, Ind. 150-pound WP. John Howard, owner.

Advance-Rumely 22-HP 9x11 single simple, 175 pound WP. Dean Shellhouse, Livonia, Mich.

Advance-Rumely 1921 18-HP. 100 pounds. Harold Janris, Washington, Ia.

15-45 Case 1909, 125 pound WP, 9x10 single simple.

Early 1-cylinder Avery, 250 RPM, 125 pound WP, J. L. Schubert, Burlington, Ia.—AMW

Wood Bros. 22-HP, 150 pounds. Dallas Kerr, Montrose, Ia. and Bill Seyb, Donnelson, Ia., owners.—AMW

Rare 1906 Kitten owned by Neil McClure and Son. 24 HP, 250 RPM, 2½ MPH, 100 pounds, single simple.—AMW

Advance-Rumely 1918 20-HP, Marsh valve, 250 RPM, 125 pounds, 2½ MPH, 1 cylinder 9x11. Mark Heston, Donnelson, Ia.—AMW

Rare 18-HP Colean 1905 2 cylinder simple. Milo W. Mathews, Mt. Union, Ia.

1886 Case 12-HP, 2 speed, 3 and 5 MPH, Link valve, 225 RPM, 100 pound WP, 1 cylinder. Note seat and footboard for teamster when pulled by horses. Charles McMillan, Mt. Pleasant.—AMW

Advance Rumely 1922, 150 pounds, 9x11 single, Ray H. Ernst, Wayland, Ia.

1903 Rumely 16-HP, Arnold valve gear, 100 pounds, 2½ MPH, 8¼x10 single cylinder, 250 RPM. Roy and Tom Troute, Douds, Ia.—AMW

20-HP Jumbo built by Harrison Machine Co., Belleville, Ill. McClure.

Teeter-tottering is always a crowd-pleaser. Water sloshing forward and back in the long boiler plus the loose, worn gearing demands the utmost of the engineer's hand and eye. Above is a 1916 Port Huron 24-75 tandem compound owned by Edwin Saltzman, Winfield, Ia., with an Old Port Huron veteran at the controls, Pete Bucher, Beckwith, Ia. Below is Pete's own 1916 19-65 Port Huron Tandem compound with himself at the throttle. Both engines have Grimes valve gear, operate at 150 pounds working pressure. – AMW

1919 Russell 25-HP, 150 pound WP. Fricke Bros.

1914 Russell 20-HP, 125 pound WP. Shellabarger.

The short return-flue boiler was favored by some for its higher efficiency, gained by passing combustion gasses through the boiler twice. The hot stack right at the engineer's face was a bane in summer, a boon in winter. Left is a 1913 20-HP Avery owned by Bill Sater.

30-HP 2-cylinder Huber plowing engine below. McClure.

Return Flues

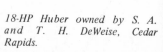

18-HP Huber owned by S. A. and T. H. DeWeise, Cedar Rapids.

New Giant 20-HP 1902 return-flue originally threshed Nebraska grain as a straw-burner; note spark catcher on stack. Was converted to coal burner. Square tank holds water supply. 8¼x10 single cylinder produced 2½ MPH at 250 RPM, 100 pounds working pressure. Built in the state prison at Stillwater, Minn. Mathews.—AMW

The Bull has one large drive or "bull" wheel. "Weather vane" on front wheel post is a guide for plowing straight furrows.—AMW

Gasgasgasgasgasgasgasgasgasgasgasgasgasgas

"Happy Farmer" tractor. Former owners say the farmers got happy when they got rid of 'em.—AMW

Massey-Harris 4-wheel drive called the Wallis. Bill Sater, owner.—AMW

Bates Steel Mule, 1922, owned by Paul Waters, Mt. Pleasant, who donated it to the Association.—AMW

25-50 Avery 4-cylinder owned by J. L. Schubert, Burlington, Ia.

12-24 Waterloo Boy 1917 2-cylinder Shellabarger Brothers, Mt. Pleasant, owners.

Early International 8-16 owned by Bernard Carroll Jr., Brighton, Ia. Apparent smoke jets come from steamers in background.

Carl Bruckner, Cedar Rapids, built this tractor in 1928. Pulling a Rockford engine.

Below: Chantry 25-HP engine was bought at 1893 Chicago World's Fair, operated a mill in Otter Creek, Ia., until 1937. Owned by DeWees Bros., Cedar Rapids.

Coonrod Specials. The one below was assembled by W. J. Coonrod, Toddville, Ia., from a 1910 Reeves 25-HP engine and a 25-HP 1920 N&S boiler mounted on a Mack truck. With a truck transmission and a full range of gears, the speed potential is formidable. He's never dared let 'er out despite hydraulic brakes.

Below: Another Coonrod Special, built by Virgil Coonrod, Cedar Rapids.

Models line up for parade. They can't dilly-dally because they haven't much reserve water.—AMW

Cavalcade of Teakettles

A. J. Goodban, York, Neb., on his model of an A. W. Stevens; took him 2,000 hours to build. Rates it 3 HP.

Another Goodban, driven by Claude Murphy.—AMW

Jewel-like replica of a Case.—AMW

His and Hers. Ralph W. Shelbourne built these free-lance models, drives one, his daughter the other.—AMW

Lester Roos, Geneseo, Ill. pulls bottle gas fuel supply and a train of wagons. 4-HP model Avery is powerful enough to pull trainload of children.—AMW

Even the kids like models. Can you imagine that?

Roos built this 4-HP, 1,500 pound freelance steamer in 1965, calls it "a rolling brass junkyard."

Built by L. H. McKinney, Cairo, Mo. on a 14-inch Solomon boiler. Joe Steinhagen, Dodge Center, Minn.

Ralph Kain operates model Avery, 4 HP, owned by Kain, Bros., Milan, Ill.

Non-scale Case-patterned 3½ HP owned by Wendell Turner, Oakland, Ia.

Minneapolis model.

J. B. Bannister, Farber, Mo., on his 4-HP Case. Weighs 2,760 pounds.

Free-lance 3½-HP 1,430 pound model engine built by Wendell Turner, Oakland, Ia., at the controls. Separator is a 1/3 scale 32x54 Case built by L. Vandervort.

O. R. Morey, Kewanee, Ill., built 3-HP, 1,800 pound engine in 3 years.

Unidentified.

Built by John Stratmann, owned by Doug Berggren, both of Wilcox, Neb., modeled after Case.

Half-scale 20-HP Advance-Rumely owned by Bob Snow, Palmyra, Mo., delivered 11.75 HP on Prony brake.

1911 Rumely model makes 5 HP, called "Little Dixie Belle," built by Harold George, Mexico, Mo., owned by Basil Dare, LaBelle, Mo.

Half-scale 16-HP Rumely weighs 3,650 pounds soppin' wet, develops 10 HP. Built by L. H. McKinney, Cairo, Mo., (nearer camera).

Free-lance built from scrap by G. P. Lain, Atkinson, Ill.

L. H. McKinney with 5-12 HP model Rumely.

Advance 3-HP, 2,000 pounds built by Ross Naylor, Platte City, Mo., driving. Took 2 years.

Judy Shelburne, Zionsville, Ind., driving a model made to look like an Aultman-Taylor, built by her father, Ralph. He also built this small separator using combine parts and home-sawed frame. Separator actually works.

Hybrid put together from odds and ends by Charles Vornholt, Solon, Ia. Rates 2 HP.

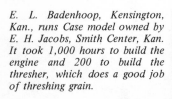

E. L. Badenhoop, Kensington, Kan., runs Case model owned by E. H. Jacobs, Smith Center, Kan. It took 1,000 hours to build the engine and 200 to build the thresher, which does a good job of threshing grain.

116

You'll encounter a whole herd of horse-drawn conveyances at Old Settlers. 2-HP schoolbus was ridden by some of the audience when they were school-children.

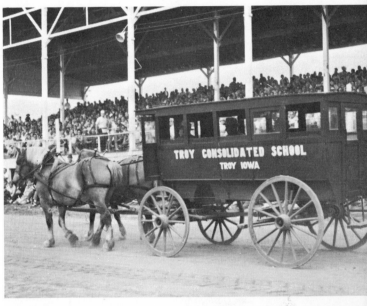

Midwest Central Railroad

Like Rockin' and Rollin'?

Then you'll love riding the Midwest Central to the rhythmic click-clack of the rail joints and the chug-chuff of the exhaust and the rattle and clank of the gear and the shower of the cinders.

12-inch bore, 18-inch stroke.

Among the trees you toot, around the curve, across the trestle, past the popcorn stand, through the squarest roundhouse in the world, up the slope (push hard on the footrest to help her make the grade [but one passenger told me, "I heard Conductor Charlie say, 'Nobody's ever been asked to hop out and shove yet!!'"]), past the firehouse and steam back to the station with its potbellied stove and agent.

The busiest one-mile railroad in the country, the little Toonerville-type cars carry capacity loads every trip. The MC has more conductors per square passenger than any other railroad in the world—needs 'em to collect the tickets before the end of the line. And that's enough to make the president of any long line drown himself in his red ink.

Queen of the Railroad is Ol' Maria No. 6, the 1891 Baldwin logger tipping the scale at a dainty 32 tons. She may not keep a cast-iron schedule, but by cracky she always runs the right direction. "19th-Century travel at its finest!" crows Old Settlers promotion.

Everybody comes down to meet the train 37 times a day.

You can tell she's a wood-burner by the cabbageness of her stack—if the cordwood ricked in her tender doesn't tell you that. Should a cinder set your hair afire, please mention it to a conductor so he can stop the train at the water tower for you, next trip, 'cause they don't want you burning down their carefully hand-crafted coaches.

Maria hauled logs for a living over 50 or 60 years and once rescued a trainload of women and children as a brushfire roared down upon their mountain village. Her 12-inch cylinder and 18-inch stroke @ 160 pounds give her a top speed of 25 MPH downwind. Her 37 flues make her little insides real busy.

Known as a Mogul type 2-6-0, black Maria has Southern valve gear. She was built in 1891 by Baldwin, as we said, for Surrey, Sussex & Southhampton RR Co. The locomotive is 24 feet 3 inches long; add the tender and she comes to 44 feet 2 inches. She arrived at Mt. Pleasant from Hardeesville, S. C., Feb. 26, 1960.

Nobody's been asked to push Ol' Maria up the grade yet.

Sometimes the engineers unhook Maria and run her off onto a siding and hitch up Ol' No. 9, the oil-burning Shay, likewise a logger. If you like bolts and nuts, you'll be interested to note that the Shay has a 3-cylinder vertical engine mounted on the right side of the boiler just ahead of the cab. The crankshaft is bevel-geared to all wheels on engine and tender, making every wheel a drive wheel for real mountain-climbing traction—all 150,000 pounds of her!

Shay came from the Hetch—Hetchy and Yosemite Valley RR of California, where she, too, was a logger. Running gears came from California and Pennsylvania. Old Settlers craftsmen built the cars.

Stan Mathews went to California and operated Shay for two days before buying her in time for the 1966 Reunion.

Real operating station.

Injun Joe, left, is for show. Ol' Maria, right, is for go.

Oil-burning Shay No. 9 was built about 1923.

Crankshaft is geared to all locomotive and tender wheels, which are all the same size. Thank goodness.

3-cylinder side-crank.

"Line of the wood-burners"

Real live bride and groom, just married in Village church, make their post-nuptial getaway via MCRR.

Steamin' 'round th' bend!

The natives are friendly.

Cupola gives ideal view.

This 18-HP New Giant was once a straw burner when it was used on the Great Plains for threshing. It was converted to coal burning. The smoke stack, covered with a spark catcher, is located at the rear of the boiler. Large tank in front to carry water. New Giant built in 1902 in Stillwater, Minn., 18-HP, 100 pounds W.P. Bore 8¼", stroke 10". Milo W. Mathews, owner, Mt. Union, Iowa.

Symbolizing the Age of Steam for farmers at Old Settlers & Threshers Reunion, this 1902 New Giant marches in review past the grandstand.

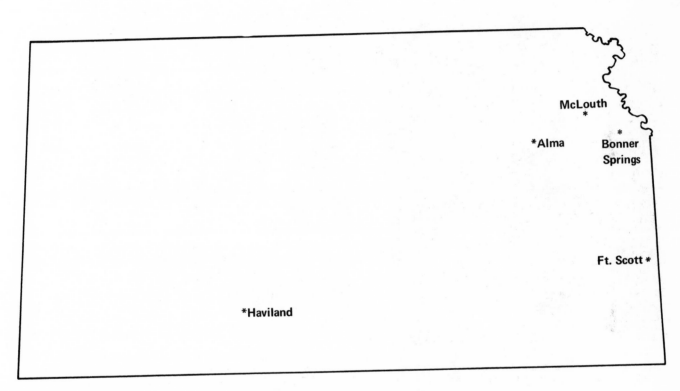

McLouth
*

*Alma

*
Bonner
Springs

Ft. Scott *

*Haviland

Kansas

AG
HALL
OF
FAME

AGRICULTURAL HALL OF FAME AND NATIONAL CENTER · BONNER SPRINGS, KANSAS

THE AGRICULTURAL HALL OF FAME
AND NATIONAL CENTER
Bonner Springs, Kan.
Open every day except
Thanksgiving, Christmas and New Year's
Steam threshing 3rd Sunday in July

Here, finally, is an educational-historical complex honoring the men and women who helped make American family-farm agriculture the miracle, the envy and the hope of the world.

Here is not just a dead museum but a living, growing, working demonstration of old and new ways of producing food and fiber. Located on a 695-acre tract near the Kansas Turnpike (I-90) and other main highways, 3 miles north of Bonner Springs, Kan., and 12 west of downtown Kansas City, it is near the geographical center of the Old Original 48 states. You can get there from almost anywhere.

Presently on display are farm machinery from a crooked-stick plow on up through a self-propelled combine with plastic sides so you can see the innards go 'round, worked by an electric motor. You can see hand tools, pioneer household gadgetry and all the many items of farm hardware from the era when hardware was mostly wood. Here is the original 1903 milking machine which, with a hand-pumped vacuum pump, tried to duplicate the 1-2-3-4 progressive squeeze of human fingers.

A library of 7,000-plus volumes tells the story of agriculture, as do the furniture, furnishings and crafts of pioneer homes. Right out where you can look at it is a collection of photographs of typical farmsteads in every state, hobby of a retired farmer. A complete electrical museum is planned.

Plans to 1975 include $12 million invested in 10 new buildings in addition to a pioneer village, an Indian village and a model farm where visitors can watch actual farming operations performed by hand, ox, horse, tractor and combine. The nation's 3,000 soil conservation districts are laying out a 275-acre model conservation farm, including a lake. Here will be demonstrated logging, butchering, cattle roundups, hive-robbing, corn-shucking contests and plowing contests.

The conservationists also built a one-mile nature trail through the woods.

A quick rundown of exhibits, present and future:

All the state flowers.

Examples of all the cream separators and milking machines DeLaval ever made.

Spinning wheels and spinning demonstrations.

Bell Telephone exhibit of equipment from the earliest to the latest.

Agricultural library.

Blacksmith shop.

Country store.

One-room school

Log cabin.

Sod house.

Hundreds of hand tools and household "appliances" from pioneer times.

The Hall of Fame, as the name suggests, will memorialize the leaders of American agriculture.

Exhibited will be different soils and rock structures as they relate to agriculture. A transportation building will show how, over the centuries, farmers traveled and hauled their produce to market—from wagons and buggies to a 1903 25-HP truck that could go 25 MPH on a clear day.

You'll see displays of food and fiber; of the care, breeding and feeding of farm animals; conference and convention facilities; a glass beehive full of living, working, buzzing busy bees that fascinate youngsters already. An industrial building will display manufactured items and processes as they relate to farming and crops. A horticultural building will portray activities in this field.

Anticipated is a complete series of 75 tractors, showing each major step in their development from the most primitive to the latest.

The pioneer village will include a church, school (just finished), store, city hall, jail, railway depot and train, all from the pioneer era.

The first exploratory meeting was held by farm and agri-business leaders in 1957. A year later the institution was incorporated for educational and historical purposes and to honor American men and women for outstanding work in agriculture and related industries.

More than 60 localities asked to be selected as the Hall site. A land agency investigated all the sites before choosing the Bonner Springs tract.

Congress gave the Hall a Federal charter in 1960, but the institution receives no tax support whatever. All funds come from the 95-cent admission charge, sale of souvenirs, donations (deductible) and bequests.

Only a few of the planned buildings are up yet. Plaza is ringed by flags of all states.

The farm machinery exhibit, instead of an unorganized mass of junk picked up helter-skelter, with a dozen of this and none of that, shows a carefully-selected one-each example of major steps in machinery development without duplication. While gaps still exist in the collections, hopefully these will be filled in time.

A model steam railway hauls people around the grounds. An old-time steam merry-go-round delights kids young and old. An old steam-operated popcorn wagon is one of the most popular attractions, as is a hay-operated Texas Longhorn named Tex who glowers at photographers through a barbed-wire fence, ominously shaking his 6-foot-wide horns and twitching flies with a long, practiced tail.

We suggest you not plan a quicky visit. Take 90 minutes at least. If you can spend a full day, you'll find it well-filled and well-spent. There's plenty of parking for cars, campers and buses. A county park directly across the road offers ample shaded picnic facilities. A steam threshing show is held the last two Sundays in July.

The idea of an Agricultural Hall of Fame originated more or less simultaneously in many minds.

The Federal charter describes the Hall: ". . . a non-profit corporation organized for . . . fostering . . . a greater sense of appreciation of the dignity and importance of agriculture, historically carried out through owner-operated farms, and the part it has played in developing those social, economic and spiritual values which are essential in maintaining the free and democratic institutions of our republic; and to maintain and operate a library and museum for the collection and preservation for posterity of agricultural tools, implements, machines, vehicles, pictures, paintings, books, papers, documents, data, relics, mementos, artifacts and other items and things relating to agriculture. Also to honor farmers, farm women, farm leaders, teachers, scientists, inventors, governmental leaders, and other individuals who have helped make this nation great by their outstanding contributions to the establishment, development, advancement or improvement of agriculture in the United States of America."

The first building opened in June, 1965. Over 100,000 visitors trooped through in 1966, double that in 1967, and the 1968 total approached a quarter-million. An ultimate visitation of over a million a year is anticipated. The institution is a favorite touring target for school groups, 4-H

126

clubs, FFA chapters and visiting dignitaries from abroad.

Present president is Orma E. Mackey, Mexico, Mo. Doris J. Enright, acting administrator, is the active manager in daily charge of Hall affairs, assisted by a staff of clerks, guides, machine operators and skilled mechanics who lovingly restore the old relics to mint condition in the Hall's machine shops.

As PROGRESSIVE FARMER said, "When the Agricultural Hall of Fame is fully developed, it will be the most complete, authentic agricultural collection in the world."

You'll see farming by hand, ox, horse and machine at the Agricultural Hall of Fame and National Center. This is a working, living museum.—Dr. Newell O. Feeley Photos

Watch your step, Mister!—Feeley

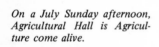

On a July Sunday afternoon, Agricultural Hall is Agriculture come alive.

The pause that refleshes.—Feeley

The Separator Man: King of all He Surveys!—Feeley

Living history.

Single tandem compound Port Huron 1919 24–75 HP, 12 and 14-inch bores, 12-inch stroke, 175 pound WP. Cost new $2,300. Engineer is L. E. Baumgardner, Shawnee, Kan. Ag Hall, owner. Cast iron wheels.

A whole generation has never ridden a steam train. Now they have their chance!

Even the water wagon is authentic!

Hay-powered long-horned meanness!

Windmill runs cordwood saw.—Feeley

Nothing like an umbrella to keep the chaff off.

Pony-pulling contest is a threshing-bee feature.—Feeley

The art of feeding bundles head-first is not quite lost.

Folk music is one cultural heritage Ag Hall preserves.

Steam-popped popcorn with real butter on is another.

Patterned after Case, from ½ to ¾ scale. 5½x10 engine makes 10-HP. Owned by Bob Harschberger.

1924 Avery 45–65 cost $3,200 new. 4-cylinder horizontal opposed 7¾x8, 600 RPM 2 speed up to 3½ MPH.

Looks like an Aultman-Taylor.

136

Touring Argentine agriculturists get the red carpet.

See reaper progress.

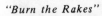

"Burn the Rakes"

June 26 — Another trial of reapers took place in Maj. Stone's rye field today. A large crowd of farmers and town people were at the exhibition. The old sickle and the cradle and the rake might as well be piled together out upon the old turnpike roads and burned.— Yankton, S.D., PRESS & DAKOTAN, 1878.

Header and barge are on display.

Kids get to operate dowel-cutter.—Feeley

Steam merry-go-round pleases all. An old Herschel-Spillman twin-cylinder 8-HP, she's operated lovingly by "Doc" Spry of Kansas City. To her steady chuff-chuff he said, "Isn't that music? I can listen to 'er all day!"

Old crawler awaits rejuvenation.

Frick Eclipse center-crank: 1914 19-HP 9½x10 owned by Floyd Atkinson, Harrisonville, Mo.—the only one in the state. Engineer today is Walter Hale, Belton, Mo.

"Jewel" is homemade by Morris Cleveland, Lawrence, Kan., except the 1892 6-HP 4 5/8x6 engine.

See windchargers, milking machines, bullet molds, gunsmith's tools, including wooden rifling machine.

International Motor Cultivator.

Early mower had center cutterbar that cut horses' tendons better than the hay they'd tromped down. This model was not a commercial success.

Museum features exhibition of today's rural artists.

If donations come in fast enough, this is what the institution will look like $12 million later—in 1975.

1919 International 8–16 pulled two 14s, weighs 3,300 pounds, cost $975 new. Four-cylinder vertical engine runs at 1,000 RPM, produces 1.8–4 MPH.

1908 Titan 25-HP 1-cylinder weighed 12,000 pounds, had Hit and Miss governor. She'd fire, then coast "whoot-whoot-whoot" for 30 seconds, then fire again.

Unidentified

he Hall of Fun

Open All Year

AGRICULTURAL PIONEERS HONORED

Men and women of all times and races will be honored here for their contributions to agriculture. More names will be added each year.

GEORGE WASHINGTON
1732–1799

Mt. Vernon consisted of more than 12,000 acres. At first Washington grew tobacco and corn, but finally declared his independence from the English market and showed American farmers how to prosper on the domestic market. He abandoned tobacco for its deleterious effects on soil.

Washington gave much attention to soil conservation. He proved prevention was better than cure—that even with slave labor he couldn't afford to haul silt back to the hillsides from whence it washed.

He milled his own wheat into flour and personally oversaw its quality, branding each barrel with his own trademark. Washington's flour was widely famed for its high quality.

A successful farmer himself, Washington demonstrated not only independence from English exploitation, but also advanced farming and conservation methods.

THOMAS JEFFERSON
1743–1826

"He is the greatest patriot who stops the most gullies," said Jefferson, twice president of the United States and the father of American scientific agriculture.

He was among the first to apply science to agriculture. Believing independent farmers were the bulwark of the nation, he worked to improve their lot. Principal author of the Declaration of Independence, he also said, "Those who labor in the earth are the chosen people of God, if ever He had a chosen people, whose breasts He has made His peculiar deposit for substantial and genuine virtue."

Jefferson invented a seed drill, a hemp brake and a threshing machine. Perhaps the most important of his inventions was a plow moldboard. He improved plants and animals. He promoted soil conservation, crop rotation, and fertilization. Throughout his life, Jefferson encouraged agricultural education.

CYRUS HALL McCORMICK
1809–1884

Not only the reaper, but a hillside plow and a water-powered hemp brake were among McCormick's inventions. He constantly improved his reaper and later manufactured binders. He pioneered large-scale farm machine manufacture. The reaper has been described as "the most important machine in agriculture." So impressed was Emperor Napoleon with McCormick's reaper and its labor-saving potential that he ordered three for use on his own farms and encouraged their adoption throughout France.

When McCormick was a boy, harvest was the hardest work on the farm. Harvesting was the bottleneck of food production, for a family could sow far more than it could reap. McCormick's reaper enabled farmers to harvest up to six times as much as they could before. And it stimulated other farm machine inventions.

The reaper and the thresher enabled mankind for the first time in history to banish the spectre of famine, to grow enough food and to spare, providing the surplus of food and labor that made possible our highly technical culture.

JUSTIN SMITH MORRILL
1810–1898

Representative from Vermont, Morrill as early as 1856 tried to get a land-grant college resolution through congress. In 1857 he introduced his first bill to grant public lands for the support of agricultural schools. President Buchanan vetoed it. President Lincoln signed a new bill July 2, 1862, granting to the states 30,000 acres of public lands for each senator and representative, the sale monies to be invested, the income to support agricultural and mechanical colleges.

Five years later, as a senator, Morrill began work for additional support for the land-grant colleges. President Harrison signed such a bill in 1890. Morrill continued to work for the land-grant college movement the rest of his life. He is known as "the Father of the Land-Grant Colleges," which have been credited, by making scientific agricultural education widely available, with enabling American family-farm agriculture to become the wonder of the world.

GEORGE WASHINGTON CARVER
1864–1943

Born a slave near Diamond, Mo., he taught himself to read and write. He worked his way through Kansas schools and graduated from Iowa State Agricultural College in 1894. Two years later he earned his master's in botany, and headed the new agricultural department at Tuskegee Institute in Alabama.

He taught farmers to minimize boll wevil devastation, while improving their farms and yields and income, by raising crops in addition to cotton. He taught improved food preparation and diet outside the classroom as well as in.

Carver developed scores of new industrial products from peanut shells, cottonseed, other farm wastes and from sweet potatoes. He refused lucrative industrial offers, remaining in his Tuskegee laboratory, dedicated to helping mankind. His guideline was, "Whatever helps the Southern farmer helps the entire South; and what helps the South helps everybody."

Late in life medals, honorary doctorates and other honors showered upon him. PROGRESSIVE FARMER, a Southern magazine, named the former slave its 1942 "Man of the year in agriculture."

Franklin Roosevelt said his life "will for all time afford an inspiring example to youth everywhere."

THE GALLIC STRIPPER
Massey-Ferguson

Sickle 300 BC

Scythe 1800

Patrick Bell's Reaping machine 1820.

Hussey's Reaping Machine-1833.

Woods Patent Self-Rake Reaper.

Massey Harvester 1877.

Harris Brantford Open-end Binder 1890

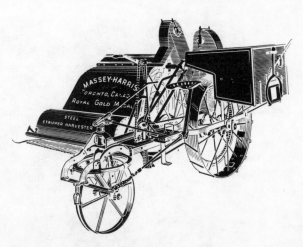

Massey Stripper Harvester 1901.

147

Many an overall bib proudly sports an admission button. This practice, common to steam shows, gave birth to a new hobby: collecting buttons. Last year's button sells for as much as this year's but it won't get you in.—Photo by Dr. Newell O. Feeley

HEART OF AMERICA
ANTIQUE STEAM ENGINE & MODEL ASSOCIATION
SW corner of town
McLouth, Kan.
First full weekend in August

This is the club that was organized at midnight.

Les Wagner's daughter found a 1919 Advance-Rumely 22-HP. When she got home late that night she got her dad up and told him about it. He went over to H. C. Watson's right away and they organized the Association right there, at midnight in 1957. They held their shows on his farm near McLouth until 1965, when they moved to the southwest corner of McLouth where they bought 53 acres. Wagner is president.

One of their prized possessions is General U. S. Grant's own threshing machine from his farm near St. Louis, now owned by Lentz Bros., Oregon, Mo. It's a wooden hand-fed web-stacked hand-sacked Little Giant built by Hiebner & Son, Lansdale, Pa., about 100 years ago.

Another prize is one of the last two 45-HP freighting engines J. I. Case built, one of two built on special order in 1912 after Case went out of the 45-HP business. It's No. 28302. With special freighting wheels (smaller and heavier than farm wheels), Baker valve, heavy boiler, it's set up as a contractor's special. It pulled a rock crusher at Manhattan, Kan., and is now owned by Del Seuser, director, Leavenworth, Kan. When he got it, it consisted of a boiler and three wheels but in six months he rebuilt it. "We have the only existing set of Case freighting wheels, so far as we know, on this engine."

Seuser explains that the 5-foot freighting wheels have an 18-inch face with ¾-inch steel lugs only 2½ inches apart, so there are three lugs on the ground at all times. "Rolls real smooth on the pavement." Heavier-than-normal 1-inch spokes, 1¼-inch cross-spokes and a 2¼-inch flanged bull gear also mark it as a beefed-up engine.

He replaced the 7/8-inch throughstays with 1-1/8-inch. "I learned every part. I put it in myself. I learned the restoration business right here.

"These are the greatest people in the world," he declares. "As soon as they found out I was working on it, they began scrounging parts." Folks who had originally scrounged parts off this same engine brought them back and sold them to him for a fraction of what they would have brought at any fleamarket.

General Grant's own personal threshing machine: 100-year-old Hiebner Little Giant.—Feeley

Hand-feeding the Gen. Grant is a dusty job.—Feeley

Gen. Grant and power compared to Case separator.—Feeley

Bob Havetter, Parkville, Mo., tends his 8-HP ½-scale model of a 20-HP Rumely. Nameplate indicates it is ASME coded for operation in any state.—Feeley

Half-scale Rumely built in 1965 powers the Gen. Grant, 100 years its senior.—Feeley

Steam pile driver and hoist from Topeka supplies live steam to 25 models.—Feeley

149

Del Seuser & Son fire up their 45-HP Case freighter.

Teaching his boy the business.

Farmall spins out trying to locomote the Case.

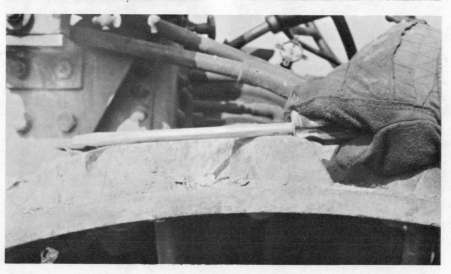

Rare freighting wheels put three cleats on pavement at once.

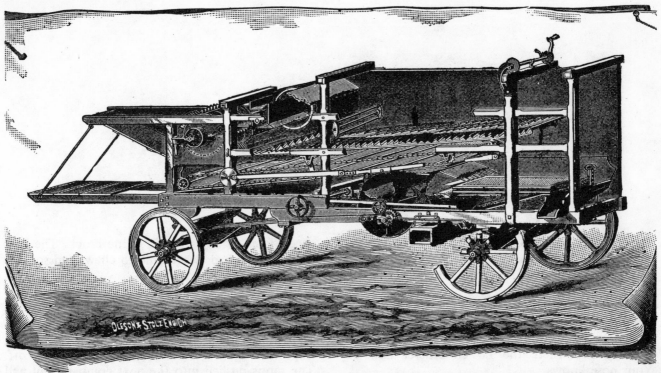

We give herewith a good illustration of a "skeleton view" of the Minnesota Chief threshing machine, made by the Minnesota Thresher Company, Stillwater, Minn. The setting of the cylinder, and the whole arrangement of the working parts, make this one of the easiest managed and most effective threshers now in use. There is no waste of grain either from failure to thresh out, or imperfect separation, and it will even do good work in hulling clover seed, without a regular hulling attachment, which can be obtained if desired. There are very few belts needed, and altogether the machine is very simple, and durable.

What
Can't Pull Out?

Why the

Non-pull-out

Bow on the **Jas. Boss Filled Watch Cases,** made by the **Keystone Watch Case Company,** Philadelphia. It protects the Watch from the pickpocket, and prevents it from dropping. Can only be had with cases stamped with this trade mark. Ⓒ

Sold, without extra charge for this bow (ring), through Watch dealers only.

Ask your jeweler for pamphlet, or send to makers.

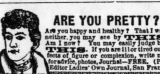

MOLASSES DAYS
at Alma, Kan.
Last two Sundays in September

Every Fall since 1874 the Thierer farm west of Alma, Kan., has repeated the sorghum molasses-making ritual. You can join the fun.

Take the winding, scenic Skyline Drive from Snokomo School west of Topeka, through Alma and Alta Vista. If the wind's right, you won't have to ask where the Lowell Thierer farm is. Your nose knows.

Here where the sorghum cane grows thick and tall, Pat, the horse, plods the circle at the one-horse mill, rotating the three-barrel press bought from the 1909 mail-order catalog by Lowell's grandfather for $27.60. The cooking-vat cost another $16.

Civil Air Patrolmen swarm through the field, cutting the cane with corn knives and laboriously stripping off the leaves and grain heads. Carefully—if the cane touches the ground it's ruined—it's hauled to the mill. Willing children thrust the stalks between the rollers. The thin green juice dribbles into a stone crock. The kids grab the crushed sweet cane to chew, and so does Pat.

Strained several times to remove bits of stalk, the watery sap goes into one end of the compartmented vat over a slow wood fire. As it boils, impurities float to the top to be skimmed off. The sap is pushed into the next compartment and fresh sap is added. Three hours later, 10 gallons of raw cane squeezin's have become one gallon of thick brown molasses.

Stop in sleepy little Volland where time stopped some years ago and visit the Kratzer General Store, which is everything a General Merchandise Emporium ought to be.

And enjoy the famous Flint Hills while you drive. And in Alma stop at Mill Creek Museum and see the dog-powered treadmill and other ancient delights from Kansas' pioneer past. Campgrounds abound around. Ask at the Museum.

"Pat's m' pal!"

Pat knows the route, now.

Collecting and trying recipes her pioneer ancestors (they called them "receets") ate by is the hobby of Mrs. Ruth E. Stone, Topeka.

She graciously typed off a couple especially for you, a reader of DAYS OF STEAM AND GLORY, at the request of Dr. Newell Feeley, DDS, Topeka, our photographer for this section. Minsky Pie came from John Sexton, who fed it to threshing crews in 1903.

MINSKY PIE
serves 21

3½ cups pumpkin
6 beaten eggs
1 quart milk
1½ cups brown sugar
1 tsp. cinnamon
1 tsp. nutmeg
1 tsp. salt
3 cups mincemeat
3 unbaked pie shells

Combine and mix throughly the first seven ingredients. Pat one cup of mincemeat into the bottom of each shell. Pour in the pumpkin mix. Bake at 350 degrees 40 to 50 minutes or until pumpkin is set.

Kids feed cane to mill and to--

BEEF PIE
serves 25 to 30

12½ lbs. stewing beef cut into ¾-in. cubes
1½ lbs. flour
¼ lb. salt
1 tsp. pepper
1½ gals. water or vegetable or meat stock
1 qt. onions
3 qts. peas
3 qts. carrots

Dredge the meat in ½ lb. seasoned flour. Brown in hot fat. Cook in Dutch oven until tender. Remove. Pour in the gravy stock or water. Make a paste of the remaining flour and water, stir in the stock. Cook until thickened. Combine meat and vegetables. Pour in the gravy. Mix. Put in two dripping pans 12x20x½. Top with pastry or biscuits and cook until done. May be used without the topping.

Our thanks to Mrs. Stone.

Lowell and Mrs. Thierer are top molasses cooks.—Photos by Dr. Newell O. Feeley

153.

PIONEER HARVEST FIESTA, INC.
"Where Machines, Tools, Articles & Methods of the
Past Re-Unite with Friends"
Fairgrounds
Ft. Scott, Kan.
First Weekend in October

You'll see old steam engines, gas tractors, over 50 types of stationary gas engines, sorghum mill, antique baler at work, farm light plants, old guns, papers, books, coins, stamps, Indian relics, pony-pulling contest, etc.

Headed by George Jackson, these men have done a loving job of restoration, as you can see from the photos, many by Dr. Newell O. Feeley, Topeka.

Reeves No. 3248, 1910, 25-HP cross-compound, 11 and 16-inch bore. Could start a heavier load by directing steam into both cylinders simultaneously. When this engine was found in Labette County, Kan., parts of the engine had been removed and a Cadillac engine installed and belted to the belt pulley: used for about three years pulling hedge trees around McCune, Kan. Restoration is scheduled to take four years. Owned by Lyle Hoffman, Worthington, Ohio.

16-HP 1908 Aultman-Taylor owned by Everett Rohrer, Denver, Colo, who brought it here for restoration. She's in excellent shape for restoration except she needs a boiler and a 12-year search has failed to locate one. If you've got an extra boiler for her, please mail it to Pioneer Harvesters, so this fine old engine can sing again.

18–55 Avery double simple has 6-inch bore, 10-inch stroke, operates at 150 pounds and 250 RPM. George Jackson spent six years, five trips, 1,500 miles acquiring parts. Boiler has been inspected and approved by the state boiler inspector. The under-mount was designed for easier accessibility and belting-up from the ground.

154

Spare parts dept.

This will be a Bates Steel Mule again someday, George Jackson swears as he pays respects to her rusty bones. A half-track tractor is said to be in production again in Oklahoma City.

Little Fooler–Townsend 15–30 Oil Tractor, 1926, built to look like a steam engine to help woo farmers away from steam. Has 2 cylinders, both pistons on 1 crank, firing alternately. Newspaper publicity promised you could use it day or night. Anybody know what was inside the "boiler"?

Rock crusher turned stone fences into roads: powered by a steam traction engine, she was used from 1920–35 in NW Bourbon County, Kan., owned by a community group. As farmers were able to buy barbed wire, they fed their stone fences into this monster to improve farm-to-market roads. Stone fences were disliked because they harbored snakes and rodents.

Two Engines Were Dead——

——They Live Again!

Case 1914 80-HP No. 31474 was delivered new near Pratt, Kan., to the Axenger Bros. They plowed and threshed with the 11x11 engine until the late '20s or early '30s when she was roaded 250 miles under her own power to Bourbon County, Kansas. There she threshed until 1935 when she went on a sawmill until 1950. She sat there until George Jackson, Pioneer Harvester's president, found her in 1954. He and other Pioneers made her young again.—Pioneer Photos

The Wreck of the Case, No. 31474, when George Jackson found her at a sawmill.

RESTORATION: A LABOR OF LOVE

Pioneer Harvesters' 1916 Case 80-HP cost about $2,500 new. Bottom scrap value was about $100. The men spent $1,200, maybe $1,500, for parts, travel, welding, machine work, paint, etc. Does not include the hundreds of hours of labor lavished on her. "This work is fun and satisfying but not a financially profitable venture," says Jackson.

Frick No. 17628 twin-cylinder. 20-HP 7x10, 150 pounds W.P., built about 1921, worked her entire life on a Neosho River island south of St. Paul, Kan. During low water she forded the river to the island, where she threshed every year until 1935, when she was abandoned. There she sat while five floods completely covered her. A 10-inch tree grew through a driver. In 1961 Jackson & Friends towed her 17 tons back across the same rocky ford with a bulldozer and set to digging the river mud out of her boiler, tanks, pipes, gears, bearings and engine. They re-flued her, made some boiler repairs, put in a new deck, new coal boxes, new canopy, patched up the water tanks and did a heck of a lot of scraping and painting and got her going again 30 years to the month after she was abandoned. Photo shows her as she was "stored" under her own power in 1935. This is a winter picture. In summer you couldn't see her for trees and weeds. Frick is rare in Kansas, although some 200 are known in Eastern U.S.

Case's first public appearance during her convalescence: partly restored, she's steaming toward the show grounds in 1956, preceded by a 20-HP Minneapolis operated by Roberta Jackson, George's daughter.

Mike Cordell, Ft. Scott, used to work on the threshing rig this Case engine powered. When he learned one of his favorite engines had been restored to youth and life, he stopped by in his Model A to admire her again.

C. C. Withers and John Gains preparing Pioneer Harvester engines for annual boiler check. L—R: 19-HP Port Huron, 16—HP Aultman-Taylor, 80-HP Case, 16-HP Reeves Special, 50-HP Case and 20-HP Minneapolis.

157

This 12–25 Avery and 22-inch separator broke farmers away from their steam engines and 40-inch machines.

Do-All 4-cylinder experimental tractor used from 1927-38, forerunner of Allis-Chalmers. Note Model A Ford radiator, standard equipment.

1926 Moline 4-cylinder with integral implement units. Note ground-driven mower.

Hay tedder stirred the windrows to dry after a rain. Then you had to rake 'em up again. If all the leaves weren't worn off the hay by then—well, you must not have let it dry enough.

Wood-frame 2-row corn planter, c. 1875, formerly carried two seats and was hand-checked. This improved model is wire-checked.

One-horse hay jack (rake) c.1865. Wooden frame. Doubled as hay sling.

Two-row corn cutter, 1910. First you tied four corn stalks together at the top to form a skeleton for the shock. Then two men rode this thing, gathering the cornstalks as the knives cut 'em off. When they had enough for a shock, they stopped, piled it around the four tied stalks. I'd rather drive a SP chopper.

Who Did What

How a Threshing Crew was Organized
Information supplied by
George Jackson, Ft. Scott, Kan.

Based on a 25-80 HP Case engine and a 40-inch Case separator they operated in central Missouri 40 years ago:

The threshing run starts about July 4 and is geared to serve about 36 farms, most of them one-day stands. Two general plans are followed: either the run starts at one end of the line and proceeds to the most remote point, where equipment is shut down until next year, then works back to the starting point—or the run is laid out in a rough circle so the rig returns home for the winter.

Someone must always be last. As it takes six weeks to complete a threshing run, to prevent the tragedy of spoiled grain, the farmers at the end of the line stack their grain. Stacks are paired so the separator can pull closely between them and the bundles can be pitched directly into the feeder. There is no need for bundle haulers; four pitchers are all that is needed to feed the separator.

Such a big outfit required a 25-man crew (pity poor Mom who had to feed 'em!) Three men stayed with the outfit throughout the run: the engineer, the separator man and the water boy.

1 Engineer—the owner or his hired man; operates and maintains the steam engine. Sometimes a fireman and flunky were used, also. Straw-burners required still another man.
1 Separator Man—in charge of setting, belting and operating the threshing machine.
1 Water Man or Water Boy—responsible for arranging for the cleanest possible water for the boiler and fetching same with team and water wagon. This might include pumping or bailing the water by hand.
4 Field Pitchers—stay in the field and help load bundle wagons; they pitch onto the wagon while the bundle hauler stacks the bundles, heads-in, around the wagon.
12 Bundle Haulers—each driving his own flat-bed wagon to haul bundles from field to machine. Two wagons unload at the same time, one on each side of the feeder.
1 Chute Man—handles the grain discharge chute and distributes the grain in the wagon box.
1 Grain Hauler—hauls wagon full of grain to the granary, puts empty wagon into position, hitches and unhitches team, transferring from one to the other.
2 Grain Men—stay at the granary to scoop out the grain from the wagon into the bin.

Some outfits pulled their own cook car and provided a cook.

Boys Will Be Boys

With such a large crew it was often impossible to supply enough manpower from the farms, so outside help was hired. Many men traditionally "followed the harvest." They were drifters, shifters, school boys and teachers on vacation and men seeking adventure. Many were not conditioned to heavy work under the scorching sun so it didn't take them long to learn that some relief could be obtained by slugging the separator with a few extra bundles. Then everybody got a drink and a breather while the separator man crawled inside to claw out the lodged straw. (The absolutely unhappiest-looking man I ever saw was the combine operator who had choked his machine hard-packed full from concaves to tailboard with overripe cuckleburrs.—dcj) This was an expensive way of getting a rest because grain was blown into the stack as the machine lost and then regained speed—since constantly correct speed was critical to the threshing-cleaning process. These bundle bunglers who indulged in separator sabotage probably were, back in the city, trolley-pullers.

A Dakota Outfit

The daily break-even point for a steam rig even in those pre-inflation days was staggering. G. B. Gunlogson threshed for many years in North Dakota. He reports he bought a $3,500 rig in 1905 on four-year terms and paid up in 1909. He lists crew, daily wages and other daily expenses for 1908:

1 Engineer	$5.00
1 Fireman	3.00
1 Separator Man	5.00
1 Water Man & team	6.00
1 Spike Pitcher	3.00

10 Bundle Haulers
  & teams @ $5   50.00
4 Field Pitchers
  @ $2.50   10.00
2 Cooks @ $1.75   3.50
  Total daily wages   86.50
(He occasionally used 11 bundle teams and two spike pitchers)
Supplies & oil   6.00
Food   10.00
Fuel & incidentals   8.00
Roughly $110 per day—repairs extra; interest, taxes and depreciation also extra.

From Steam to Gas
(Geo. Jackson)

The introduction of the gas tractor produced a marked change in harvest customs. Smaller outfits required fewer men and permitted a three-week run.

For example, a 12-25 Avery belted to a 22-inch separator used nine men and threshed about half as fast as the steam outfit discussed above. Whereas the larger outfit took six weeks to make a 36-farm run, the smaller outfit made a nine-farm run in three weeks. The large crew usually had to be supplemented with outside hired hands while the nine-man crew most often was composed of work-trading farmers in the ring. Threshing then became a neighborhood operation with nine farmers pooling their resources to buy and operate the rig:

  1 man operated tractor and separator
  5 men hauled bundles
  1 man hauled grain
  1 field man helped load bundles
  1 man cleaned up or filled in as needed.

The cost of a small gas outfit, tractor and thresher, was about the same as the cost of the larger steam traction engine alone. Also, in the three-week run there was less chance of bad weather than during six weeks.

Railroader Makes Model Parts

Want to build a steam engine model? Don't know where to get the parts? Check with Ed Alexander, 710 W 44 St., Kansas City, Mo.

A railroad engineer and a draftsman, he takes his measurements off the original, draws the plans to scale, oversees the making of the patterns and the casting of the iron. Started to help a model-making friend, this developed into a hobby which Ed plans to expand into a post-retirement business.

Steering wheel, intermediate gear housing, steam gauge, steering mechanism.

Showing ¼-scale Case parts, here's Ed with a smokebox door, flywheel and bull gear.

Whistle, boiler feed pump, water column and—well—YOU know.

SOUTHWEST KANSAS ANTIQUE ENGINE & THRESHER ASSOCIATION
Haviland, Kan.
2nd Weekend in August

Originally held in Wichita, the show got squeezed out. Haviland offered its sponsorship and formed a local association, electing William Arnett president. The three-day show always starts off with a downtown parade, led by the Boy Scouts and the community band. It starts officially each day when the engineers get steam up and blow their whistles. A minister invokes the Lord's blessing on the activities to follow.

A 40x100 tent shelters models, hobbies and small exhibits. A community weiner roast is held on Thursday evening, followed by a talent show. Friday sees two Little League ball games.

Featured are not only steam threshing, but a tug-of-war between model steam engines, a Baker fan test, separator setting contest, steam engine slow race and log sawing.

How He Got the Bug

Steam engineering, like fishing, is an incurable disease. Whether it is fatal or not depends on your wife. Of course, anyone who threshed when young is already susceptible. Then it takes only one exposure to a bundle fork in his extra-susceptible later years, or one lungful of that heady steam-smoke-hot cylinder oil to give him an acute case of the galloping steamers. Symptoms are a bright eye, inability to talk about other things, a hand on the throttle and a life span increased by 20 to 40 years.

R. D. Yoder, whose letterhead says YODER'S HOBBY LOBBY AND DAIRY FARM, Yoder, Kan., tells how it happened to him, as reported by Weston F. Cox, Haviland, Kan.

"I hope my story will tell why men and women folk relive their teenage years, when mechanical power was replacing live horse power in all farming operations. This conversion was so fantastic in wonder that, now in our age, we want to look back and retell this period to our grandchildren."

To this end, in the early 1950s, "We began to look around and see where these big, powerful steam engines and machinery of yesteryear had gone. We found them few and far between . . . A group of collectors developed, who restored their finds into nice operating show pieces, all finished in their original factory paint, striped and lettered beauties."

Gas is practically as exciting. Near Kempner, Tex., in the Austin area, 1960, Yoder found a wooden 1916 Avery "Yellow Kid" thresher, 24x36, and a 1921 Avery 14-28 tractor. The separator was preserved in a shed, but the tractor had stood outside since 1947 and a tree six inches thick had grown through a driver.

The whole town of Haviland pitched in to help restore the Avery outfit, leading to Haviland's sponsorship. The man who did much of the restoration, John Ondabu, Kisii, Kenya, Africa, a student at Friends Bible College, Haviland, got so much paint on himself that his friends kidded him about being "more yellow than black."

The whole town of Haviland pitched in to help restore the Avery outfit. This led to Haviland becoming the SWK sponsor. Many local folks pitched in with blacksmithing, carpentry and automotive repairs.

The outfit's maiden voyage was in the parade that launched Miss Kansas, Debbie Barnes, on her way to Miss America 1968.

Half-scale "Star" with undermounted engine, exhibited by F. H. Massoni, Kismet, Kan.

R. D. Yoder shows off his 1913 Avery Undermount.—SWK photos

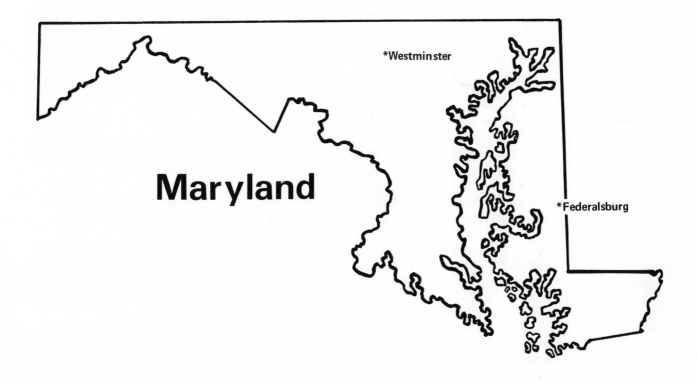

Maryland

*Westminster

*Federalsburg

A Layton pet is 1921 8¼x10 16-HP Frick.–Emory Dobson

EASTERN SHORE THRESHERMEN & COLLECTORS ASSOCIATION, INC.
James Layton Farm
Federalsburg, Md.
Late July or Early August except the year after leap year
when it's different

Just for old times' sake, Jim Layton fired up his 1929 Frick 8½x10 in 1961 and threshed a little wheat, neighbors helping.

He didn't realize what he'd started.

The next year, quite a crowd turned out. The shows kept getting bigger. On June 11, 1966, 19 steam buffs elected him president of the country's easternmost steam show, only 40 miles from the ocean. They elected his daughter, charming 15-year-old Shirley, the world's youngest steam engine secretary.

She reports membership includes the Eastern Shore of Maryland, Delaware and Virginia, "steam and gas threshermen and collectors of almost everything." Spectators number around 12,000.

Besides wheat threshing you'll see shingle sawing (better say that slowly), sawmilling, parades, broom-making, cornmeal grinding, etc. VP Col. Ross Rhodes, auctioneer, likes to rattle off a mock coon or dog auction for the crowd's (and his) amusement. No money is exchanged but full many a jocular jest is.

Feature of the 1967 show was a 13-inch rain which put an engine into the mud, firebox and all. "Nothing can stop real steam show lovers!" reveals Secretary Shirley.

The show also boasts, besides the last steam traction engine Mr. Frick ever built (No. 30519), the allegedly only Model B Oil-Pull east of the Mississippi, owned by "Oil-Pull" Pete Lovelace; scadallions of gas engines (100 on one truck); live

steam models; antique cars and household gadgetry; balers, tools, threshers, a colonial Olde Blacksmythe Shoppe; hydraulic rams that pumped water with water before REA came through, and even that rarest of all farm machines in the East, a windmill.

This is the only show on the Eastern Shore; there are but two others in the state. Area folks offer the kind of hospitality that's hard to find.

With a start like this, Secretary Shirley opines, "We're on the verge of a breakthrough with no way to go but forward!"

Since the show date is a movable feast, you'd better check with Miss Shirley, Rt. 2, Federalsburg, Md. 21632.

Jim Layton on the last Frick built at the first among-friends threshing bee, 1961. New cost was $2,800 plus freight on 10 tons. Runs 3 MPH at 250 RPM. Separator is a 28x47 all-steel Frick.– Robbins Hollyday

Thought to be the only Model B Rumely Oil-Pull 25—45 east of the Mississippi, "Oil-Pull" Pete Lovelace belongs to this jewel.—Lovelace

World's youngest steam secretary's secretarial chores include cleaning Keck Gonnerman flues and twisting bolts off a 12—24 Hart-Parr. Look how she's bent that wrench!—Layton

MASON-DIXON HISTORICAL SOCIETY
Carroll County Farm Museum
Westminster, Md.
Steam-Up Days mid-May
Show early September

Sawmill is 1/5 scale '01 Frick. Built by Ted Gowl (back to camera) and operated by son Dick, it has a 12-inch blade, saws logs 5 inches by 4 feet, "works like a clock," according to Gowl the Elder. Has three head blocks and belt feed. Ted also built a ½-scale steam engine and a scale model web-stacked thresher that works just like a real one. Check show date with Ted Gowl, 2913 Northwind Rd., Baltimore, Md. 21234.

Most popular with the children is William Handley, Cambridge, Md., and his oxen.—Hollyday

New for the 1969 show, this 1926 Keck Gonnerman is owned by Paul Singer, Denton, Md. Rated 19 HP, it has an 8¾-inch bore by 12-inch stroke, does 3 MPH at 240 RPM, weighs 20,000 pounds. Bearing serial No. 1819, it cost $2,900 new.—Lovelace

"Oil-Pull" Pete Lovelace, Wye Mills, Md., owns this cute li'l 8-HP 1895 Nichols & Shepard. It weighs 6 tons, does 3 MPH at 250 RPM, has the Stevenson link valve gear, cost $900 new.—Lovelace

*Constantine

Michigan

EARLY DAY GAS ENGINE & TRACTOR ASSOCIATION, INC., Br. 4
Constantine, Mich.
Leland Warren Farm
1½ Miles West Mottville, Mich.
First full weekend in August

Events include daily parade, teeter-totter, corn shredding, fan test, sawing, plowing, baling and threshing, with two steam engines, 40 gas tractors and 100 gas engines.

Organized with 20 members in 1960 with Elwood Dieffenderfer as president, Early Day has grown to well over 200 members with its own clubhouse.

The first four shows were held at Constantine, Mich. Needing more room, the members voted to move to Mottville where it rained and rained. In fact, it rained cats and dogs, judging by the ground covered with poodles. The tractors did most of their 1966 performing pulling cars out of the mud. Every year has been a bigger success both in exhibits and attendance, in 1968 reaching well over 3,000 people.

New equipment includes an old sawmill which has been restored fully. Members in 1968 pitched in and built a new 24x36 clubhouse, which also serves as a chow hall during showtime.

Present officers are Frank Farmer, Eau Claire, Mich., president; Russell Bergersen, Cassopolis, Mich., vice-president; Warren Bachtel, Millersburg, Ind., treasurer; and Mrs. Daisy Wagner, Constantine, secretary.

"We think this book, DAYS OF STEAM AND GLORY," says Mrs. Wagner, "will do a lot to further interest in all our clubs. In so doing, maybe many engines will be saved from the junk yard and be used as an enjoyable hobby for years to come."

22-inch Advance–Rumely. Lou Rineholt, owner.

Double-header teeter-totter. Below, 1920 12-20 Rumely Oil-Pull owned by Leland Warren; right, 1923 16-30 owned by George Baumeister, Burr Oak, Mich.–Donald Knepp photos

Andy Baumeister, Burr Oak, Mich., demonstrates his Maytag. Says Sec. Wagner, "We're glad to see this age group interested in engines and tractors. They will determine whether our clubs will continue to grow and the hobby be preserved."

1924 12–20 crossengine Case, the only one in the club. Al Troyer, Sturgis, Mich., owner

Crawler garden tractor lays its tracks under the control of Don Knepp & Son.

1914 20–80 Baker provided a little excitement during the show when a gasket blew. Lou Rineholt, Vicksburg, Mich., calmly pulled his fire, cooled 'er down some, repaired it and had steam up again in an hour.

1925 22–80 HP Advance–Rumely owned by Ray Wenger, Sturgis, Mich., on the fan. 9x11-inch, 240 RPM, 150 pounds, No. 15058, weight, 14 tons.

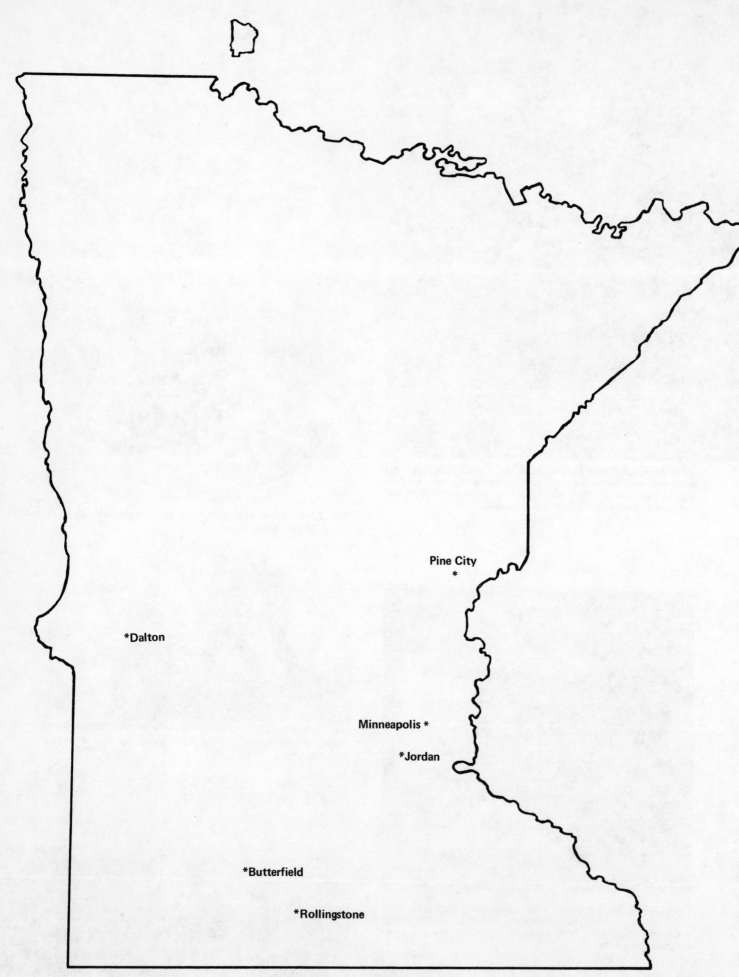

Pine City
*

*Dalton

Minneapolis *

*Jordan

*Butterfield

*Rollingstone

Minnesota

1917 Case 22–65 R&L No. 33,276 owned and restored by Otto Wolner, Butterfield. Prior to the Butterfield Threshing Bee, Wolner fired her up once each fall so people could get a glimpse of threshing as in days gone by. Now it is one of the central attractions of the Bee.

BUTTERFIELD THRESHERMEN'S ASSOCIATION
Voss Park
Butterfield, Minn.
Third Weekend in August

S tarted "as a sort of a lark," the Butterfield Threshermen's Annual Steam and Gas Engine Show outgrew its didies before it was one day old.

Reports historian-publicist Bill Paulson, Butterfield, Minn., publisher of the BUTTERFIELD ADVOCATE, "There are many little shows—one-man deals—in our area of southern Minnesota, where the farmer may have an old steamer, decide to fire up on a Sunday afternoon, and charge $1 a head. In Butterfield, population over 600, as we say (601), we decided this type of thing might be good for a village celebration. Several area farmers had started refurbishing old tractors as a hobby but had no place to show them."

Delivering milk to Butterfield creamery in 1912.

172

Mrs. Helen Harder astonished show visitors by demonstrating the near-forgotten spinster's art.

The late Ned Gustafson first broached the idea at a November, 1966, Butterfield Community Club meeting. Members were so enthused they appointed a committee and voted $100. The club organized Jan. 24, 1967, and elected Wayne Kispert president. The board decided right away quick that the show theme should be Early Americana and it should be as non-commercial as possible. Beards sprouted all over.

"We publicized the one-day 1967 event as much as possible," Paulson relates, "and figured we might get 2 to 3,000 people if the weather held. What happened was fantastic.

"The highway patrol and sheriff's office estimated the crowd at close to 15,000. Our parking and ticket-taking plans went awry under the crowd pressure.

"In 1968 we stretched it to a two-day show. We were better organized. The crowd was as good as the previous year."

Events include steam threshing, gas tractors and engines, wood sawing and splitting, spinning, churning, an antique display and a costume contest.

"The unprecedented success of the first show impressed upon the Association the need to organize a permanent body," says the publisher-historian. Once incorporated, the Association was able to lease the park from the village. Money received over expenses goes into permanent improvements. Already the Association has paid its early debts, lighted the park and installed the only electrically-lighted privies in the county.

Butterfield gives cash prizes for the best-costumed customers.

The Real Farm Power

Courtesy of Paul Fabick, R.D. 1, Sharpsville, Pennsylvania. This ad taken from the Farm Journal Magazine of the year 1915.

States Paulson, "As is true in so many events, the history and the future success of the Butterfield Steam and Gas Engine Show can be summed up in two words: community cooperation."

Outdoor worship services are conducted on the grounds Sunday morning.

Information and illustrations courtesy Paulson and his BUTTERFIELD ADVOCATE.

AN OLD BEAUTY
by
John F. Buschena
Fulda, Minn.

The thresher I recently purchased from friends in Kentucky is one of the early models of the J. I. Case Agitator thresher which came out in 1880.

This machine was bought new by John Mack about 1885. He moved to Kentucky then and settled in Franklin. This machine was built for sweep horse power. It required from 10 to 12 horses. This power was slow and very uneven speed, so it required slow threshing to about 250 or 350 bushels a day, so this machine was not used too much after it was shipped down South, as the steam engine slowly took over the horse power work.

In 1905 the horse power attachment was removed and a belt pulley put on. Mack bought a used 12-HP Huber steam engine. Then there was plenty of good power and they could thresh from sunup to sundown and thresh much more grain per day.

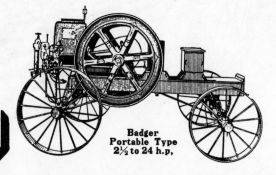
F. HAL HIGGINS Agricultural Engineering Research Collection.

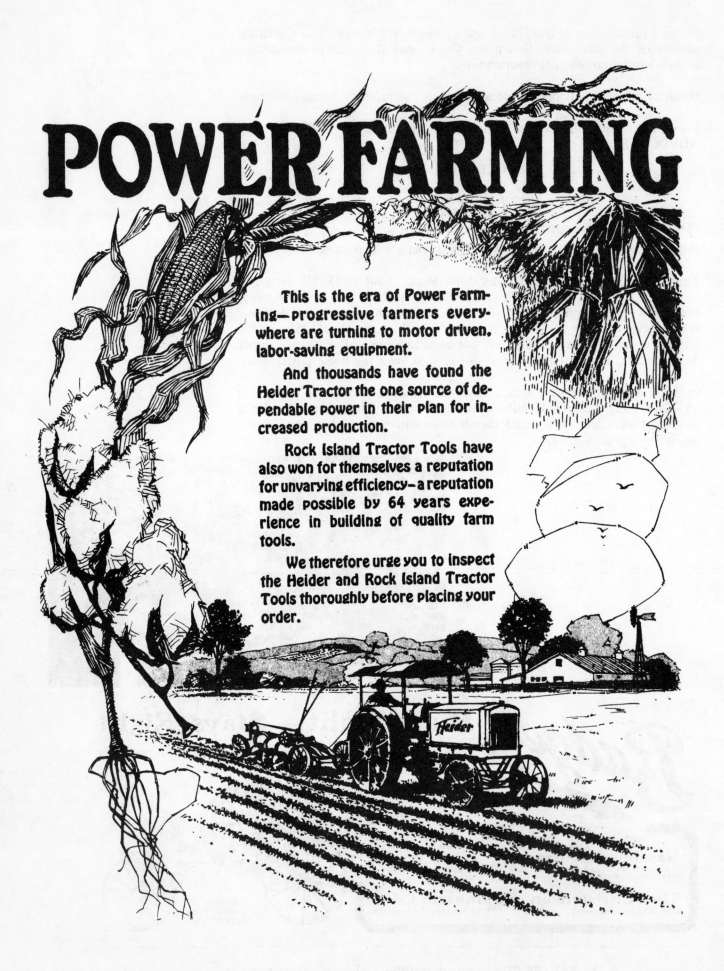

POWER FARMING

This is the era of Power Farming—progressive farmers everywhere are turning to motor driven, labor-saving equipment.

And thousands have found the Heider Tractor the one source of dependable power in their plan for increased production.

Rock Island Tractor Tools have also won for themselves a reputation for unvarying efficiency—a reputation made possible by 64 years experience in building of quality farm tools.

We therefore urge you to inspect the Heider and Rock Island Tractor Tools thoroughly before placing your order.

176

Before...

George Samuelson found this 1924 variable-speed 12–20 Heider near Welcome, Minn., in such tough shape he didn't know where to begin. It had a 4-cylinder Waukesha 4½x6¾ engine that produced 1 to 4 MPH at 900 RPM, weighed 6,000 pounds. Like so many of the old relics found in farm groves or in junk piles, many of the Heider's giblets were missing. With the aid of friends, the blacksmith and a lot of scrounging, George restored the Heider to its original condition (below). He won't even estimate how much time he put into it. Butterfield area men restored 11 old tractors in a single year—all running in the show.

...and After

But there was another handicap against this machine. It required so many men to run it: two to cut the bands, two to feed, three in the straw stack, and four to sack the grain and haul it to the granary.

This was the first machine I worked on in 1905 as a boy of 13.—(Adapted from THE IRON-MEN ALBUM Magazine)

Another turn-of-the-century classic powers this separator at the show: a 9-HP Frick portable steam engine owned by Raymond Peets, Truman, Minn.

Left: Minnesota's forests are both a resource and an obstacle. Pioneers had to clear land—but the trees provided lumber, shingles and fuel. John Pankratz found this unusual cordwood splitter at Fairfax, built from the complete front end of a small Rumely Oil-Pull. A rear wheel of the same tractor mounts the splitting wedge. The wheel is constant-running; you hold the chunk's sawed end against the wheel and the wedge comes around ker-whack! Beats the arm and ax, they say!

Wayne Hanson's 1-cylinder 8–16 1915 Mogul which he found behind the Schlach Bros. shed in the Comfrey-Darfur area with the head off. "A tree had fallen on top of it and mice were running in and out of the water hopper. They said they had sold the head to a guy from Hector. So . . . off to Hector I go. Out in the grove we found the head. After a little dealing ·I got the Mogul home in Frank Janzen's garage. We had to rebabbit the connecting rod, make rocker arms, but finally got it running." 2-cylinder 8x10; 2 MPH at 500 RPM.

John Pankratz with some of the 50 gas engines he shows at Butterfield.

178

A COLLECTOR TELLS "WHY"
by John Pankratz

The enthusiasm for and the experiences gained in restoring gasoline engines as expressed by some of my friends aroused my curiosity, interest and nostalgia. This was the beginning, about 1963, of the collection of more than 50 engines you'll see at the Butterfield Threshing Bee.

Taking an engine which hasn't run for 30 or 40 years and maybe junked, and restoring it to running order creates a challenge and a satisfaction which must be experienced to be understood. In a less significant way, it parallels the process of taking a useless, wrecked life and restoring it to meaningful place in society.

Much work is involved in taking an engine apart, piece by piece, cleaning off the layers of dirt and grease and rust accumulated through the years, repairing or replacing broken or missing parts. (Often it requires two identical engines to restore one completely, as you must cannibalize one for parts.)

Recognition and credit is due the older generation whose ingenuity precipitated our present highly mechanized, mobile society. They were content with a simple, quiet life, but were not oblivious to progress and convenience. Without the foregoing generations, our present accomplishments would be lacking.

Perhaps my strongest motive in pursuing this hobby is a desire to preserve for future generations concrete evidence of some of the ways of their forefathers. As a youth habitually turns the ignition key in a powerful, multi-cylinder vehicle, he would do well to remember preceding generations. It was their efforts which laid the foundation for our modern convenient life.

Star of the show, Wolner's Case powers a 36x58 Minneapolis separator. Note two feeder wings. Three rigs thresh 15 acres of oats during the 2-day show.

179

LAKE REGION PIONEER THRESHERMEN'S ASSOCIATION
"Home of the Giants"
Dalton, Minn.
Just North of I-94
Second Weekend in September

"Saga of the past" is what the Lake Region folks call their show. Besides steam and gas threshing, plowing, saw mill, Baker fan and shingle mill, you'll see a lath mill, a big steam parade and displays of interest to all ages.

Says the club's brochure, "In 1954 the Lake Region Pioneer Threshermen's Association held its first show. Only a small one was staged as no one knew just how successful it would be. To the surprise of everyone, without any advertising about 500 people came to view the first steam threshing demonstration held in the community in many years.

"Since 1954, the club has grown beyond our imagination. To date the association has built three large buildings (12,000 square feet) to house the antique farm machinery . . . common in the pioneer days.

"Thousands of people from many states attend regularly to view again and enjoy the engines and tractors they were so fond of in their younger years, and to give the younger generation an insight into the glamor of days gone by.

"Steam and large gas tractor plowing is performed daily to show how the great northwest lands were broke, making the fields ready for crops.

"Lake Region Pioneer Threshermen's Association is a non-profit organization. Neither owners nor operators are paid for their services. If there is a profit, the money goes into new buildings, etc., to make a better and more interesting show from year to year." President Dale Akerman has a big job overseeing all this. Seems like he does a good job.

Meals are served on the grounds. "Our aim," say the threshermen, "is to make this show one of the best in the country from every angle. Courtesy and good will is our aim. Without this the show could not be the success it has been to date."

Pitching bundles into the 40–64 Minneapolis thresher. Wing carriers are later additions. Says a club spokesman, "Wings were used in stack threshing as much of the grain was stacked in 4-stack settings and threshed later in the fall. The wings saved two pitchers and made it easier for the others as the wings were put in the middle of the stacks."—All photos and information courtesy Lake Region.

A few of Lake Region's engines. They have everything from 12 to 32-HP, all of 'em running!

Skinrud Bros., Underwood, Minn., owned this complete 25-HP Northwest rig threshing on the Borst farm north of Dalton in 1916. Henry Skinrud, a Director, is fireman on the Reeves engine at our show.

32-HP Reeves on 10-bottom plow at the show.

Sec. Ralph Risbrudt painting the Minnesota Giant which he and his brother restored. It was built about 1885-6 and is the oldest engine on the grounds.

The same engine, a 14-HP return flue, was built by the Minnesota Thresher Manufacturing Co., Stillwater. Chain drive was the company's first traction engine and was intended only to propel the engine, not to pull loads. Several companies were making chain drives about this time but all went to the gear drive. This engine has a 7x12 cylinder, normal speed of 200 RPM.

25-HP Garr-Scott built by M. Rumely Co. about 1916. Has ½-inch butt-strap boiler, 56 2-inch flues, 6-inch drive gears and pinions, 26x76 drive wheels, heavy shafts, 3¾-inch bore and 11-inch stroke, 42-inch flywheel. Used for threshing and lumber sawing in the Dalton area. George Melby, owner. J. B. Hilling, Coal Valley, Ill., "one of the best in the business," engineer, according to the club program book.

Reeves 32-HP cross-compound plow engine used to break prairie sod in Montana, built about '08. High pressure cylinder is 8½x14, low-pressure 14x14. WP 165 pounds. 7¼-inch drive gears and pinions, 24x76 drivers designed for plowing virgin sod. Reeves made engines from 13 to 40 HP and were a leader in heavy engine design. Restored by Ralph Melby, Dalton. Reeves made only one larger size, a 40-HP cross-compound. Reeves never made a 1-cylinder engine.

80-HP Case 11x11 operated at 240-250 RPM. Case built engines from 6 to 150-HP. Only three 150s were built. The 80 was the most popular engine for plowing and threshing.

30-HP Russell owned by H. N. Johnson & Melby. 10x13 cylinder, boiler shell of 3/8-inch plate, 36-inch diameter, butt-strap seam; 4-inch bull gears and pinions. Although Russell did not build heavy-geared engines, the company called them "Road Locomotives." They were used for belt work like threshing and sawing. Russell built engines as big as 150-HP.

Left: 25-HP Wood Bros. 10x11; 26x72 drivers, 5-inch bull gear and pinion, 3/8-inch lap seam boiler, 56 2-inch flues, built about 1910. Considered a plow engine. Normal speed 240–250 RPM. Wood, Des Moines, started late in the steam business. It is not known how many engines they built—the Dalton Boys think about 400. They also built small grain threshers and the large Hummingbird separator.

Below: Back end of the Gaar-Scott; reverse lever on left, clutch center. Small lever in front of steam gauge is the throttle. Reads 120 pounds steam pressure. Multiply this by the number of square inches of boiler surface and you get a high-tonnage figure on the internal force the boiler contains. That's why you don't want to let your crown sheet get dry and red. BOOM.

25-HP Advance—Rumely, the largest this company built, about a 1917. Had 10x12 cylinder, 6-inch bull gears and pinions, 3/8-inch butt-strap boiler, 56 2-inch flues, 26x72 drivers. Olin Thompson is the engineer, Elton Helleckson is firing.

A late Huber, 30-HP, owned by Henry Johnson, Dalton. Gilbert Kirkeby is at the throttle. As are all Hubers, this is a return-flue, as Huber never built a straight-flue. Built for plowing, has 5½-inch drive gears and pinions, 30-inch drive wheels, 10x12 cylinder, 7/16-inch butt-strap boiler. Used for threshing and sawing in Wisconsin.

Nichols & Shepard 25-HP circa 1912, owned by Kenneth Bratvold, Ashby, Minn. 6-inch gears and pinions, 26x76 drivers. Had ½-inch butt-strap boiler 36-inch diameter, 45 2½-inch flues. N&S were one of the first to comply with the Alberta, Canada, boiler laws which were the most rigid.

George Melby's 12-HP Advance, about '06. Has light gears, 5/16-inch lap seam boiler, made for threshing and sawing. These small engines were used in the East where the farms were small, fields small and rough, roads narrow, hilly and crooked. They could do a lot of work for their horsepower.

One of the last Garr-Scott engines built by Rumely, this 25-HP had a 9¾x11 cylinder, 36-inch boiler of ½-inch butt-strap construction designed for 200 pounds steam; 56 2-inch flues, 29x48-inch firebox, 6-inch gears and pinions, 26x76 drivers. Owned and restored by Melby, operated here by Henry Lebacken, St. Cloud, Minn.

Henry Johnson's 22-HP Avery plow engine. Undermounting insured that engine and wheel brackets were free from the boiler so no matter how hard the pull, there was no strain on the boiler—like a locomotive. Avery built straight and return-flue engines up to 40 HP in the under-mounted style. This one is 2-cylinder, 7x10, 2-speed, has 3-bearing crankshaft, 3/8-inch lap seam boiler 33-inch diameter with 58 2-inch flues, 5-inch gears and pinions.

New 1910 Russell and crew. The photographer, Roy Willendorf, Ortonville, was part owner. He comes to the show every year to run his big old black baby again.

Double-cylinder 7x11 25-HP Garr-Scott, Richomond, Ind., 1910, rebuilt 1925, threshed in the Dalton area until 1938, then spent a few more years in a sawmill. 3/8-inch lap-seam boiler 36-inch with 56 2-inch flues, 6-inch gears and pinions, 4-inch countershaft, 26x76 drivers, carried 165 pounds steam.

Threshing from the stack about 1904, a common winter practice then. Scene west of Ashby, Minn.

Nichols & Shepard 25-HP and Advance 40x60 about 1914.

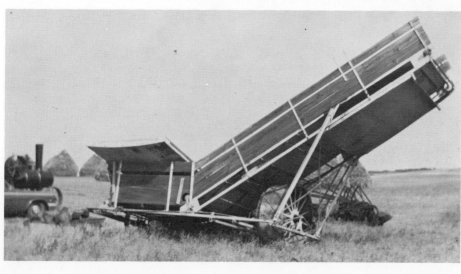

Shock loaders such as this were used extensively in these parts in the '20s and '30s. Could load a bundle wagon in 4—5 minutes. Ralph Melby, owner.

Another hunk of junk—a big 1912 Rumely steamer 2-cylinder 7x12. Drivers are 30x78; 6½-inch bull gears and pinions; ½-inch butt-strap boiler 40-inch diameter with 76 2-inch flues. Threshed and plowed in the Dakotas.

Peter Bitzman's home-made hybrid: a 20-HP Witte gas engine on an old Minneapolis steam engine running gear. He built this in WWI time when he was 17, threshed with it for his neighbors for many years north of Evansville, Minn. That's Pete himself at the wheel.

Lath mill making thousands of 48-inch lath out of hundreds of 50-inch basswood bolts.

Minneapolis Universal 1910, owned by David Hanson, Elbow Lake, Minn.

188

The largest tractor Aultman—Taylor ever built is Ozzie Stephen's 30—60 gasoline model, "One of the best old tractors we know of." Designed for plowing and road work, "was one of the top tractors in their day." Drivers are 2x8 feet, spread the 22,000 pounds out so the per-square-inch pressure on the ground is less than that under a woman's spike heel.

Left: Rumely Do-All 10—20 circa 1926, Richard Akerman's hand on the throttle. Intended to take the place of nearly all small tractors on the farm. Could be changed to a regular tractor with wheels in the front.

VP David Hanson, Elbow Lake, is in charge of the large collection of 1- to 40-HP gas engines running throughout the show.

Fresh from the oil fields around Cutbank, Mont., Superior 40-HP natural gas/LPG engine pumped black gold from deep within the bowels of Mother Earth. Not many of these around in running order. Single 12x15 cylinder admits gas in front of the cylinder. Piston rod and head are like a steam engine's. Force-feed lubrication throughout the bearing. Henry Johnson and Ralph Melby, owners.

189

THE SAGENG SAGA
Dalton minister invents, manufactures
self-propelled thresher

Farmers' struggles to improve their lot by inventing machinery produced some devices which appear strange to us. One of the strangest-looking was designed by a minister: the Sageng self-propelled thresher.

Essentially a threshing machine with a truck-like cab and equipped with its own engine for both propulsion and operation, it was designed to be driven from farm to farm, right up to the stacks. Two wing-feeders permitted threshing from four stacks at a setting. As you can see from the diagram, the straw came in at the same end it went out—the rear. The machine was, in the straw-travel pattern, folded back upon itself.

The Sageng Self-Propelled Thresher took itself to the stacks and threshed four at a set.—Lake Region.

We are indebted to Mr. O. R. Aslakson, past president, Central North Dakota Steam Threshers, New Rockford, for the Sageng thresher advertisement from the January 1910 THRESHERMEN'S REVIEW, and for the statement that about 21 of these machines were built.

Mr. Ralph Risbrudt, secretary, Lake Region Pioneer Threshermen's Association, Dalton, Minn., loaned us the Sageng photograph, the news item from the May 26, 1910 Fergus Falls, Minn., WEEKLY REVIEW, and the following information:

Halvor Sageng, the inventor of the Sageng Self-Propelled Thresher, was born in Norway. He came to America when a young boy. His parents, brothers and sisters lived on a farm 4½ miles west of Dalton. He received his education at the Augsburg College and Seminary, studying for the ministry in the Lutheran Free Church. He was sent by the church to the Madagascar mission field.

Rev. Sageng was in Madagascar for a number of years, and it was while there he came upon the idea for his self-propelled thresher. When he came back to the States he organized the Sageng Thresher Company, with headquarters in St. Paul, Minn. Stock was sold and production started in 1908.

Ten or twelve machines were built, but he had trouble with the first machines, as they developed gear and shifting problems. This was a real heavy machine and cast-iron gears would not stand up to heavy roads and fields. The problem was corrected in the last machines. After this, the company ran short of funds and went into bankruptcy. There were several stockholders in the Dalton vicinity, but no one was reimbursed.

People seem to think this was the forerunner of the combine, but this was not the case at all. Mr. Sageng wanted to eliminate the work of from three to six men it took to operate the steam rigs used at that time.

Rev. Sageng went back into the ministry, where he remained until his death several years ago.

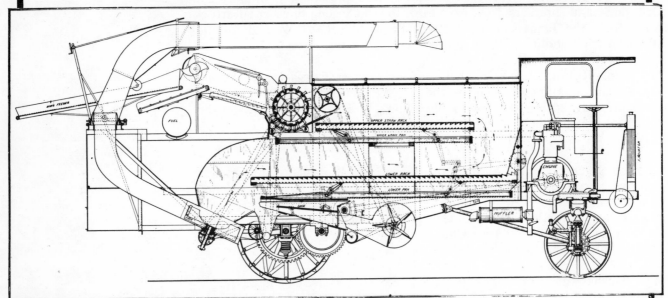
192

A TRIAL OF THE 1910 MODEL OF THE SAGENG THRESHER OCCURS IN DANE PRAIRIE
THE MACHINE WORKS TO THE SATISFACTION OF ALL, AND DOES RAPID WORK

A field trial of the 1910 model of the Sageng gasoline combination thresher was made at the farm of Ole Fossan in Dane Prairie on Wednesday and Thursday.

During the past winter the design of the machine has been materially changed, and those who saw the machine which operated so successfully this week, scarcely recognized its resemblance to the new one which they saw working last year. The thresher had just been completed at the works in St. Paul, and arrived in Dalton for its first operation. It was but natural that Mr. Sageng should want to have the first trial of the machine in the vicinity where he was raised. He was gratified at the success of his invention. Arrangements had been made with Mr. Fossan to keep his entire crop unthreshed until the machine was ready for its trial. It was run out from Dalton over a very hilly, and in some places, soft road and handled itself with perfect ease. The machine was started Wednesday noon in the presence of a large number of neighboring farmers and a lot of threshermen. Mr. Halvor Sageng, the inventor, came to the city and took out a party, consisting of Hon. C. J. Wright, Gunder Bartleson, Vernon A. Wright, E. A. Jewett and Mr. and Mrs. Elmer E. Adams to see it work.

The grain had been well stacked and when it was opened up, it was found in excellent condition, although a trifle too dry. The machine ran all that afternoon without a hitch, and at times, threshed 150 bushels an hour, which is very fair running for a 36-inch cylinder machine. Those present watched the blower very closely and found that all the grain was saved.

The machine was in charge of Mr. Anderson, superintendent at the St. Paul plant, and three assistants. After finishing threshing at Mr. Fossan's, it will be taken to North Dakota, and then to South Dakota, where grain has been saved in order to enable threshermen and those interested in the enterprise, to see a demonstration.

The machine brought to Dalton is the first one that has been completed this year, but another is practically completed and will be taken to Texas the coming week.

About 150 men are employed in the factory at St. Paul, and material has been purchased for 100 machines, which it is hoped will be completed, if possible, in time for the threshing this fall.

The test showed that the machine was consuming about four gallons of gasoline per hour. Mr. Fossan's grain was yielding well, and if it continued to hold out, he estimated that he would get 23 or 24 bushels of wheat to the acre. If the thresher continues to work as well as it did in its demonstration at the Fossan farm, it is certainly going to meet all the claims which have been made for it.

Mr. Sageng lived on a farm some 4½ miles west of Dalton, Minn. They manufactured four sizes of machines: 28x50, 50 h.p. engine; 32x54, 60 h.p. engine; 36x60, 70 h.p. engine; and a 40x64, 80 h.p. engine. All motors were 4 cylinders. At least some of the machines had Garden City feeders and wing carriers. (Story from the Fergus Falls, Minn., WEEKLY JOURNAL, May 26, 1910. Story and photo courtesy Lake Region.)

The Original **John Deere Tractor**

SMITHSONIAN INSTITUTION PHOTO

The only restored Deere All-Wheel-Drive.—Smithsonian photo

Mid-West Exhibits
Rollingstone, Minn.
Open All Year

A unique historic enterprise is the privately-owned exhibit of early equipment at Rolling-stone, operated by retired Air Force Captain Francis Hansen.

Prize possession is the John Deere All-Wheel-Drive tractor, of which only two are known to exist. Captain Hansen's is fully restored and still runs on original equipment, even down to the original Champion spark plugs. He says the other specimen has not been restored and does not have some of its original equipment.

"Our machine is No. 79 and operates perfectly," he says. He loaned it to the Smithsonian Institution in Washington, D. C.

Curious-looking to our modern eyes, the three-wheel All-Wheel-Drive was introduced in 1919. Deere promotional folders published in 1919, 1920 and 1921 report it crowns ". . . seven years of investigation and development to find the best design and materials for tractor work . . . In all respects, it is a high quality machine . . ."

Advantages claimed for the design, which featured a single rear driver and two front drivers that also steered, included weight reduction to 4,600 pounds, equal weight distribution and ability to pull and steer in soft ground. It had no differential; any wheel having traction was said to receive all the power:

"A very simple ratchet does away with the necessity for a differential," the leaflet states. The single rear wheel measured 40x20; the front wheels 36x8. All were roller-chain-driven, unencumbered by stuffy safety shields or dust covers so you could easily get to the chains and sprockets to replace them.

Another selling point was the operator's ability to shift from low to high or vice versa without stopping. The two speeds, forward and reverse, were 2 and 2 5/8 MPH. It was rated at 12-24 HP, 3-plow, with four 4½x6 cylinders. The early experimental models, at least, used a Waukesha engine.

For Hansen's history of this model's development, see page 380.

194

Ad from the Huron, S. D., HURONITE, Sept. 5 and 6, 1918.—Hansen

Capt. Francis Hansen going over his meticulously restored Deere 3-wheeler discovered in a grove near Huron, S. D.—Hansen

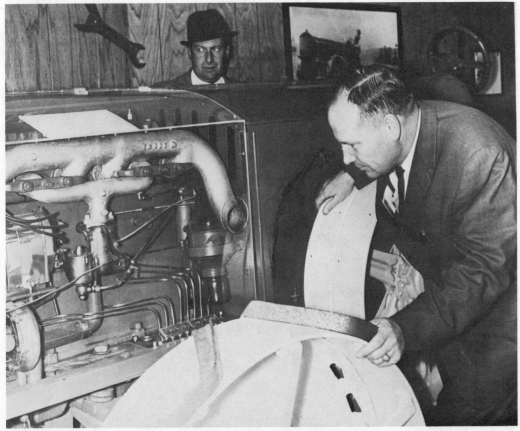

SCOTT-CARVER OLD THRESHERS
Jordan, Minn.
Last Weekend of September

This show, like so many, started out rather casually. Ermin Morrell had his father's 1914 Buffalo Pitts wooden separator and 1900 22-HP Advance steamer that didn't turn a wheel between 1945 and 1953. Then Morrell fixed up the Advance and ran it around a little, then let 'er set for another 10 years, when he decided it would be fun to see the old rig thresh again.

On a hot August afternoon in 1964 he steamed up. Bill Olander from Carver County brought his 1915 22-HP Advance. Several neighbors brought teams and bundle wagons and Loren Habegger chugged up in his '09 Model T. There was no advertising, but a nice crowd turned out.

The next year saw four steam engines, some gas engines and tractors. "We put up a lunch stand and did very well. Several thousand people turned out to see this one," reports Ronald Scott, Ermin's nephew.

"For the 1966 show we organized and became the Scott-Carver Old Threshers. Morrell was elected president, Olander vice-president, Arthur Leibbrand secretary and Ruben Boettcher treasurer."

They had rain for the '65, '66 and '67 shows "but it didn't hurt us much for the land is sand and we covered the grain stacks. In 1968 we had a shingle mill, lath mill and saw mill. Ruben brought a Minneapolis 16-HP engine mounted on a truck frame. We use this engine to advertise our show in celebrations such as Dan Patch Days at Savage."

Latter-day additions are Marvin Boettcher and his 30-60 Aultman-Taylor and Ruben's 1917 Titan. He and Scott brought their 1926 Oil-Pull. In 1968 the club bought 52 acres, erected a 40x100 shed and attracted 5,000 people. They added a 65-HP Case and some miniature engines.

"One thing we had that the people liked to see was the 1889 Watrous steam fire engine belonging to the Jordan Fire Department. It was fixed up by Ermin and Bill." Anticipated additions include a 35-70 Minneapolis gas tractor, a small Russell steamer, and a 15-30 McCormick-Deering tractor belonging to Scott, as well as his Eli hay press.

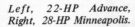

Left, 22-HP Advance,
Right, 28-HP Minneapolis.

Bill Olander's 1915 22-HP Advance on saw mill.

Machinery isn't the only attraction at the Scott-Carver show.—SC photos

1889 Watrous steam fire engine is a crowd-pleaser.

Karl is second from left. Left is his father, Paul, nearing 90, born in the Amazon Valley jungle and still in good repair. Others are brothers.—Early Day photos

SNAKE RIVER VALLEY ENGINE & THRESHERS ASSOCIATION, INC.
Marquardt Farm
6 Mi W Pine City, Minn., Co. Rd. No. 7
Second Weekend in August

"Never throw anything away," a newspaper article about Karl P. Marquardt advised. It told how he started collecting rare books and now has a football field full of "old iron."

He helped organize Early Day Gas and runs practically a one-man show on his farm. Here you'll see over 150 steam, gas, oil and diesel engines, no two alike, from ½ to 40 HP. The oldest is a 19th-century Stickney.

Among his rare jewels are a 40-60 Oil-Pull, Gray wide drum, M-H 4-wheel drive, 18-36 horizontal 2-cylinder Hart-Parr, 20-30 Wallis, Waterloo Boy, Titan, hand and self-feed threshers, 12-inch J. L. Owens pea and bean thresher, several reapers, etc.

Interstate No. 35 takes you to within six miles of the farm, blacktop the rest of the way. The Snake River show is sponsored by Early Day. Business address is Robt. H. King, Rt. 3, Box 105, Stillwater, Minn. 55082

Old-timers get large charge out of pitching bundles again at Karl's Snake River show.

1917 Minneapolis 28–90, No. 8052, 15 tons, with butt-strap boiler, Wulff valve gear, single 16x16 cylinder. "Very good condition." Looks like Karl at the throttle.

6-HP Frick is 100 years old, works.

EARLY DAY GAS ENGINE & TRACTOR ASSOCIATION
Karl P. Marquardt
National Secretary-Treasurer
2702 Polk St. NE
Minneapolis, Minn. 55418

Karl Marquardt (see Snake River story, preceding page) helped launch the national Early Day Gas Engine & Tractor Association. It now has branches in Minnesota, Michigan, Indiana, Illinois, Wisconsin, Iowa, Missouri and California.

He relates, "For about 10 years prior to 1956, many clubs were formed to preserve the once-common steam traction and portable engines. Yet, no group gave any thought to the preservation of the early one-cylinder, two-flywheel gas engines and early gas tractors."

Late that year he started correspondence with others of similar interest throughout the country, resulting in the incorporation, April 7, 1959, under Wisconsin laws as a non-stock non-profit national organization with local branches, of Early Day "to promote the collection, restoration, preservation and exhibition of gas and oil engines, gas and steam tractors, power driven farm machinery and other equipment of historical value."

The Association publishes a directory of old equipment so you'll know where to find a 13/57th bolt hole for a 1492 Gopher or whatever.

IHC 1912 45-HP Mogul weighs 10 or 11 tons, has original equipment: starting engine, make-break igniter, original magneto, instruction and parts book. "Runs very good."

Marquardts bought Fordson new in 1928, added lights and muffler, still use it.

Palmyra *

*Hamilton

*Platte City

Missouri

Most show members are engineers. Both engines are Case—the 16-HP owned by Willis Mercer, Kearney, Mo. The show has been held every year since 1961.

JAYCEE STEAM ENGINE SHOW
Fairgrounds
Platte City, Mo.
Second Weekend in August

Not only big steam engines but little steam engines, a quilting bee and a 100-foot-long Bar-B-Q are features of the annual Jaycee show. More than 10,000 people attend, thus financing next year's civic events.

You can see antique gas tractors and cars and watch a frog-jumping contest (no buckshot allowed), bike races, turtle races, horseshoe pitching, tether board, parade, with steam threshing all day both days.

In the hay pitching contest, pitchers pitch through a ring which is raised until the last fella can just barely pitch through it. Basketball coaches spy on this event.

Ross Naylor teetertots his 2/5-scale model of a 16-HP Advance. This one puts 5.5 HP on the belt, has Marsh valve gear. Weighs 2,000 pounds. Took him two years to build it.

203

NORTH MISSOURI STEAM & GAS ENGINE SHOW & DEMONSTRATION
American Legion Park, north edge of city
Hamilton, Mo.
Third Weekend of August

Some of the folks around Hamilton had seen other steam and gas engine shows and started talking it up here.

"We held our first show in 1963," reports Ryland A. Miller, secretary. "Each year we add something new to make it bigger and better. A draft horse pulling contest, promoted by President Robert Baker, Hamilton, was added two years ago and attracted many."

Paul Allen, Kingston, supervises an antique gun show, and C. O. Drumm is chairman of the antique car show. Many local organizations cooperate to make the show successful. "Old Threshers' Dinners," furnished by the Harrison Club, please folks, too. There's plenty of room in the park surrounding a covered amphitheater and an exhibit building.

Among the founders were Clarence McCutchins, Russell Moss, Bob Baker, Jim Henry, Dale Oldfield, Jack Neil, Ryland Miller, Dale Hartley, Reuben Hartley, Drexel Hill, Virgil Rains, Blake Corbett, Bob Michaels, C. O. Drumm, Leroy Huey of the Hamilton and Kingston communities, and Casey Rhinehart, Nelson Rhinehart and Paul Bryant from the Braymer area.

A Nichols & Shepard 50–116 HP owned by Roe and Claude Maxwell, Ridgeway, Mo., runs a 20-inch New Racine separator owned by Clarence Otto, Hamilton.–Strade photos

Organizations helping to make it a success include the Hamilton saddle club, garden club, Lions, public schools, Legion, Boy Scouts and chamber of commerce.

The young folks see how it was done and the old-timers relive old times. Separator furnished by Russell Wilson estate, Sampsel, Mo.

He is warmed twice who saws his own wood.

Model T Ford dates from 1927, makes every parade. Antique cars are a part of the North Missouri show. Owned by Robert Kirkpatrick, Jameson, Mo.

How many modern kids ever get to ride behind a team? Leonard Jones, Cameron, Mo., sees to it that some do. He provides rides every year.

Roland Russell, Richmond, Mo., provides his 1923 Rumely Oil-Pull. Weighs 16,000 pounds, pulls 8 to 10 plows, features positive lock differential.

Runs like new, but half-canopy and water tank on H. K. Peterson's 50-HP Case were not original equipment. He's from Trenton, Mo.

It doesn't look like Grandpa's steamer, but W. J. Early's built-up engine saves Granma's feet at the show and entertains the young'ns. He's from Trenton, Mo.

OLD SETTLERS & THRESHERS
Palmyra, Mo.
Second Weekend in July
Rain Date 1 Week Later

Besides threshing and sawing, this Palmyra Jaycee-sponsored show features a slow race, steam plowing, Baker fan, Prony brake and a wide variety of engines.

You'll see a 20-HP Advance-Rumely steamer, 25-90 Nichols & Shepard double cylinder rear-mounted, 16-HP Advance, 20-HP Aultman-Taylor, 20-HP Case, 18-HP 9x10 Advance-Rumely, 23x70 Baker 10x10 and 9-HP Case 7¼x10.

There are 15 steam models snorting about, too.

Bullwheel of the show is Bob Snow, Palmyra, old-time steam thresherman and sawyer whose father and grandfather were the same and who married the daughter of a steam railroad engineer.

Says Snow, "I hear some hot argument about different engines and valve gear. They all will do their job if maintained proper. I have never seen a poor engine or valve gear. I like 'em all."

We'd guess he's seen some poor engineers, though. Wonder if he likes them, too.

Snow's 25-HP Advance–Rumely No. 15171, 10x12 Marsh valve gear, pulling John Deere 8-bottom 1902 plow during the '68 show.

Mrs. Snow at the throttle of Bob's ½-scale model of a 20-HP Advance–Rumely. It weighs 4,450 pounds, has Marsh valve gear and Allen double-ported valve. Its 4½-inch bore and 5½-inch stroke developed a measured 11.74 HP on the Prony brake. Took him 2,000 hours to build.—The Brothers Studio photos

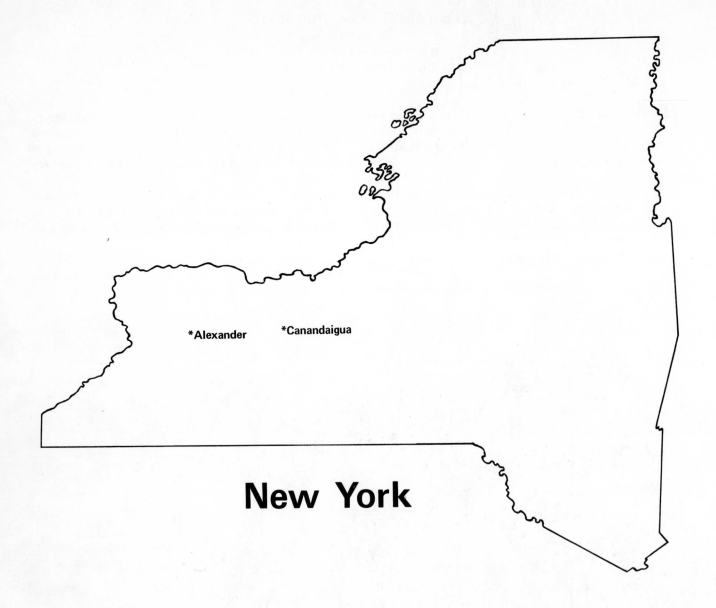

New York

*Alexander   *Canandaigua

NEW YORK STEAM ENGINE ASSOCIATION, INC.
HQ: East Bloomfield, N. Y.
SHOW: Roseland Park
Canandaigua, N. Y.
Mid-August

World's biggest steam calliope, a steam pile driver, a big Corliss engine and a genuine hay-burning ox team are among the excitements here, as well as a wooden-wheeled steam traction engine and a belting-up race.

The interest of three men in 1958 launched the club: Wallace Wood, Edward Faulkner and Homer Prudom attended a steam-up at Sam Harrington's place at Akron, N. Y. Some of the men had some engines, and somehow the word got around and they were invited to display them at the state fair.

With the encouragement of Bob Marshall and of James McLean, president, Stromberg-Carlson, things kept a-movin' until November 22, 1960, when Wood got a meeting together in the East Bloomfield fire hall and organized the Bristol Valley Steam Club. Soon the name changed to the above, and today the Association stages a big show.

Signing the charter were Claude Abbert, Homer Prudom, Wood, Robert Marshall and Ed Faulkner. Wood was first president.

World's first steam engine was Hero's, built about 130 BC, this model of which works zippity-zam at the Canandaigua show. A fire under the kettle generates steam, fed to the hollow sphere through the pivot pipes. L-shaped steam jets on the ball rim rotate it so rapidly the camera shutter at 1/500 sec. can't stop it. Engine found no practical use. Archimede's water screw (left), cranked by hand, lifted Nile water for irrigation in 230 BC.

208

Old and new are symbolized by jet plane contrail streaking through smoke from 22–65 Frick "Eclipse" operated by G. D. Kirkland, Painted Post, N. Y. Built in 1921, No. 17326, she has a 9½x10 cylinder.

A belting-up contest tests skill of enginemen and separator men. Pulling threshing machines, engines race at full-throttle 2¼ MPH into position. Men unhitch, turn the engine around and back into the belt. The first to shoot straw out of the windstacker wins. Bundles are flying in background while belt in foreground is still slack. These guys did it in 3 minutes 45 seconds and 3:30. Record is 2:20.

Early Peerless has wooden wheels.

S. W. Wood 1912 portable steamer was pulled by horses, cranks out 6 HP. Operator is Wally Wood (not related to engine). Owned by Dick Lewis, Cuba, N. Y. Ireland drag saw belongs to Association.

2-speed 1908 16-HP Waterloo was built in Ontario and is the only one in the U. S., so far as owner Ken McCormack, Jordan, N. Y., knows. Bell was borrowed from a B&O locomotive. Notice 2-speed gear detail.

Steam threshing is a daily feature here. Due to lack of space, though, they have to make one load of bundles last for the whole show.

Glen Orbaker, Newark, N. Y., owns this Baker.

A. D. Baker No. 1564 1920 21—75 has single simple 9x10 cylinder, operates at 100 pounds. Owned by Erdle Bros., Canandaigua, N. Y.

The "Frick without a trick" was known by cylinder size rather than by HP. This is an 8½x10, owned by Hoxie & Hitchcock, Levanna, N. Y.

An unusual farm implement—this 1916 10-ton twin-cylinder Buffalo-Springfield steam roller was used on vegetable farms for producing mashed potatoes—or was somebody kidding me?

1912 Buffalo Pitts 2-cylinder is rated at 14 HP. Owner is Bob Marshall, East Bloomfield, N. Y.

Below: Another trickless Frick.

Below: Advance—Rumely and grader tidy up rainsoaked parade ground. Clarence Rounds, owner.

Huber Mystery Explained

"Why the smokestack on the back end?" People frequently ask about the two Huber Return-Flue engines seen at the Canandaigua show.

Claude Abbert, owner of one, explains: "The Huber boiler is of the two-pass Scotch marine type. The fire is contained within the large tube near the lower side of the outer shell. The burning gases travel through the tube to the front end where they reverse and return to the rear through flues. There are no stay-bolts."

Some Hubers had fireboxes running the full length of the boiler for burning sawmill slabs. Saved sawing the wood into short lengths.

Continues Abbert, "Compared with the loco-motive-type boiler usually furnished on steam traction engines, this design has both advantages and disadvantages. The safety and economy records are remarkable." Huber used to advertise "5,000 in use and not an explosion." The return flue won the 1893 World's Fair consuming only 5.32 pounds of coal and 39.50 pounds of water per HP-hour.

Abbert explains the combustion gases give up so much heat to the water, there's little left by the time they reach the stack; hence, draft in firing-up is a problem. This fact, plus the large water capacity, makes them take three hours to steam up, compared to one to one and one-half hours for locomotive-type boilers.

Association's prize possession is this 25-ton Corliss 1897 engine, originally powering a Syracuse sawmill. Flywheel is 10 feet in diameter. Permanently housed on the grounds, it is in operation throughout every show.

Bill Senior's 1925 Erie pile driver is rated at 30 HP. It drives a whole forest of piles during the show.

The Canandaigua show features several fancy-free homemade models. The Tomahanna Valley Special was built by Walter Malloy.

Levanna Special has a Leffel boiler, Farquar engine. Built by Charles Hitchcock.

ModelsModelsModels

You'll find every kind of model you ever imagined at Canandaigua, and some you never dreamed of even in nightmares. See Elbow Engine in Roy Henry's story, Alexander, N. Y., section, page 238.

Sunbonnet, classic gown, and cotton in ears.

Biggest Steam Calliope in the World

Forty whistles make the Getz Bros. steam calliope the biggest there is. Not even the Russians can top it. Truckers of Lancaster, Pa., they say, "We like steam."

No, they don't have any steam-powered trucks in their fleet, and none of their 14 school buses is a steamer, but they have two coal-fired and three oil-fired portable 5-HP boilers with which they do custom steaming: sterilizing tobacco beds, cleaning out tar cars, commercial heating, emergency heat and power—any time you need a whole bunch of steam, just call the Getz boys.

Noah, William and Robert copied and improved upon a circus calliope. Noah drew the blueprints. The whistles are cast brass and hand-machined, actuated by pilot-operated fast-action solenoid valves with only 1/10-second delay contrasted to the ¼- to ½-second lag of conventional mechanical valving. When you're playing Skip to My Lou, you don't want to wait all day between pressing the G-key and hearing the note.

This instrument is the most popular feature of any show, judging by the crowds it draws. You don't need to advertise it—soon as it begins to tootle, everybody for miles around knows about it. Besides delighting young and old at steam shows throughout the Northeast, this truckload of music leads Christmas and Memorial Day and Centennial parades.

The Getz boys worked on it two years, finishing in 1963. They ran it on steam borrowed from the nearest traction engine until they built the semi-trailer in 1966. The trailer mounts a 5-HP oil-fired boiler tended by Engineer Irvin Hoffman, Manheim, Pa. With its own steam-powered electric generator, the unit sometimes supplies emergency electricity. Hoffman earned lifetime free popcorn by electrifying a popcorn wagon at one steam show.

Calliopist is Mrs. Lorena Miller, Lewisberry, Pa.

"Farming is our life work," she smiles proudly. The calliope is her hobby. A self-taught church organist and pianist, she learned the calliope "just by practicing."

Sometimes, after the instrument has stood silent for an hour or two and the whistles have grown cold, it's off-key when she starts to play. She'll run her fingers over the keys to send steam jetting through the manifold and whistles, then start out right. It can't be tuned, and the tone of each whistle depends on temperature, whim, mood of the brass and other intangibles so she has to warm it up, determine its tone-mood of the moment, and shift up or down the scale to bring the behemoth into tune.

She delights the crowd with the old favorites: Listen to the Mockingbird, Seeing Nellie Home, Tenting Tonight, Battle Hymn. Come Sunday, she drowns out many a sermon with The Old Rugged Cross, Doxology, Christian Soldiers. She can play any tune 40 or more years old you can think of.

No need to ask the traction engineers or the children or the locomotives to be quiet—she drowns 'em all out. A little thing like another steam whistle doesn't bother a-tall.

Mrs. Miller, a chirky 79, dresses the part in sunbonnet and an 1870 gown. She wears cotton in her ears, too, as does the engineer. When I went aboard to take pictures while Mrs. Miller was playing, I had no plugs in my ears but would have used chewing gum had any been handy. It's loud in there.

Whether you call the great instrument a k'LY-o-pee as city folks do, or a KAL-ly-ope like farmers say, you're right and everybody knows what you mean. It's named for Kalliope, the Greek Muse of eloquence and heroic poetry.

Each whistle is cast-brass and hand-turned.

If you don't happen to notice the heaven-splitting sound, steam squirting above the trees will alert you.

Keyboard is like piano's. She tunes instrument by shifting up or down scale.

Mrs. Lorena Miller, a farm wife, learned to play by playing. Wonder what the neighbors thought?

WHAT? You Never Heard of the Uniphone?
Neither Did I

Between performances, Mrs. Miller entrances the crowd by performing on the Uniphone—a sort of an electrical whingading, a car-battery-operated musical thingamajig that looks like a whaddaya-callit run by doorbell buzzers. A piano-like keyboard is wired to electrical vibrators that buzz wooden hammers against the tone bars.

Getz relates that the Uniphone was in a circus in the Southwest until the depression. Patented in 1917, it is the largest made, with 49 notes. A preacher bought it from the defunct circus and used it in tent meetings until WWII. Now mananging a fireworks factory, the Reverend collects antique cars. Getz induced him to sell the Uniphone by telling him where he could buy a classic Packard.

The Uniphone, rescued from a circus and the revival tent, runs off 6-V car battery. Cotton not needed in ears, here. And you can enjoy the music 'way out on the lagoon in a paddleboat—4-knee power.

220

When Wood
Was King

You can see ancient wooden hand-fed threshers and a reaper at Canandaigua. Osborne reaper is owned by Carrol Burdick. Champion hand-fed (top) belongs to the Association. Burdick's Westinghouse separator (lower right) is in top shape.

Charles Hitchcock's shingle mill is a goin' thing.

1906 Cretor steam corn popper mounted on a 1931 Model A makes all the shows around here (see closeup of its steam engine in Alexander, N. Y., section, page 236) with Don Thomasson at the controls. Does a booming business, too. There seems to be something special about popcorn from this old timer with its wee steam engine, clown and whistle. That's Master of Ceremonies Dayton Nichols (left), sampling the wares.

Goodies for the Kiddies at NYSEA

Two-horse sweep powers stationary wooden hay press.

Dave and Dan, 3-year-old Holstein steers, do all the farm work for their boss, Irving Lamb, Friendship, N. Y. Cart is over 100 years old and features the linch-pin wheel bearing and you can't hardly get that kind no more. Oxen weigh 1,700 pounds now, will top a ton when they get big. Irving shoes them himself because you have trouble enough finding a blacksmith who can shoe horses, let alone cloven ox hooves.

Early Internationals cooled themselves by running water over open hailscreen. Left is 1906 IHC famous 10-20 owned by George Marshall. Right is 1907 20-HP IHC stationary engine owned by Harold Embling, Churchville, N. Y., belted to a generator.

Ford's Fordson tractor did for farming what his Model T did for transport. More Fordsons were built than any other tractor.

1912 Avery had mowing-machine wheels for drivers, featured friction clutch. Operator is Richard Snyder, Covington, Pa.

McCormick-Deering was forerunner of IHC.

Massey-Harris produced 4-wheel-drive in 1930.

224

Gas Goes Good at NYSEA

President George Knab, Spencerport, N. Y., keeps in touch with his far-ranging chairmen by walking-talking radio.

Dave Shearns, Marion, N. Y. Whizzes by at 2¼ MPH on his 1924 Aultman–Taylor that puts out 22–45 HP with its 4-cylinder horizontal engine of 5½-inch bore and 7-inch stroke. Cooling system holds 75 gal. How'd you like to buy Prestone for that?

Gas bugs, as well as steam nuts, imagine-up their own. Novo 3-whistle Mini-Bug was built by Hines and Cook.

George Knab's 1916 30÷60 HP Aultman–Taylor plowed, graded roads and powered the belt. Takes 130 gallons water.

WESTERN NEW YORK GAS & STEAM ENGINE ASSOCIATION
Firemen's Park
Alexander, N. Y.
Second Weekend of September

It's a young show and a gas show, but WNY can assemble a pretty respectable lineup of steamers. Trouble with the East, though, is lack of room. Whereas the western shows keep one to several threshing rigs going every day of the show, the easterners have to stretch one load of bundles over the full three or four days. So mostly they just run around with their steam engines. This 1922 23–90 A.D. Baker is owned by John Farrell, Honeoye Falls, N. Y. Has a 10-inch bore and 11-inch stroke in its single simple cylinder, carries 130 pounds steam, weighs about 15 tons and, new, cost between $2,500 and $2,900.

Few engine clubs have their own newspaper. Fancy this one, then, that had a goin' newspaper before the club was two years old! FLYWHEEL NEWS, they call it.

"It all started with a gas-up at Donald Weisbeck's in Alden, N. Y." reports FLYWHEEL NEWS, "when many of the fellows asked how come we couldn't form an association in western New York." Roland Reigle, Tonawanda, held a meeting in his home in early 1967. Finally, in June, they got a-goin' with Wilfred Schneider, Darien, N. Y., president. Even with this late start they held a rally that fall, took in over $3,000 and 408 members.

Their second rally made a mighty good showing, as these pictures show. Of the spectators, THE FLYWHEEL commented, ". . . many had never known such activities existed. All ages seemed to enjoy looking back into by-gone eras."

The 1968 rally included 223 gas engines, reports the new president, Keith Alwardt, Alexander, N. Y. There were some complaints that I took so many steam engine pictures and so few gas engine pictures because the club is primarily gas.

Well, this book is primarily steam.

Three views of the 1911 Frick "Eclipse" Contractors' Special rated at 18 HP with simple center crank 9x10 single cylinder operating at 80 pounds. Weighed 15 tons and cost over $2,500 new. Owned by Ernest Wells, Delavan, N. Y. Called "the turtle on wheels" because of its long, low shape and ground-hugging velocity.

Advance–Rumely, 1919, No. 15003, 20–45 HP, simple, 155 pounds pressure, weighs 15 tons, cost between $2,500 and $3,000 new. Owner: Clarence Rounds, Lockport, N. Y.

Port Huron "Longfellow" was built about 1920, rated 25–50 HP, has a tandem compound engine, weighs some 16½ tons, used to sell for nearly $3,000. Owned by Francis Keem, East Aurora, N. Y.–WNY

James Erdle, Canandaigua, N. Y., brought his 1920 Baker 21–75 over.–WNY photo

Hand-made 3-whistle runabout generates about 20 HP with its 5x6 cylinder at 100 pounds. Chain drive.

A Gaggle of Gas

1918 IHC Titan 10–20 pulled 3 14-inch plows with its 2-cylinder. 6½x8-inch cross-mounted engine at 500 RPM at 1.85 and 2.5 MPH. L-head engine burned kerosene, gasoline or distillate. Tractor weighed 5,710 pounds. This one is owned by Allen Bushman, Spencerport, N. Y. New cost was $1,000 to $1,200.—WNY

Belting up to the 2-step pulley of an unidentified Titan.

1918 Titan 15–30 had 4 cylinders, was formerly owned by the highway department at Ft. Plain, N. Y., now owned by Ronald Rolfe, Schoharie, N. Y.

Detail of Titan chain drive.

The 1924 Bates Steel Mule, made in Joliet, Ill., was rated at 37 HP capable of pulling 3 or 4 14-inch bottoms. Four 4-1/8x5¼ vertical cylinders with valves in head burned kerosene or gasoline in Midwest engine. Boasted enclosed transmission gears. Tracks are 52 inches long, 10 inches wide. Speeds were 2.4 and 3.5 MPH. 8-foot turn radius. Weighed 4,300 pounds. Note details of chain drive, latest thing in 1924 operator comfort. Owner: Ronald Rolfe, Schoharie, N. Y.

1920 Samson Model M owned by Ben Schultz, North Tonawanda, N. Y., has many beautiful features. —WNY

Minneapolis Farm Motor, about 1917, 40–80 HP, has a 4-cylinder, L—head horizontal motor 7¼x9-inch producing 2 MPH in low gear and 2½ MPH in high gear at 500 RPM. Weighed over 11 tons. Owner: James Erdle, Canadaigua, N. Y.

Wallis 1916 12–20 is operated by Mrs. Charles Sumner, wife of the owner. Rubber tires came later.

Another 40–80 Minneapolis, circa 1917, 4 horizontal 7x9-inch cylinders, owned and operated by Sherwood and Mrs. Hume, Milton, Ont.

No excuse for getting lost on this cross-engine Case 10–20 from 1919: you always know which-away you're a-headin'. Rated for 3 14s, its 4-cylinder vertical 4½x6-inch engine burned gasoline, kerosene or distillate. At 900 RPM you had your choice of 2¼ MPH. Weighed 5,080 pounds. The right drive wheel was the main driver; the left had its own clutch and was supposed to idle except for pulling out of a mudhole. This design did not survive into the Space Age. Owner is Allen Bushman, Spencerport, N. Y.

Rumely Oil-Pull owned and operated by Charles Summers, Springville, N. Y. No data.

Unidentified Rumely offered optional head and tail lights.—WNY

Huber survived to 1939 with this Model B owned by Ross Smith, Dale, N. Y.

232

Starting 'em gave you lots of fresh air and sunshine.

George Knab brought his 1916 30–60 Aultman-Taylor from the Canandaigua show.

233

Clifford Rugg, Cattaraugus, N. Y., made and sold cider from his 1863 Hutchinson cider press during the show. It's driven by a 3-HP International back gear.

Classic cars make a long line across Firemen's Park. This is a 1919 Pratt-Elkhart.

Farquhar saw mill is powered by George Knab's 1916 30—60 HP Aultman—Taylor gas tractor. The Association owns the mill.

Ottawa 4-HP drag saw. Paul Wahl, Palmyra, N. Y.—WNY

Horse-pulling contest pulls a whale of a crowd away from the engines.

Cretor steam corn popper was pulled from Chicago to N. Y. by a pony in 1906 and has delighted the palates of western New Yorkers for over 60 years. It wasn't on its present 1931 Model A Ford chassis when the pony pulled it, however. Sam, the clown who turns the peanut drum and makes the little steam engine go chugalug, is nearing his threescore and 10 years. Owned by Don and Nancy Thomasson, Castile, N. Y.

If you like real runnin' live-steam models, you'll love the Alexander model tent—but every one of 'em is a No—No! Mustn't touch! Note revolutionary elbow engine, center foreground.

Vegetable Farmer Invents
First New Steam Engine
Since The Turbine

"I got to thinking there hadn't been a new kind of steam engine invented since the turbine," a 73-year-old vegetable farmer told me.

"So I made one."

I was browsing the huge model tent at Alexander, N. Y. Here were rows and rows of steam engines from half-inch to two-inch bores all going chuggity chug. They were of every shape and size. Some were singles and some were doubles. There were verticals, horizontals, marines, stationaries; even a model steamboat flapped its stern wheel. Some had walking beams and some drove flywheels. But they were all alike in one respect—they were all reciprocating piston engines.

Then I came upon one going lickety split, *stststtttt!* It was unlike anything I'd ever seen. Six cylinders surrounded and connected to a single crank—just like an aircraft radial engine but without the master connecting rod. The piston rod was the con rod, going straight to the crank. The cylinders, pivoted at their lateral centers, gently oscillated, eliminating wrist pin, crosshead and guides.

The farmer, Roy E. Henry, Elba, N. Y., told me how he got interested in steam.

"Well, it started while I was in the first grade in country school. When I heard a threshing engine whistle I used the normal indication of two fingers on a raised hand." This gained him teacher's permission to go to the "accomodation room out back" and to stay awhile. He went right on past the priv and stayed all day.

"This went on until my parents and I were bankrupt for excuses for my absence. Then other arrangements, not to my liking, were made. But steam continued to be of great interest to me all the rest of my life.

"When the internal combustion engine came into practical use, all of the science used to develop steam power was gradually forgotten and no more interest was applied to practical designs for steam.

"It has always seemed to me that energy generated from pressure, whether steam or compressed air, would eventually fill the gap which will come when the natural resources of the world are dangerously diminished, causing grave problems for human existence. A way can and must be found, although it is said the impossible takes longer.

"In my opinion, steam is the nearest thing to automatic power. When the injector replaces the water in a boiler under a full head of steam, it seems like pulling yourself up by your bootstraps.

"I think a small oscillating steam engine has advantage over the conventional design. This little six cylinder model can be used as a foundation when scientific research develops a heating unit with which small atomic reactors can be safely used.

"The basic principle in my oscillating engine is that ALL connecting rods drive on ONE crank pin. Thus the engine can be more compact and smoother in operation. I believe it would be more economical to operate than a turbine. It can be made any size and power. I hope this small model proves food for thought for better steam engines."

Unable to lick 'em in his youth, however, he joined 'em. Mr. Henry studied internal combustion engines and, in 1915, became mechanical road engineer for International Harvester. After army service, he started, about 1924, the first sales and service station for IHC trucks in Rochester, N. Y., The Million Dollar Garage.

He bought a muck farm in 1931 near Elba, where he invented and patented the first vegetable bagging machine, which he built and sold. He also invented the onion combine and some smaller vegetable-farming machines.

"I now take pleasure in seeing that many of these machines have been further developed from my foundations." He enjoys retirement because, "This spare time gives me opportunity to design and make the model steam engines which have been in my mind for many years."

Built like an aircraft radial engine, this little steam engine's oscillating cylinders eliminate wrist pin, cross-head and guides.

Intricately-routed backplate and gasket guide steam to the right place at the right time. Engine is its own safety-valve: if pressure gets too high, spring-loaded plates separate slightly, letting steam escape.

A possible competitor for the new steam engine title is this "elbow engine" I saw at Canandaigua, N. Y. Three reciprocating elbows work in holes in flywheel hub and fixed nubbin or whatever they call it. I could find out nothing about it other than it fell from the space race. Don't even know which direction the steam flows.

Muck Farmer's Invention Puts Success 'In Bag'

From January 20, 1969 issue of BUFFALO COURTER-EXPRESS by Bill Lamale

Roy Edward Henry and his wife, Beulah, lived down on "the muck" north of Elba, in Genesee County. They had 25 acres of the black loam that once was lake bottom.

It was 1931. They were building their own home, a place with a hip roof and gables. Beulah Henry commuted by train to Buffalo, working as a cost accountant. At night she'd help Roy finish his chores.

Out from their home stretched fields of onions. The rows were so long and so straight and so uniform that the fields looked like corduroy. Roy worked in the muck, directing the helpers in cultivating and harvesting. Everything about the work was back-breaking and repetitious. Roy knew what it was like to look down the long, endless rows at dawn, and face the same unending rows at dusk.

When weather kept him out of the fields, he used to head for the little machine shop built into his house. There he repaired farm equipment and fussed over mechanical things.

Before coming to the muck, he had worked for an industry in Milwaukee, traveling and helping farmers assemble harvesters. He could listen to machinery and tell what needed adjusting.

When Roy took up onion farming, he was appalled at the labor that went into it. The fastest hand couldn't gather more than 40 bushels a day, and growers couldn't make a profit paying more than 15 cents an hour wages. Onions, bagged in 50- or 100-pound lots, were shipped to city markets where they sat in storerooms.

The trouble was that times weren't good. How many housewives could afford that many onions at a time?

"Talk was going around among the growers about packaging the produce in consumer size bags," Roy relates. "The idea was that a good many housewives would find a 15-pound bag a lot easier to buy and carry."

One day Roy watched a grower trying to package onions in a new "consumer size" paper bag. Workers with hand scoops were doing the job. They spilled the onions, guessed at the weight and got everything mixed up.

"It was a pathetic attempt," he notes. "I knew there must be an easier way."

So he drew up some sketches. He knew others had tried to devise bagging machines and failed. But finally he went to work, using scraps of sheet metal and discarded equipment. Every night he was in the machine shop, cutting, boring and fitting.

In August, 1933, he called his wife in to see his invention. It didn't look very fancy; no motors, pulleys or gears about it. The base was an old feed mill scales. The top was two metal chutes with clamps below. "That," Roy announced, "is a two-man bagging machine." Then he and a hired man demonstrated it. That night Mrs. Henry helped her husband get the plans and specifications off to Washington.

While the patent was pending, Roy unveiled his machine to the local growers. "We held a demonstration out in the barn," he says. "While one man tied a bag, the other filled and weighed his. At the end of an hour we counted the 10-pound bags. There were nearly 400."

Roy was assembling bagging machines but still worked in the onions. His wife went out to the field one evening, waving an envelope. Roy was on his knees, weeding.

"What are you doing down there in the muck?" she called. "Don't you know you were awarded a patent today?"

Roy's first customer for one of the Henry Bagging Machines was a shipper in Elba. Then came an order from a market chain in Buffalo.

After that Roy didn't get back into the fields very much. He designed and produced his own packaging equipment. From the first primitive models he progressed to powered machinery that sorted, graded, weighed and bagged, all in one operation. They moved into a large concrete block house on a knoll, and Beulah Henry set up an office for the company.

Roy hit the road with model machines, and set them up at farm equipment shows and fairs. He built up a mail order business, mostly with onion growers.

But he did all the assembly work himself, calling into the office for his wife when he needed help. In 1953, he produced an automatic bagger that had such capacity it required four men just to shovel the onions.

That was the ultimate so far as Roy was concerned, and he left it to the big manufacturers to develop the modern automated bagging machines used by the fresh produce industry. But Roy is still in his machine shop, working over blueprints and constructing model steam engines on a table near a chunk stove.

239

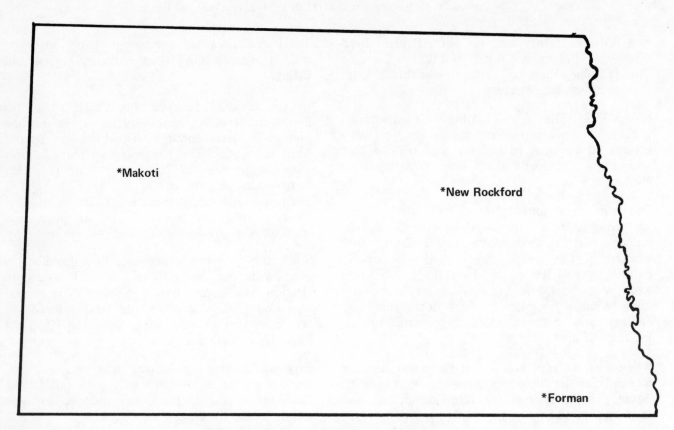

*Makoti

*New Rockford

*Forman

North Dakota

CENTRAL NORTH DAKOTA STEAM THRESHERS REUNION
Fairgrounds, SW corner of town
New Rockford, N. D.
Weekend of next to last week in September

New Rockford is a small town but it entertains large crowds during the show.—ND

Nine steam engines reign in this prairie town, population 2,000.

It started, sort of, in '54 when aerial sprayer Ole Aslakson fetched his old Advance strawburner from the old home farm 11 miles to the airport after 15 years of idleness (the steamer had been idle, not Ole).

"I steamed up several times during the next few years." Meanwhile he acquired some more engines until today he owns five of the nine.

C. A. Anderson brought in his Nichols & Shepard 25-85 double side-mounted. When New Rockford celebrated its 75th birthday in 1958, Ole's N&S double rear-mounted 25-85 and a 20-70 N&S double owned by John Aarestad, McHenry, N. D., ran in the big parade which was considerably longer than the town. That was so much fun that on March 31, 1959, they organized with Ole as president and incorporated 364 days later.

The first organized show was held Oct. 3, 4 and 5, 1959, in perfect weather. Three days later, snowdrifts stood as high as the engines. Of late, 10,000 to 15,000 people have attended on a Sunday—pretty good for a county of maybe 5,000.

240

Says Ole, who gave up the chair to Gilbert Pross, Fessenden, "Some of our more unusual attractions besides the straw-burner are a shock loader, a hand-fed thresher built about 1890, a 32-HP Reeves and an 11-HP Case owned by Howard and Norman Pross of Luverne, N. D. They also brought in two outstanding wooden threshers—an Avery Yellow Fellow and a Buffalo-Pitts built about 1900 with a geared windstacker."

The program book answers "Questions Most Often Asked at Steam Shows": The average 25-HP steam engine weighs 13 to 16 tons, ranging from seven to 22 tons. "In 1905 a Case 25-HP 11x11 cost $2,050, a 36x58 thresher $475 but feeder, weigher and stacker extras total $900; in 1915 the 80-HP Case was listed at $2,350, 110-HP $3,055 and a 36x58 thresher $1,045 complete. Mr. C. A. Anderson tells that in 1913 the Nichols & Shepard double listed at $2,800."

It also explains that each boiler is tested before the show by a state boiler inspector. Filled with water to the very top, the boilers are pumped to at least 50 percent over working pressure. Sharp hammer blows reveal any weak spots. For added safety, boilers are operated at 100 to 125 pounds instead of the design pressure of 140 to 175 pounds and up.

The late Jake Arndt restored 1898 reaper. Behind it is 1918 Case 20–40 2-cylinder for which Siebert, Obert and Martin Hoveskeland paid $3,100, plus $900 for a 28–56 Case separator. Tractor threshed in the Hamar, N. D., area until its retirement in 1944.—NEWS

Reeves 32-HP double simple and Avery Yellow Fellow are locally considered "about the finest showpieces in the country."—NEWS

"Ready to move," says the faded inscription on this yellow photo, "Threshing outfit owned by Homer S. Ballard. Larrabee Township, Foster Co., N. D." Aslakson says the engine is an Advance 30-HP single-cylinder strawburner, and "am fairly sure the separator is also Advance. Note the 4-wheel water and straw tender behind engine. This was the most common way to provide water and straw for moves." Engine, tender, separator and cook car (can you see the long-gowned ladies by the cook car door?) made quite a train on the move.—Aslakson

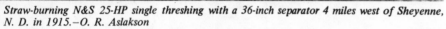

Straw-burning N&S 25-HP single threshing with a 36-inch separator 4 miles west of Sheyenne, N. D. in 1915.—O. R. Aslakson

Above: "Hard at work," the photographer scribbled on this print, which proves that though cameras don't lie, photographers do. Engine flywheel is motionless—straw coming out of windstacker was painted in by hand. Bundle wagon in foreground is loaded with bedrolls and suitcases.—Aslakson

Avery undermount pulling a seldom-seen steam-lift plow near Barlow, N. D., between 1908 and 1914. Hose hanging from crane sucked water from tank wagon on the go. Left to right are Leonard, George and Frank Schmid. Leonard was the father of New Rockford Mayor Chester Schmid.—Aslakson

243

Huebner Little Giant hand-fed thresher was built about 1890. Has overshot cylinder, web stacker. Aslakson is owner. N. D. Gov. Guy at right on platform.—ND & MINOT DAILY NEWS

Teeter-totter always holds the crowd breathless because such skill is required on the reversing lever to balance the loose-geared engine. Water sloshing forth and back in the long boiler upsets the equilibrium, requiring quick correction. This is a rare strawburner, a 26-HP Advance tandem compound.—ND

Cinder's eye view of N&S 25–85.—ND

City fathers view steam engine parades with mixed emotions. Nichols & Shepard is still 5 or 6 feet from bottom of sewer main. Ole's pet, it is a 25–85 double-simple rear-mounted with a direct-flue, very heavy butt-strap boiler sometimes called the Canadian. This engine is thought to have been built before 1917.—ND

George White single cylinder rear-mounted engine was built in London, Ontario, 1913. Ole Aslakson moves it for loading by winding a rope about its flywheel and pulling the rope with his family car.—Central ND Steam Threshers photo

1907 Stanley Steam Car, gleaming red-and-brass, can still top 90 MPH, has more power and pickup than modern autos with their claptrap internal combustion engines. Operates on 600 pounds pressure. Art Haga, Bergan, N. D., takes show visitors from steam engines to airplane rides. Other prize autos at the show include a 1903 Orient Buckboard, owned by E. P. Mattson, New Rockford, descendant of the original buyer. J. G. Buckwalter, Jamestown, N. D., licenses his 1917 Paige every year and drives it regularly.

Aslakson invested 6 years' spare time building 1/3-scale N&S. Having no plans, he took his measures off his 25—85, made his own patterns, had casting poured in Fargo, did his own cutting, welding and lathe work in his aircraft shop in his hangar. Weighs 1,320 pounds, has 2-foot drivers, 6 2-inch flues, puts out about 6 HP at 350 RPM (big brother runs at 220). Model, like the big fellow, is a double-simple. Has 2¼-inch bore, 3¼-inch stroke. Powers 1/3-scale separator.

MAKOTI ANNUAL THRESHING ASSOCIATION
Makoti Threshing & Antique Show
Airstrip
Makoti, N. D.
Third Weekend in September

GROWTH is the word for the biggest thing in Makoti, N. D. (population 200)——the show began with 0 members in 1961, now has over 100. First parade displayed 30 units; today 100 chug down Main Street, making a line longer than the town (44 out of the 100 were kerosene units and four more wouldn't go). Some 3,000 people came to the first show. Today they tally over 8,000. The Association built two huge steel buildings to shelter their precious cast-iron jewels.

Biggest thing in Makoti is the annual threshing bee. A 1906 Minneapolis 25–75 separates the oats from the chaff.–Minot DAILY NEWS

Reports LeRoy Quandt, Ryder, N. D., "The Makoti threshing and antique show had its beginning with the Makoti Golden Anniversary celebration July 12-13, 1961. The late Clarence Schenfisch, rural Makoti, who began collecting old tractors in 1957, had seven of his 13 tractors in the parade and threshing show. They included a 1917 Gray, 1920 Titan 10-20, 1913 Pioneer 30-60, 1916 Avery 40-80, 1913 Case 20-40, 1915 Avery 14-28 and a 1929 25-40 Rumely.

"Also in the parade was a 25-75 Minneapolis 1906 single simple steam traction engine with the owner, William Zimmerman, as engineer and Carl Yahnke, Roseglen, N. D., fireman. Clarence later added this engine to his collection. Gerald Johnson, Douglas, N. D., brought his 1916 Waterloo Boy and has returned each year for the show. A 28-48 Twin City separator owned by Ed Ouradnik, Makoti, threshed."

Oswald, Wilmar and Orlan, brothers of Clarence, retained his collection when he died. Local men labored long and lovingly to restore the rest of his collection (see list).

People come from many states and Canada. Some show up a day early in their trailers and campers.

Association members, Quandt continues, bought five steamers from the Torske Bros., Conrad, Mont., and added four of them to the show: 1913 Case 80 bought by Ed Larson, Minot, N. D.; 1910 Nichols & Shepard 25-85, Ed Dobrinski, Oswald Schenfisch and Herbert Markwardt, Makoti; 1910 N&S 20-70, Elmer Wolff and Dorance Heise, Ryder; and a 1920 Russel 25-75, Ted Simmons, Art Oberg, W. L. Morris and Wayne Jones, Ryder.

1913 Pioneer 30–60 HP has 4 horizontal opposed cylinders 7x8-inch, operates at 650 RPM, weighs 23,000 pounds. Obviously wooden separator is 1914 Aultman–Taylor 43–64.—Minot NEWS

Unloading two new 30–60 Pioneers at Makoti April 15, 1916, bought by John Boss, Makoti farmer, and Henry Clare, Sanish farmer. New plow is lower left; its steering apparatus is at center. Still living are Ed Heise, 2nd from left, and John Holst, 4th from left. Fred and John Holst were Pioneer dealers from 1913.–MTA

Heider 1916 Model C 12–20 HP has 4 cylinders 4-1/8x6-3/4 inches; 750 RPM, friction drive 7 speeds, weighs 6,000 pounds.– Newtown NEWS

Geiser "Peerless" threshing near Hope, N. D., in the early days.–MTA

It took the 27-ton, 25-foot lowboy and L-190 tandem truck of Oberg & Folden Construction, Ryder, to transport the brutes, one at a time.

Minot in December, 1968, retired its 1919 American-LaFrance pumper and 1930 Howe Reo fire truck and lent them to the club. Both are operational and join the shows.

Adds Quandt, Dale Hopkins and Marvin Franklin, Ryder, display over two dozen stationary engines on several flatbeds: a ¾-HP Maytag, 1½-HP IHC, 3-HP Dan Patch, 4-HP Success, 5-HP Wolverine, 6-HP United and 15-HP Fairbanks-Morse.

Separators used in the show are the Association's 1914 wooden Aultman-Taylor 42-64; 1928 Case 28-46 owned by Nels Fjeldahl, Plaza, N. D.; 1924 wooden Goodison 24-42, Tom Lampert, Makoti; 1920 wood IHC, Jim Blowers, Makoti and a 1928 Twin City 28-48, Loren Quandt, Makoti.

Inspired, other Association members have started collections. Past President Ed Dobrinski has 12, some of which are a 1919 Moline Universal, 18-35 Rock Island, 28-50 Hart-Parr. Wayne Jones bought a 1916 Emerson Brantingham 20-35 Big 4, 1926 Original Farmall and a 17-28 16-valve Twin City, among others, Quandt reports.

Oberg restored a 1920 20-35 Twin City. Marvin Franklin has a 1925 15-30 McCormick Deering. Lyle Bergeson has a 1924 McCormick-Deering. Roy Peterson, Ryder, got a 1917 Aultman-Taylor 30-60 and a 10-bottom hand-lift P&O plow which plows at each show. Rensch Garage, Makoti, has a 1920 Samson M donated by Louis Wahner, Parshall, and restored by Art and Alvid Anderson, Makoti. Bob Van Eckout, Plaza, has a 1924 John Deere D.

Continues Quandt, the late Oscar Semmen, Douglas, loaned a Caterpillar Model 30 restored by Robert Tellefson, Makoti. Melvin Jacobson, Douglas, has a 16-30 Rumely. Bob Reinhart, Des Lacs, a 27-44 Twin City. Ray Patton, Plaza, has an 18-36 Hart-Parr. Clarence Butler, Parshall, has a "beautifully-restored" 1913 30-60 Big 4. Orris and Clifford Bakke, Stanley, have a 1915 Aultman-Taylor 30-60, 8-bottom JD plow and a 36-56 wooden Aultman-Taylor separator. John Tysee Jr., Crosby, and Bill Krumwiede,Voltaire, own a 1910 Type C Mogul, a 35-70 Minneapolis and a 1913 15-30 Rumely restored by Dorance Heise. Max Harris, Des Lacs, got a 20-40 Eagle and a 10-20 Mogul restored by Fred Reinisch, Ryder.

Old cars also come rattlin' in to the show–like a 1913 Model T, a 1916 International, 1915 Samson, and other such goodies.

Arnold Olson, Makoti, brings his horse Nick to pull a buggy loaned by Jack Igelhart, Emmet, restored by Alice Ouradnik and Eugene Rensch, Makoti. Alfred Olson, Bowbells, had his scale model 1915 Case 75 there.

Each Fall, Lial Peterson, Makoti, oils up his old JD binder and cuts oats, which are stored inside for the show.

Other attractions, Quandt relates, are a Baker fan and Orin Hanson, Sanish, with his 30-HP 1914 double simple Minneapolis.

The cook cars aren't just for looks, but feed the hungry throngs.

The half-mile marked airstrip is much used by fly-ins and barnstormers.

Each year the Association prints souvenir booklets with pictures and descriptions of the units. Such a show, of course, takes community-wide cooperation not only from Makoti folks but from surrounding towns and cities and the neighboring counties of McLean, Mountrail and others—cooperation which the Association gets in full measure.

The Association, with volunteer help from the community, erected two 40x96 steel buildings to house many of the showpieces, financed by loans and donations. "The two museum buildings are open to the public at any time with Fred Markwardt as caretaker," says Quandt. One building is dedicated to Clarence Schenfisch, 1920-1964.

Officers are Elmer Wolff, president; Wayne Jones, vice-president; Glen Warner, secretary (all of Ryder), and Gilbert Fischer, Makoti, treasurer. The non-profit corporation's objective include obtaining, restoring, maintaining, exhibiting and housing antiques of all kinds.

Clarence Schenfisch collection restorations

UNIT	RESTORED BY	ADDRESS
1919 Avery 12-25	Alfred Janz	Ryder
2-cylinder opposed	Oswald Schenfisch	Makoti
1921 Advance-Rumely 16-30	Janz, Oswald & others	
1913 Rumely Model E 30-60	Dorance Heise	Ryder
	Oswald, Janz	
1924 Fordson	Janz	
1920 Wallis 15-25	Herbert Markwardt	Makoti
1916 Heider Model C 12-20	Carl Yahnke	Roseglen

Loren Quandt and son Mardon erect sign in front of Makoti Threshing Association's two big steel storage buildings. Better check that date.

Big and little threshermen are lost amongst iron mountains in MTA storage building.

"Hey, Dad! Lookit what I found out here in the weeds!" The same 10-bottom Parlin and Orendorff plow delivered with the Pioneers!

251

RATHERT'S STEAM THRESHERS' REUNION
Forman, N. D.
ND Hiway 32 north edge of town
Weekend after Labor Day

One of the few private-enterprise shows staged by an individual, Rathert's includes not only gem-like antique steam traction engines but rare early gas tractors, gas buggies, motorcycles, and early nickelodeons. They all work.

Jim Rathert earns his bread-and-oleo in road construction. But in real life he hunts, moves, restores and shows these ancient gems, assisted by his son, Rudy, a carpenter, and some Forman folks and, of course, Mrs. Jim.

Just a wee part of Jim Rathert's iron yard (in the off season).

"I've been collecting and restoring old autos for about 20 years," he reports. Sometimes when hot on the trail of an '03 Lizzie, he turned up an '02 steam traction engine instead, and this was what infected him with the incurable Steam Disease.

Some of his autos in which he takes the most pride are an '02 Olds one-cylinder curved dash, '03 Model A Ford, '06 four-cylinder Model R Ford (Jim explains Ford's first Ford was the Model A, the next Model B, then Models C, F, K, N, R, S, and T, where the designation stuck for a spell; then Henry started all over in '28 with the Model A again), a '07 one-cylinder Model K Cadillac runabout, and an '08 Sears Motor Buggy two-cylinder Model J fresh out of the mail-order catalog.

Also in his barn is a 1910 four-cylinder in-line Pierce Arrow motorcycle with nickel-plated longhorn handlebars which looks as streamlined as a rocket and as sexy as a 1999 experimental. He revved her up to 88 MPH before he chickened-out.

Rathert's non-farm collections include early nickelodeons that not only play zylophones, drums and cymbals via punched paper rolls but have little foot-high musicians that go through the umpa-umpa-boom-boom-boom motions, including a trombonist who really lets things slide. A mechanical violin's automated fingers play four parts at once plus piano accompaniment. Another early juke box switches 3-foot-wide metal disks like a modern juke box changes 6-inch records. Each disk is punched, the resulting prongs strumming music-box-type steel reeds. All these five-cent marvels date from around 1875 to Ought Hundred.

BEFORE . . . .   *1910 Aultman–Taylor 30–60 No. 133.–Rathert*   *. . . . AFTER*

WHY DO WE CALL A STEAM ENGINE "SHE"?

BECAUSE SHE'S JUST LIKE A WOMAN:

SHE DEMANDS LOTS OF TENDER LOVING CARE

AND CONSTANT ATTENTION.

AND IF SHE DOESN'T GET IT

SHE BLOWS UP ALL OVER YOU!

Some of his gas tractors that pleasure him most are a 1912 30-60 Big Four and a 1914 40-70 Flour City with drive wheels 96 inches high, 1910 30-60 Aultman-Taylor No. 133; 1909 one-cylinder Mogul and a couple of 1912 30-60 Rumely Oil-Pulls.

Some of the steam engines that stuck to his fingers include a 1914 20-HP Reeves double simple, 1906 25-HP Huber return-flue, 20-60 HP '03 Case and an '09 25-HP Minneapolis.

1909 IHC 25-HP Mogul No. 276.
1 cylinder 10x14 at 240 RPM
pulls 5 plows at 1.9 MPH. Hit
and Miss governor.

253

Free engine, anybody? That other boiler in the mud is the rendering boiler from the Marquis de Mores' 1883 packing house fiasco at Medora, used here as a base for the steam pump.—O.R. Aslakson

How Jim & Rudy Rescued Big Minnie From the Little Missouri River

Jim and Rudy's Big Adventure—pulling a huge steamer from the Little Missouri River mud—started like a lark in 1957. Jim wrote it up in the August 3, 1968, DAKOTA FARMER, but his adventurous seeds were sown in the early '50s.

When out on the job, he kept inquiring about old cars. Out in western North Dakota a persistent rumor kept cropping up: "Every so often someone would say, 'I don't know of any old cars, but I know where there's a big steam engine in the river.' I took this rather lightly, but after hearing this rumor several times it began to arouse my curiosity. The engine was supposed to be in the roughest part of the Badlands, and I wondered what a big steam engine would be doing in this rough country."

Year after year, Jim watched Minnie settle into the muck.—Rathert

Finally, in 1957, finding themselves only a few miles from the reputed location, Jim and Mrs. Jim got directions and started thataway. Driving over what had been trails but now were washouts, and ignoring his wife's many excellent reasons, often stated, for going thisaway again, he drove "until the clutch smelled right out loud." He drove some more and finally reached the bank of the Little Big Muddy 12 miles north of Medora. He recognized the hulk as an unusually big Minneapolis.

"The river and its spring ice jam had done everything in their power to destroy this huge steam engine. If it had been just an ordinary-size engine, I'm sure the river would have rolled it over many times and buried it in the quicksand. The engine had been vandalized for nuts and bolts, brass, the connecting rod, bearings, etc. Someone had removed the main bearing caps and the ice had picked up the crankshaft and flywheel assembly, weighing more than a ton, carrying it downstream, maybe to St. Louis for all I knew."

Jim snapped some pictures, realizing "this must be the biggest steam traction engine I had ever seen." He took a pious vow never to be so foolish as to try to salvage it. "At that time it would have been relatively easy because it had not sunk in and the boiler was not yet full of sand."

The thought of that great engine sinking deeper year by year kept bugging him. Like the criminal returning to his crime, he kept going back, taking more pictures to gauge her settling into the mud year by year.

When the front wheels were out of sight and the mud was halfway up the boiler, and after the ice broke the big drive gear on the countershaft, the boiler and firebox filled with tons of sand, he decided Somebody Otta Do Something. Rancher Don Short, the owner, said he'd be happy for someone to rescue the old elegant elephant. "With her tummy full of sand, she must have weighed 30 tons."

Jim's 1966 resolution was to save her. An early freeze delayed him a year. November 14, 1967, when the water was lowest, Jim and Rudy took off from Forman in southeastern North Dakota with two big trucks and a machinery lowboy.

The first bit of good news was the sight of the flywheel rim showing above the mud downstream. "It gave us a real lift to find the flywheel and crankshaft still existed."

After Big Minnie sat here idle for 20 years, the high water and ice of '47 tore out a chunk of 40-foot bank and Min toppled into the drink. Ice carried away the crankshaft and flywheel.—Aslakson

With a little Melroe Bobcat they'd salvaged from a burnt barn and rebuilt, Father and Son dug a long, deep ramp down the bank—a cut so big it made the Bobcat in it look like a bean in a bucket. They built a dam around Big Minnie and dug out around her by Bobcat and by hand. They had to chain ol' Bob to Minnie's wheel to keep quicksand from swallowing him, backhoe and all.

The rescuers dug a 15-foot trench four feet deep and buried a deadman to anchor the winch. When the 1-inch steel cables didn't pop, the winch gearbox did "like a melon dropped on a rock." The best they could do that time among the snow and sleet was drag her (the drivers were rusted tight) above the river's reach.

They got her high enough to determine she was a rare four-cylinder 1911 Minneapolis 45-135 HP double tandem compound with 7½-inch high and 11-inch low-pressure cylinders and a 10-inch stroke.

The Rescuin' Ratherts wondered long and loud as they shivered in the old log cabin nearby "that was about as cozy as a corncrib" what a big old lady like Minnie was doing 'way out here in the Badlands. Don Short, who lent them his Cat and then countless hours of hard labor and, soon, a warm bunkhouse, told them the engine had been bought new at Killdeer, North Dakota, with a 14-bottom plow. She'd plowed and threshed around there. Then in 1917 Don's father started driving her to his ranch across the Badlands but got hung up and broke the bull gear. There she sat for some time until he went back, fixed her up, abandoned the plow and drove her back to Killdeer. He loaded her on a flatcar for Belfield. She hung out over both sides of the railroad car so far she looked like she'd topple off.

After plowing and threshing with her into the '20s he decided to irrigate some of the river bottom flatland that's so good for farming in amongst the Badland buttes when it gets water. He parked her on the river bank and belted her to a 12x12-inch pump, fired with lignite dug right on the spot. Later he piped steam from Big Minnie's boiler to the pump's own engine.

The Depression killed that project. For maybe 20 years she sat idle. Then the record high water of '47 toppled the aged beauty into the briny deep. She lay in the mud and water for another 20 years. When I was photographing the Medora restorations in the summer of '68 I heard about "the big engine in the river." The grapevine failed to carry news of the fat lady's salvation.

For save her Jim and Rudy did! They went back in December and by monstrous effort got her up onto the lowboy. The two trucks pushed and pulled her out of the Badlands, across the state to her new and happy home at Forman.

"We don't have much money," Jim explains. He and Rudy substitute muscle for machines and money on their salvage jobs.

Restoration slowly proceeds. If anybody knows where any of the "salvaged" parts are (hey—have *you* got the valve gear?), or has parts that will fit, Jim and Rudy would sure like to hear from you, else they're going to have to make a lot of parts by hand, because there weren't many of this model made.

And Jim and Rudy are dedicated to making Big Minnie steam again.

Cables and winch popped.—Rathert

Fired with lignite dug right behind her, Big Minnie pumped irrigation water in the '20s. Right front wheel was removed to make room for belt to pump 40 feet below in river.—Don Short

Loaded with gravel for traction, trucks struggle up out of Badlands.—Rathert

256

Little Minnie when Jim found her at Sun Prairie, Wis., in 1958. He paid $250 for her in this shape.—Rathert

Her bones scattered about Rathert's yard, Big Minnie waits for new life.—Rathert

Rudy and Jim with the 2,000 pound crankshaft and flywheel that almost floated to the Gulf.

Little Minnie—1909 25-HP single simple Minneapolis—today sparkles and purrs. Big Minnie someday will be beautiful again.—Rathert

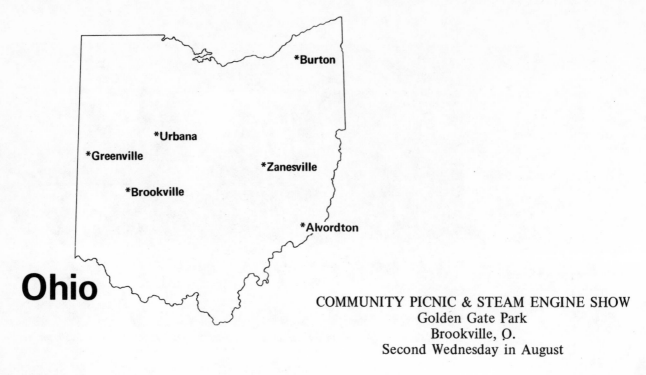

Ohio

*Burton

*Urbana

*Greenville

*Zanesville

*Brookville

*Alvordton

COMMUNITY PICNIC & STEAM ENGINE SHOW
Golden Gate Park
Brookville, O.
Second Wednesday in August

Winner takes all the prizes in the one, the only, the original Brookville steam engine race.

Sawmill, thresher and Baker fan give the steamers something to do like Ed Troutman's 1916 Case 50-HP No. 33618 on the 1915 Enterprise sawmill. Sawyers are Lawrence Bretz and Dale Hypes.

Paul Cole, Morristown, Ind., shows off the model A.D. Baker he built.

Brookville celebrated its centennial in 1950. This went over so big the chamber of commerce decided to have some kind of celebration every year. Thus arose "The Picnic," as local folks call it. Merchants, business and professional people donate time, money and prizes. Your 25-cent gate ticket gets you a chance at frequent drawings throughout the day. Grand prize is a new car.

In planning the first Picnic, the committee was looking for events attractive to people of a rural community. "Someone suggested they get a few steam engines, a thresher, a sawmill, a couple of loads of wheat, some logs, all of which were available, and do some threshing and sawing like in the good old days," report Edison Troutman and Kenny Mears of the engine committee. Merchants display wares; there are carnival-type rides, games, musical events, ball games, a magician, drill teams, beauty contest, tractor or pony pulls and—most of all—steam engines.

"We try to have 10 steam engines, three or four old gas tractors, a thresher, sawmill, Baker fan, model steam engine and farm-type gas engines. We always have a steam engine race. The engine committee feels this is the original steam engine race for steam shows." Fireworks cap the day at 10:30.

The 25-cent admission does not begin to pay the costs, of course. "The business people's time and money make the Picnic possible."

258

First Scheidler Traction Engine
Had a Curious Life:
Portable-Traction-Portable

The first Scheidler traction engine was originally manufactured about 1895 as a 10-HP portable. Traction and steering mechanisms were added in 1897, but in '98 these were removed and the unit was reconverted to a portable.

Edison H. Troutman, Brookville, O., got the story from 83-year-old Lawrence Brown, Dayton, O., son of the original owner, Robert. Relates Brown the younger:

The elder Brown bought the engine new from the Scheidler Company, Newark, O., and used it about two years in his sawmill at White Cottage, about seven miles southwest of Zanesville. When the manufacturer, Rinehard Scheidler, returned from studying traction engines in his native Germany, he was eager to apply his new knowledge. Being good friends and frequent visitors in each others' homes, Brown and Scheidler made a deal to add traction and steering gear. Brown thought the traction engine would be useful for skidding logs.

However, the traction gearing could not stand up to the mud, roots, and frozen ruts. After a year of trouble, Scheidler reconverted it to a portable, which Brown odd-jobbed around for several years. He sold it to a Zanesville wheel company which used it to generate steam for bending the wooden felloes. The engine's fate is unknown.

Scheidler was killed by one of his engines about 1900. He insisted on giving each engine the final brake test himself. While he was testing an engine, a part flew off and crushed his skull.

A Scheidler employee, John McNamara, left that company and started building his own McNamara engines in Newark. He took over the Scheidler Company about 1904 or '05, Brown recalls.

Brown says the Scheidler family in Germany was associated with the Krupp munitions family, and it was locally believed Krupp financed Scheidler's American operations.

Roscoe Shivedecker's Baker.

Baker boils apple butter.—Darke photos

McClain's ox team and 150-year-old prairie schooner.

DARKE COUNTY STEAM THRESHERS ASSOCIATION, INC.
Harvey Estey Woods
Rt. 571, Greenville, O.
Labor Day Weekend

The Darke County show started out as too much of a good thing.

Elmer Egbert and his son Jack held their own little home show each year at Anna, Ohio. It got so big that in 1953 they couldn't handle it any more so the next year the Miami Valley Steam Reunion was held on the Gilbert Lease farm at Greenville. Here it was decided to alternate between Darke County and Bellefontane year to year. The Bellefontane boys decided in 1955 the show was so nice they'd just keep it, so Greenville had to start its own.

The Greenville boys selected the Harvey Estey woods on 571 east of Greenville and organized the Darke County Steam Threshers Assn., Inc. The first show, 1956, had eight steam traction engines. The next year the corporation got its charter. Sylvester Ditmer was elected president and served 10 years. Today he has a lifetime vice-presidency. Raymond Hollinger succeeded him.

Added to the steam engines have been antique gas tractors and engines, old-fashioned cops and paddywagon, ox team, sky divers and a stage coach that always brings a surprise (ed?) guest. The ladies take a large hand in the celebration, many of them operating engines. Thelma Ditmer rides around in an engine's drive wheel. Mildred Ary, secretary, claims to be the first woman to balance a steam traction engine on a teeter-totter.

After the show, the steam fans gather 'round a vat and cook apple butter on steam coils supplied by an engine, under the genial direction of Charles Ditmer and Hugh Hartzell. "People drive for miles to get some lickin'-good homemade apple butter," says Mrs. Ary. "They go wild to taste it. Steam coils cook apples in no time." People scramble to pay $1 a quart.

The Egberts still have a little home show and make sorghum. "No end to what can be done at the steam show," says Mrs. Ary.

Today the Darke County show boasts 23 big steamers, several models, sawmills—full size and miniature—big and little Oil Pulls. "We like to claim we may not be the biggest show, but one of them"

MUSKINGUM VALLEY THRESHERS' ASSOCIATION
Zanesville, Ohio
Ralph Bowden Farm, Co. Rd. 64
Second Weekend in August

Success comes hard in any worthwhile venture. The Muskingum Valley Threshers' Association almost died a-borning.

The first show was held on the Ralph Bowden Farm near Zanesville, Ohio, in 1962, with two steam engines and a few other items. There was little improvement and in 1965 no show was held.

This got Bowden's dandruff up, however, and he determined not to let it die. Inspiring the others with his own zeal, they worked hard securing, restoring and painting equipment for another try. They added a steam-powered sawmill as a permanent attraction and installed electricity on the grounds.

Now each show boasts six steamers and entertains folks with a larger number and variety of items. Each day's program includes threshing, baling, the Baker fan, sawing, and grinding meal on a stone burr mill. Open air church services are held Sunday mornings.

A feature at the Muskingum Valley show is this upright boiler and engine owned by Jim McCall, Bloomfield, O.

GEAUGA COUNTY THESHERMEN'S CONVENTION
Geauga County Historical Society
Burton, Ohio
Last Weekend in July

You see not only steam and horse-sweep-power threshing, but a veneer mill and shingle mill as well. Sawmill and drag saw, stone flour mill and other equipment are among the Russell, Frick, Port Huron, Case, Keck-Gonnerman, Westinghouse, Baker and Peerless steam traction engines.

Amish steam engine enthusiasts and the Society started the annual show in 1966.

The Thing is obviously of mixed ancestry.

The Crossroads Store and other historical buildings add much to your enjoyment.—GCHS photos

The Baker seems to be rated 19—65 HP.

Peerless engine must be a real oldy; note the wooden wheels.

262

263

MIAMI VALLEY STEAM THRESHERS ASSOCIATION, INC.
Urbana, O., Fairgrounds
Third Weekend in July

Three span of oxen in Urbana grand parade pull Conestoga wagon built by Carl Swaney (on pony). Carl, wife and son of Jackson, O., own oxen and wagon.

Nearly 300 members pitch in to bring over 30,000 spectators to the shady fairgrounds for the four-day event. Association-owned equipment includes a Chase shingle mill, Frick sawmill, Baker separator, Advance corn shredder, McCormick grain binder and horse power drag saw. Members operate 30 steam traction engines and smaller units.

A daily parade steams past the grandstand. On Sunday, some 100 antique autos join the parade.

For many years after its 1949 start, the show was held on various farms and places. In 1964 it moved permanently to the Champaign County fairgrounds at Urbana. "Here it has enjoyed the splendid cooperation of the Champaign County Agricultural Society and the entire community," says Treasurer E. L. Wilkins.

The next year the show joined the Urbana Area CC annual Pioneer Days featuring sidewalk sales, antique displays and artsy-craftsy exhibitions. The steamers parade through the town Friday night, stepping as lightly as possible to save the pavement. Then in 1968 the Association won coveted membership in the Ohio Festivals and Events Association.

President George Edinger, Urbana, states the show is the largest of its kind in Ohio and, in terms of equipment operated, one of the largest in the nation. "We feel our annual show presents to the younger generation an idea of the role that steam and early gas power played in developing the agricultural Midwest."

Other show activities include sawmill, flint mill, barbershop quartetting. (Photos courtesy Miami Valley Steam Threshers Assn. Library)

Canadian-built 1917 Sawyer-Massey shows pneumatic front tires and tractor-tire treads bolted to drivers out of respect for city dads' love for their pavement. Operator is Emil C. Jones, Kennard, O., and associate director. Owner is O.W. Nichols & Son, Pikerington, O.

1917 20-HP Minneapolis drives Association-owned Baker separator. Engine's owner is Lewis Meachem, Lancaster, O.

Separator in foreground is 1893 Case, hand-fed and web-stacked, powered by 6-HP Advance, H.R. Holp & Sons, Brookville, O., owners.

Long veneer strip from belt-driven Coe mill will make a whole bunch of take-homes for spectators. Owner/operators: Luman Kranz & John McAllister.

Chase shingle mill owned by the Association manufactures free souvenirs for guests.

THE NATIONAL THRESHERS ASSOCIATION, INC.
LeRoy Blaker Farm
Alvordton, Ohio
Late June

Port Huron engines owned by NTA and LeRoy Blaker: 1921 19-65 HP No. 8635; 1917 24-75 HP No. 7948; 1920 24-75 HP No. 8503, winner three times in the economy run using less than 23 lbs. water per HP-hr.—Photo courtesy NTA

Why Threshermen Thresh

Steam threshing was hot, dirty work in summer and cold, dirty work in winter. The engineer had to get up as early as the cook to steam up, and work at maintenance chores long after the crew was rolled up in the hay.

Economic studies show that competition was so fierce and threshing fees so low (3-5 cents a bushel) that few threshermen made expenses. Barn-door bookkeeping was so imprecise that few threshermen realized they were subsidizing their neighbors and that their own farms were subsidizing an unprofitable hobby—steam threshing.

So why thresh?

". . . once it got into a man's blood it was harder to kill than leprosy," opined E. W. Hamilton, Ed, CANADIAN THRESHERMAN.

Wik* quotes an old-time thresherman, "Well, I reckon I have swore off this durn threshing business a hundred times . . . I swear off and durn if I ain't crazy as a kid just as the threshing season starts."

A Missouri veteran of 56 years' steam threshing

said, "I love the whistle of the engine, the hum of the cylinder and a yellow-legged chicken dinner as well as ever." Sad case, Doctor.

Another remarked there was the Keeley cure for drunks but no help for threshermen.

Boiler explosions were frequent due to carelessness, drunkenness or stupidity of the engineer. I was told of one who had the bad habit, when he stuck his engine on dead center, of reaching up with a foot against a flywheel spoke to shove 'er off. The owner kept warning him this was bad business. Once he forgot to close the throttle. She came off dead center like a rocket and the engineer was meat.

Champion thresherman, according to Wik, was James Morrill, Mankato, Minn., who spent 72 years on 20 engines and 21 separators.

The industry supported three journals:

THRESHERMEN'S REVIEW, St. Joseph, Mich.
AMERICAN THRESHERMAN, Madison, Wis.
CANADIAN THRESHERMAN, Winnipeg, Man.

*Wik, Reynold M., STEAM POWER ON THE AMERICAN FARM, U. Penn. Press, 1959.

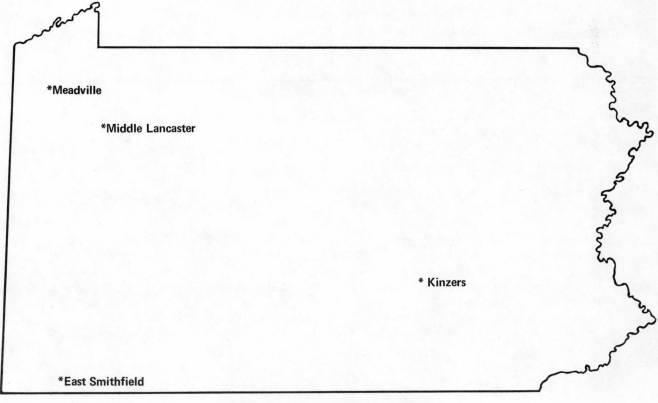

*Meadville

*Middle Lancaster

* Kinzers

*East Smithfield

Pennsylvania

NORTHWESTERN PENNSYLVANIA STEAM ENGINE
& OLD FARM EQUIPMENT SHOW
Community Park
Middle Lancaster, Pa.
Last 3 days following the last full week of July, yet!

This show started, as did so many, when some neighbors regenerated old-fashion neighborliness in 1963, helping Charles McMurray fire up his 1911 Case 12-36 to saw some lumber on Harold Bupp's sawmill at the Lawrence County Farm Show.

Some of NW Pennsyvania's equipment, left to right: 1911 Case 12-36, Wendell Bintrim, owner; 1915 Case 50-HP, Pres. Charles McMurray; 1926 Buffalo-Springfield 24-ton steam roller, Clyde Lightfoot. L-R are Harold Bupp, Harmony; McMurray, Slippery Rock and W.K. Matteson, New Castle.—Butler EAGLE

Reports Mrs. Bupp, now secretary, "That Fall, eight persons attended a meeting. Since sawing with steam was such an attraction, they would try to interest more people and add threshing and baling the next year." They elected McMurray temporary president next February, wrote a whole gob of letters to folks they thought would be interested, and held an organizational meeting April 7, 1964.

Everybody put a well-greased elbow to the wheel "and by Farm Show time we had quite a nice display," reports Mrs. Bupp. Highlights of that show were the Case threshing and sawing, and a one-dogpower treadmill working a wooden dasher churn called a Daschchurn out of respect for its prime mover although he was a sort of a shepherd, partly. They also ran a stone flour mill and a 10-HP portable Russell steam engine.

268

The Farm Show kicked in $50 toward expenses which gave the club a big boost. A still bigger boost was an invitation to return next year (nothing like being wanted). That November the Butler County Fair offered $500 for the club to put on its show there. This, plus money raised by a tureen dinner, mostly went for transporting machinery. It takes quite a bit to lug a steam engine around.

"So we went back to our tureen dinners," recalls Mrs. Bupp. The Community Club also extended an invitation and offered to help with advertising and insurance. Neighbors got together to bind and shock grain for the affair, and Mrs. Harold (Thelma) Schott cooked a real old-time thresher-men's dinner for the crew, aided by neighbor ladies.

Trouble was, people got Lancaster and Middle Lancaster mixed up. Please note THE SHOW IS HELD BETWEEN ZELIENOPLE AND PORTERSVILLE ON Rt. 19.

They ended the 1966 show with money in the bank toward the next, bigger and better show.

"To celebrate a successful show, we had a tureen dinner and didn't pass the hat," Mrs. Bupp reports.

"The Middle Lancaster group had borrowed money on their signatures to put a basement under the old one-room school to use as a community center so the young people would have a place for scout meetings, square dancing and parties in their community. They credited the steam show with paying off their mortgage." The steam club incorporated in time for the '67 show.

Featured at the '68 show were a 1915 Case 50-HP steam traction engine, the 1911 Case, a 16-HP Frick steamer, 15-HP Westinghouse steam engine, 10-HP Russell, 10-ton Buffalo-Springfield steamroller, Spencer return flue, sawmill, 1872 shingle mill, 1898 Champion thresher, 1907 West-inghouse thresher, Red River Special thresher, chaff piler, some old gas tractors and trucks, engines and accessories.

Activities included steam threshing and sawing, musical events, garden tractor pulling contest, teen night, square dancing, country and western music, pony-pulling, and those good ol' thresher-men's feeds.

Says the secretary, "Putting on these shows, working and planning together are bringing back the old neighborliness."

15-HP Westinghouse owned by Morgan Hill; operators are Matteson & McMurray.—EAGLE

10-HP 1914 Russel.—Bupp

Frick Portable sawmill.—Bupp

The Bupps' son-in-law, Wendell Bintrim, Harmony, caught a bad case of steamitis, too, and, in his search for a cure, bought a 50-HP steam engine, which of course only made the disease worse, as such medicine always does.

Says Mrs. Bupp, "Our daughter says it has one advantage: he can't put it in the cellar to work on in the winter the way he did his gas engines."

269

PIONEER STEAM & GAS ENGINE SOCIETY
Fairgrounds
Meadville, Pennsylvania
Weekend after Labor Day

"A bunch of the guys got together in 1967 and decided to have a little show," relates Dillon Wescoat. The guys were Parley Carpenter, Guys Mills; Oliver Rhead, Meadville and Ellis Wellman, Erie, Pa.

So they had a little show over at Wellman's, where he has a whole herd of gas engines. "They set up with that and Oliver's Rumely and Morgan Hill's vertical-tube Westinghouse traction engine.

"The response was so great they decided they'd better be organized. They called together all the people on the register." They organized and had their first formal show in the Fall of 1968.

For a first, it was quite a show, complete with steam calliope, parade, a homemade steamer that went 50 MPH.

Their shows to come will be even better, I think.

Pretty respectable line-up of steam engines for a first show.

Here you get a good look at the flat-blade Baker fan construction.

1913 16-HP 8½x10 Huber owned by George A. Nicholas. Designed for 135 pound WP, but in respect for its gray hairs he carries 113-125 pounds

Slow race separates the steam men from the grease monkeys. Object is to run the engine as slowly as it will go and still keep moving. Once you stop, you're out. This requires perfect alignment of valves, cranks, bearings— because if there's a sticky spot you have to run 'er faster to get past the hang-up. Last man across wins.

Farquhar 1927 pulls & powers (through hose) steam calliope. Note engine is "backwards" compared to usual cylinder-flywheel arrangement.

Steam calliope was one of the most popular attractions. Calliopists are Morgan Hill and Mrs. Ellis Wellman. Built by C. A. Fisher Mining Co., Stoneboro, Pa.

rtable 1920 20-HP Birdsell owned by Clair Carpenter & Sons, Guys Mills, Pa.

Hybrid 18-HP 2-cylinder is made up of Gaar-Scott & Port Huron & truck parts by Fred J. Hart, Williamsville, O. Will go 50 MPH, has hydraulic brakes.

Westinghouse vertical-tube boiler was built in 1895, cranks out 10 HP. Morgan Hill, Linesville, Pa., owner. Although she's self-propelled, you wouldn't want to pull more than the water wagon with her. What appears to be a second steering wheel is really a crank for the variable-sheave V-belt drive that gives you an infinite range of speeds.

Unidentified.

1924 Advance-Rumely 20-HP owned by J.J. Sutzman.

Says an old-timer about Margaret Peters, Espyville, Pa., "She never seen a threshin' machine before. Somebody talked her into cuttin' bands. I seen guys who cut for 5 years couldn't hold a candle to her." Better be careful how you hold them-there candles around all this straw, and a wooden machine to boot. Hand-fed thresher is a Pioneer with windstacker built in 1925. Pioneer began building steel machines in 1927.

Moppet is fascinated by grain pouring into half-bushel tally.

Forrest Carpenter, Blacksmith.

Truckload of models, owned and many made by
L.D. Johnson, Sagertown, Pa., retired machinist
and tool & die maker, run on 10 pound air.

Herd of Rumely Oil-Pulls. Number 14 is number 3833, a 1924 15-25 2-cylinder 730 RPM; pulls 2 14s. Runs on water & kerosene. A.G. Dougan & Son, owners. Others are unidentified.

1904 shingle mill.

Youngsters are catching on.

Titan.

Huber 1928 40-62 owned by O. Nelson.

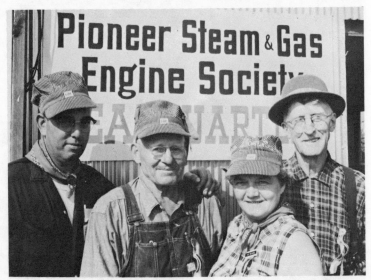

Officers, L–R: Al Van Slycke, Meadville, field supervisor ("Money, men & grounds!"); Oliver B. Rhead, VP & operator, Meadville; Mrs. Mary Van Slyke, sec.-treas.: and Parley Carpenter, president, Guys Mills.

C.J.L. Williams likes whistles by the carload. They run off the exhaust.

Wellman puts more drag on the Prony brake.

ROUGH & TUMBLE ENGINEERS HISTORICAL ASSOCIATION
Spring Steam-Up Early May
Fall Reunion Late August
Engine-O-Rama Early November
East of Kinzers, Pa.

In the heart of the Amish and Pennsylvania Dutch country, you see some traditional farming practices still practiced. See hex signs on the barns going and coming. Enjoy Pennsy Dutch cooking, the real original.

Huber Return-Flue.

Eclipse.

Peerless.

Avery Undermounted.

1-horse treadmill runs groundhog.

Right: You can crank the groundhog by hand if you wish. Someone has to fork the straw away. Grain still has to be winnowed.

The dark maw of the groundhog thresher, resembling a ground-hog's hole, gave it its name.

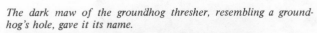

Fanning mill.

1-horse grain mill.

Sweep power runs hand-fed, web-stacked, hand-sacked wooden thresher.

You'll see some fine horseflesh in the Amish country.

Corliss engine is on display.

Take a steam ride. —OT photos

How to take all the work out of gardening.

The old order restored: Old Order Amishman has replaced worldly rubber tires with plain steel wheels. Looks like a stationary engine on an old John Deere chassis.

BRADFORD COUNTY OLD TIMERS
VFW Grounds
East Smithfield, Pa.
Write for date

A daily parade, sawmill, shingle mill making free souvenirs, stone crusher making fireproof souvenirs, threshing, baling are regular delights. Other features offered from year to year as available include free ox team rides, antique cars, spinning, knitting, steam traction engine and sawmill built by member Miles Stone.

Started in 1963, Old Timers didn't get out of the red until their third show. Their main attraction is the model steam railroad owned by Sullivan Bros., Horseheads, N. Y., who gives free rides to young and old and in-betweens.

"We're a non-profit organization and shy away from concessions," says Secretary Bono Van Noy. "We try to provide entertainment for everyone and a place where a family can go and have a good time. Food and soft drinks are available at a reasonable price."

One prize item is an 1898 Westinghouse vertical boiler steam engine which William Van Netta found in a Michigan brush patch. He restored it to operating condition.

For show date write to Bono Van Noy, Rt. 2, Troy, Pa. 16947.

Threshermens Galvanized Steel
WAGON TANKS
The Original and only 3 Point Bearing Wagon Tank Made.

Patented May 10, 1904.

What would you think of a man, or set of men that did not have the ability or self mechanism to produce an article of merit. But were so unscrupulous as to imitate what others were doing. Would you expect such People to give you an honest deal? Those who try to take such advantage, we all know will do us in the end, in some way. See what some other tank makers are trying to do. They are trying to produce a tank looking just as much like ours as they possibly can, without getting so close to our patent that they are liable to prosecution by us. We, after 16 years' experience in tank making, had this tank patented to keep just such unscrupulous imposters from copying every idea we had produced in the steel tank line, and they dare not make our exact tank, but have the gall to offer something just as near like it as possible. And let the People believe it is the same, if they will. This tank is supported on the wagon by a heavy steel truss, with a heavy steel Channel lapping down 2 inches on each side of the Bolster.

The front truss is made rounding, or so it rocks on the bolster which gives it a 3 point bearing on the wagon making it impossible for the tank to be the least twisted over rough roads. It fits any common wagon. And is sold at prices no higher than those ask that are trying to have you believe they make one just as good. We have put out about six thousand in six years, and we have yet the first dissatisfied customer to hear from. We make this assertion and defy its contradiction. Send us a card and get full particulars. Preserve this ad., as it may not appear again in this size.

PIONEER MFG. CO.,   Box 327,   Middlebury, Indiana

Northwestern Agents, Sachse & Bunn, Cherokee, Iowa.   Kansas Agents, Wichita Supply Co., Wichita, Kansas
Port Huron Machinery Co., Des Moines, Iowa, Agents.   Southwestern Port Huron Co., Peoria, Ill.
Bowen & Quick, Agents, Auburn, N. Y.   Port Huron Engine & Thresher Co., Port Huron, Mich.

Some Men Take Care of what They Have and Always Have Something

A good cover is a necessity if you take care of your machine.

A thresherman of 20 years' experience made the remark that covers were not as good as they used to be. That is true if you buy the general run of covers.

But you can get good covers now as well as 20 years ago, if you buy a good make. Most cover manufacturers think any kind of goods is good enough for a cover. We think the best is none too good. Get our samples and prices.

R. O. KUNKLE & CO.

P. O. Box 575,   Peoria, Illinois.

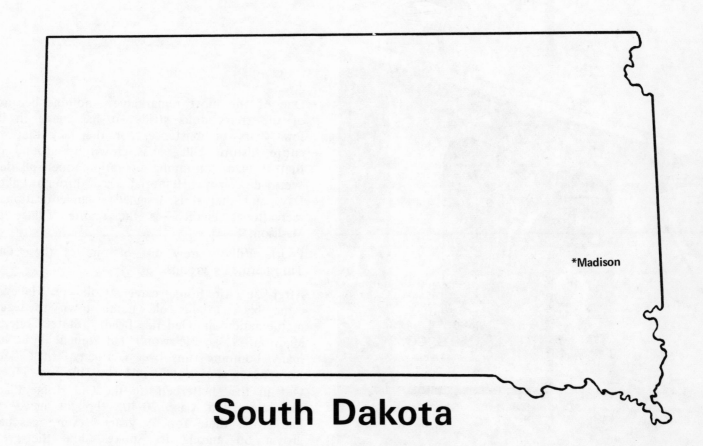

South Dakota

Prairie Village, South Dakota

where the past comes alive

One of the most remarkable——notable because of the tremendous strides it has made in its few years of existence, for the fact that an entire historic village has grown up around it, that it is a continuing operation, open all day every day from Memorial Day through Labor Day, and that it is designed as an educational-recreational facility——is the Prairie Village at Madison, S. D.

Prairie Village grew out of one of these Old Threshermen's groups.

After an Air Force career, Col. Joe Habeger came back to his old home town to teach mathematics at General Beadle State College, Madison, S. D. He won't talk much about his many bombing runs over Germany——just, "We were never shot down; just shot up."

Out in the shelterbelt on the Old Home Place stood a 1915 Case 20-40, "bought new." It had stood there for 25 years——even trees had grown up among its spokes, like the great oaks between Atlas' toes. Joe tinkered it back to life. Old Ralph Leonard, who had run that

Prof. Joe Habeger, left, hands over the "key" of his 1915 Case 20-40 gas engine to Jerry Prostrollo, Prairie Village fund drive chairman. Joe's gift was the first property it owned.

Portable horse-drawn steam engine. Photo provided by John J. Menchhofer, who can say only that "It's an old one." Floodlights growing out of stack are not part of machine.

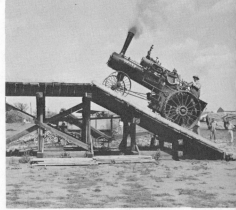

Hill climb used to be quite a thing at fairs––to see if you could get up the hill without losing steam. There's no draft at this angle. Case 50-HP; date unknown.––J. I. Case Co.

tractor for 30 years but hadn't heard it for 25, listened a moment. "She's runnin' about 65 RPM too fast, Joey," he said. Joe slapped his tachometer on it.

She was running 60 RPM over her rated 475.

Powering an old separator with the Case, Joe got some friends to help him thresh in 1961. This gave them the idea of an annual threshing bee, but they never got around to it in 1962. That winter, Joe and friends organized the Eastern South Dakota Threshermen's Association. The next year they got Adolph Rude to bring his Case steamer over from Flandreau, and some 6,000 people came to watch that one steam engine work on Joe's farm. The next year came 8,000 people during the three-day event, and in 1965, 10,000 people thronged to Joe's farm 13 miles north of Madison.

The Greater Madison Chamber of Commerce began thinking it was a pity these 10,000 people had to gather so far from the comforts of civilization. They voted it would be a kindness on the merchants' part to make the pleasures of their stores, cafes, service stations, etc., more accessible to the crowd, and suggested to ESDTA that they move their show closer to town next year.

Nobody will say who thought of it, but history will speculate it was Joe––somebody got the idea of recreating a turn-of-the century pioneer town to show folks how their forefathers lived while taming the raw prairie, and to stage the annual steam threshing jamboree at the village site. This grew into plans for an all-year-'round educational-recreational non-profit enterprise which could be used by tourists and scholars alike, where would be preserved some of our pioneer heritage. People started speaking of the idea as Prairie Village and the name stuck. ESDTA reorganized into the Prairie Historical Club, Inc. and elected Joe its president.

A church parading down the highway, jaunty bird's nest bonnet atop her steeple and followed by depot, ranch house and country bank headed for Prairie Village, got pictured in national and European papers.

Madison civic and service organizations jumped into a drive to raise $100,000 to buy land and build necessary shops and shelters so this irreplaceable equipment wouldn't have to sit out in the weather. Mrs. Irma Lyons made an ideally-situated 120-acre farm available to the club at far below market price because she liked the educational-recreational-preservation-restoration idea. Nestled between S. D. 34/U. S. 81 and Lake Herman, just two miles west of Madison, the land offered plenty of room for parking, displays, activities, the village itself and for growing the big grain crops required to keep a whole herd of classic threshing machines busy throught the three-day annual Steam Threshing Jamboree.

The project got not only local support but amazingly enthusiastic help from businessmen in Sioux Falls, the state's metropolis (pop. 55,000), 50 miles away, who contributed.

Volunteers pitched in and hauled turn-of-the-century buildings from a wide area: a church, a one-room country school, store, depot, country bank, farm and ranch homes, jail and a claim shanty. A photo the author took of the church marching down the highway, followed by bank, house and depot for the Madison Daily LEADER, was published in papers all over this country and in some European papers.

A log house was discovered near Canton, 100 miles away, built in the 1870's but clapboarded early so it was in perfect condition. Volunteers picked this two-story structure up and set it on the village site, where a tornado promptly scattered its logs over a wide area, mixed with pieces of barn.

Show Day 1971. The six new old buildings [opp. page] that were moved here in 1972 made quite an. addition. Biggest oldie hauled in was the basketball-court-sized Oldham Socialist Hall, where Lawrence Welk made his first stage appearance. Lake Herman shore is an added attraction.

Along with all this other work the volunteers rebuilt the barn and gathered up the logs. The log house is back in running order, for the tornado didn't hurt the logs any——just mixed them up.

Even before Prairie Village had a home, East River Electric Power Cooperative, Madison, was asking its 55,000 members throughout eastern South Dakota to donate or lend pre-electric or early electric household and farm gadgetry for a museum which it has since built at the Village. Dusty treasures flowed from attic and basement all around.

Those bundles don't just jump from the windrow into the shock——from shock to bundle wagon and then into the feeder. Somebody has to do the work. And every time they're moved, some of the grain shatters out. These were some of the sales pitches used in selling combines: less work, less wasted grain, no threshing crews to feed.

No, that's not a double-barrelled thresher. You see windstacker and weigher of a Case looming above and behind the Aultman—Taylor. Bundle-pitchers had to lay bundles in heads-first, had to keep machine up in the collar without slugging, and had to keep from falling into the clawing, chawing feeder because meat and bones gum up the cylinder.

The separator man was boss

There was always a running argument among early railroaders as to who was boss of the train——the conductor or the engineer. Legend has it that one conductor and one engineer settled the question for all railroaders and for all time with their fists: the conductor won.

The separator man is undisputed boss of the threshing crew. Everything centers around the threshing machine that it may do the best possible job. At 3 cents per bushel, wages and profits depend on getting the most bushels out in the shortest time. The engineman maybe was King in the old days——King in the sense of romance and glamour and prestige——but when the separator man says, "Jump," everybody still says, "How high?"

When he isn't oiling, inspecting and adjusting his machine and feeling bearings to make sure they aren't getting hot, he's standing atop his thresher, keeping an eyeball peeled.

Daring Young Lady of '74 shows some bare ankle at the Prairie Village old-time costume contest. Cheesecake not only caught the judge's eye, but the prize as well.

No, she doesn't have jets in her 1870 bonnet. Author snap-shot this from the hip as National Guard saluted Gov. Boe at 600 MPH during groundbreaking festivities.

What kids today have the enviable opportunity to jump in a bright, fresh strawstack? Just the kids who visit Prairie Village.

Fun for everyone at Prairie Village

The 3-day Steam Threshing Jamboree drew 13,000 people in 1966, the first year it was held at the village. You can get an argument going as to whether 20,000 or 30,000 attended the 1967 show. "Pretty good for a county of 15,000," grin boosters.

Not everybody registered, by a long shot, but those who did represented 39 states and 9 countries.

Two national-international publications sprang up to minister to steam buffs. Both represent enterprises that started as fun hobbies and grew almost to overwhelm their originators, much to their bemusement.

One is The Iron-Man Album Magazine, founded, edited and published by Rev. Elmer Ritzman, NTA chaplain, at Enola, Pa.

The other, Engineers & Engines, was started by T. H. Smith in 1955. Wrote a biographer, "Mr. Smith had spent most of his life working with steam engines on the farm, in oil fields, heavy construction and on the railroads." He died in 1961, but his widow, Mary Louise, continues the bimonthly, doing all the work including the printing, in her home at 611 Darcy Ave., Joliet, Ill. She has subscribers all over the U. S., in Canada and England.

A magazine devoted to old gas engine and tractor devotees recently split off one of these.

Squaredancers entertain the throng.

Not only lots of steam threshing and plowing going on, but auctions where you can buy everything from a lard press and a handcranked "labor-saving" wooden washing machine to a crankshaft for your '03 Goliath.

acres of models *Half-scale Avery thresher, bundle wagon and water wagon really thresh real grain. The only concession Garrett Havelaar, Hudson, S. D., makes is to open the bundles and hand-feed them.*

Have fun at Prairie Village

unique steam
carrousel

Prairie Village centers on steam-powered merry-go-round.

When Herb and Mrs. Willoughby bring their collection over from Howard, they make quite a parade. They're seated in a 1920 4-door Franklin.

Sam Johnson gives the kiddies pleasure with a sure hand on the whistle of the Herschel Spielman twin-cylinder opposed 8-HP engine.

Little Kids growed big have a ball operating the real coal-burning engines from 1/10 to 1 HP they built themselves. Every show features 1 acre creeping and crawling with real operating model. Leo Huston, Watertown, S. D., built this ¼-scale approximating the Nichols & Sheppard.

There's the soddy——and in the foreground is the one-horse breaking plow a pioneer plowed up his sod "bricks" with——and that plowed the sod strips for this soddy. Claim shanty is in background at the Madison, S. D., Prairie Village.

Where you can see how your forefathers lived

Back East, where Nature provided lots of trees, the glaciers left plenty of rocks. Settlers built log cabins or stone houses. Building materials lay at their feet. Fuel was in the forests, in David Thoreau's words in WALDEN, "an encumbrance."

Not so on the Great Plains.

An ancient sea floor, the Plains provided neither trees nor stones, but still homes and fuel lay at the ingenious pioneers' feet, though less easy to come by. Many of them, too poor to buy and freight lumber from the rail-head maybe a hundred miles away, built their first homes with the only thing at hand: the tough, matted prairie sod.

An ox team and a breaking plow turned the sod in foot-wide strips about four inches deep. The farmer, his family and friends cut the half-mile-long furrow strips into manageable lengths of two or three feet and laid them like big bricks. The tool of choice for cutting was a corn knife, but some used a butcher knife. Moderns, finding corn knives scarce, use a linoleum knife.

No mortar was needed. Mud and wads of sod plugged the holes. Wagon sideboards formed the roof, overlaid by sod.

People are still living, some with only a few gray hairs, who remember living in sod houses. An aristocracy of sorts——the Sons and Daughters of the Soddies of North America——has developed. To qualify, you must have been born in, or lived in, a soddy. Far from a dying breed, the membership increases as more old soddy residents find out about the S&D of S of NA. Who knows——perhaps having lived in a soddy will become a snob symbol like coming over in the Mayflower!

You can see a real live soddy at Madison's Prairie Village. A Madison school principal, Miss Bena Jacobs, lived in one from March to October, 1910, in Alberta while her family's proper wooden house was a-building. Far from considering her childhood deprived, she says, "I've always been thankful to my parents for giving me this heritage. I want other people to have the experience of seeing how pioneers lived."

So when Prairie Village started in 1966 she volunteered to build a genuine soddy there. It's pretty big and rather ornate, as soddies go, being 20x13½ feet inside and having a pole frame. The walls are 2 feet thick (some old-time soddies were 3 or 3½ feet thick, she recalls) and 7 feet high. "We built it higher than most because we wanted visitors to move around comfortably."

These thick earthen walls are excellent insulators, keeping out summer heat and winter cold. And they're surprisingly durable. "I recently met a woman born in one in Nebraska in 1901 who says it is still in good condition," she says. Barring accidents or the itchings-scratchings of cattle, and if the builder locates the building on high ground where toad-strangler runoff won't lap the wall, the building is good for generations.

How to build a soddy: Miss Bena Jacobs, who lived in a Canadian soddy when she was a child, shows how you build the wall. "I don't ordinarily wear my Sunday clothes for this job," she chuckles.

A fringe benefit of soddy living is the "wall garden" you can raise when prairie lupines, cacti, other wildflowers sprout out of sod wall.

Soddy even has a real storm cellar such as protected settlers from tornadic "cyclones" and kept vegetables and milk cool. Note weeds growing in roof sod. Here you can see how the gable ends are finished––another unusual feature. Most soddies had shed roofs––simpler to build.

Soddy is furnished with a real cast-iron cook-stove, just like granma used before the REA came through, and with other authentic pioneer furniture.

The roof, though, gave trouble, always. "I remember two little leghorn straw bonnets my sister and I were quite fond of, brought from the States," recalls Miss Jacobs. "A long hard rain soaked through the sod roof and stained our hats. But mother got out the sadiron and heated it on the topsy stove and cleaned them up and made them pretty again."

Miss Jacobs gives some handy household hints on building a soddy: "Choose virgin prairie sod——buffalo grass is best because the curly blades give extra adhesion." She's never tried domestic sod but scorns it, considering even sodbound bromegrass too friable for construction.

"Plow with a regular breaking plow such as the pioneers used, as deep as the roots are matted." She had to settle for 3 inches at Madison because the over-grazed roots didn't go any deeper. You're supposed to use oxen, but in our benighted space age you may have to settle, as she did, for a horse. The horse, borrowed from under the saddle, disapproved of the entire project.

You don't need a fancy foundation. The good way is to lay your base course directly on the sod and to build from there——eschewing, of course, low or boggy spots. Choose a knoll or slight slope above high water. The plot she was assigned was not firm enough, so she laid the base course on gravel fill in a trench.

Sometimes the builders simply rolled up the sod strips for transport to the building site, then unrolled them on the rising wall. It's important to place the sod upside down on the walls, right side up on the roof, Miss Jacobs says.

Bridge the roof with tree branches, brush, boards or the sideboards off your wagon——whatever comes in handy. Roof can be peaked or shedded, whichever suits your artistic fancy. Overlap the sod strips like shingles to shed rain, starting at the eaves and working toward the peak.

The housekeeper needn't worry about dirt crumbling off the inner walls, once they've settled, Miss Jacobs assures the nervous pioneer mother. For exhibition purposes she finished the walls of her soddy in the several ways of our forebears: clay, plaster, heavy paper and boards, and left as-is. She floored part of the soddy with boards, part with the usual clay, which she says, "is clean as can be."

300

The Prairie Village soddy is furnished with authentic period cookstove, bunks, churn, kitchen "safe" (cabinet), other genuine pioneer homestead articles. It can be inspected whenever Prairie Village is open—— every day from Memorial Day through Labor Day.

Also at Madison's Prairie Village you can see an original claim shanty. The Homestead Act of 1862 gave 160 acres (¼ square mile, considered a family-size farm at the time) to anyone who would farm it and build a habitable dwelling thereon. Most of the Great Plains were settled that way——people still claimed homesteads into the '20's.

The law was rather lenient in its interpretation of a "habitable dwelling." Most of these were, if not soddies, mere shanties of 6x8 feet or so made of rough boards hauled 100 miles or more from the end of steel. The door was of planks, the floor of dirt, and the single window a sliding wooden shutter. Anyone rich enough for a glass window was the aristocrat of the community.

The claim shanties and often the soddies were heated to a small degree by a cast-iron stove which also did for cooking. The settler had his choice of fuel——prairie hay or buffalo chips, and later the dried dung "platters" cattle so thoughtfully make for us.

The trouble with grass was it blazed up in fury and was gone. Then somebody invented the air-tight stove in which the grass, twisted into a tight bundle, would glow and give off heat for a longer time. Tying hay into the necessary knots was an all-family job to which even the little ones could contribute. Stories were told of families spending the entire winter just tying hay to keep from freezing.

That's how Hayti, S. D. (pronounced HAY-tie) got its name. Settlers gathered in the marshes there to tie the lush marsh grass into fuel bundles.

Many a claim shanty stands yet on the plains. Some are vacant and rotten. Others were added to, room by room, as the family prospered and today form the nucleus of a respectable, modern farm house.

Some of these built-on structures even have air-conditioning, now, and electric heat! A far cry from hay and buffalo chips.

Here's what the sod "bricks" look like up close. Pole frame construction is unusual in a soddy; was built here for extra durability.

A real topsy stove: these air-tights kept tight-knotted prairie hay twists burning a long time instead of just blazing up and away. Rubber band holds hay knot tight for display.

South Dakota Twins Invent Uniflow Steam Cylinder

August and Martin Quickstad, twin brothers, Toronto, S. D., patented a side-ported steam cylinder and piston in 1916. They offered it to the J. I. Case Co. in 1931. D. P. Davies, vice-president, declined with thanks, saying, ". . . at present there is hardly any demand for steam tractors, and we have practically given up the manufacture."

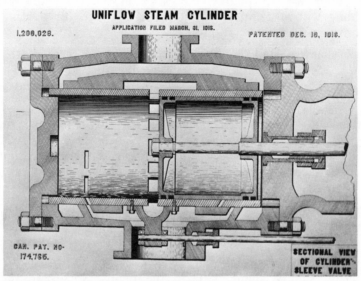

The Quickstad twins' patented Uniflo.—Quickstad photo

Plowing with Huber Return Flue.—Quickstad

"The Original Russell 10-HP built in 1892: photo about 1905," writes August Quickstad. "I am on rear of tank with fork, proud & thrilled at having job of straw monkey. Old Betsy in Utah."—Quickstad

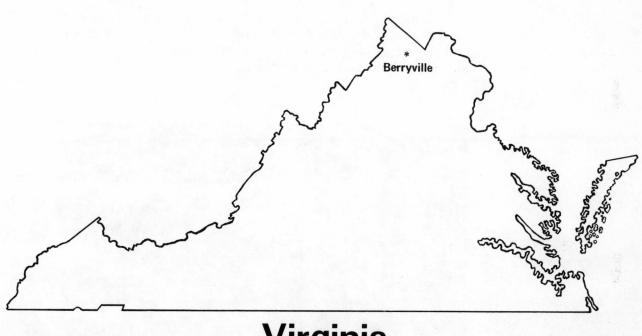

Berryville

Virginia

SHENANDOAH VALLEY STEAM & GAS ENGINE ASSOCIATION
Berryville, Va.
1 mile W on US No. 7, horse show grounds
Late July or Early August

One steam show starts another. Mr. and Mrs. Paul K. Giles of Berryville attended the Rough and Tumble show at Kinzers, Pa., in 1959. They caught the bug bad and nothing would do but they had to buy a steam engine of their own and work for starting a Berryville show.

The first show was held with a single Frick engine on Fred Stickley's farm at Waterslick near Front Royal, Va., in 1959. The next year saw a two-day show and in 1961 more engines performed. By 1963 it had outgrown Stickley's field so it was moved to R. G. Buckley's property at White Post, Va. The next year it moved to the old Berryville horse show grounds, now owned by the Clark Co. Ruritan Club. Here are plenty of space, shady groves, picnic grounds, etc., 1½ hours from the nation's capital in the heart of Virginia's Apple Country.

Now, besides Stickley's Frick, the show boasts a 120 HP ZZ, the largest Peerless ever made, owned by Buckley and Ralph Lewin, originally used to pull three huge wagons of apples to the railroad where it filled a box car at each trip. Buckley also supplies a Frick DC and Lewin a Peerless and a Farquhar.

A rare jewel is this 1885 Greencastle 12-HP owned by W.U. Waters Jr., Damascus, Md. It is thought to be the only one left. Has an 8x10½ cylinder and a non-variable cutoff. — Club photos

Jimmy fires the Huber, the last of its line, while Grandpa watches to see how to do it. Mr. Brandt is one of the few old-time threshermen left in this area. Amos take his Huber to ALL the shows in the East. — Wm. M Rhoden, Jr. photo

The club organized formally in April, 1967, with Paul Giles as president, the first chartered steam club in the state. It now has over 200 members, many of them willing and able workers, others willing and able to let the others work.

The 1968 show features 12 steamers plus many gas tractors and engines and models. The club owns a Huber 30-50 thresher donated by R. J. Sadlick, and bought a stationary boiler for the models, and a Frick sawmill. Giles' 7x10 double cylinder 60-HP Frick is one of the best-preserved engines in the area.

William H. Clem, Manassas, provides a 75-HP Case. A. F. Brandt, Bainbridge, Pa., brings the very last Huber steamer ever built, and his 11-year-old grandson Jimmy comes along to run her!

Both the Frick and the Peerless engines were built in nearby Waynesboro, Pa. "More than 30,000 Frick engines were built," insists Mrs. Giles, club secretary. "I dispute the 27,506 given elsewhere in this book. Frick engines list serial numbers from one to 27,506 from 1884 to 1936.

Before 1884, they had built 3,130 not listed, and at least 75 after 1936, according to the Frick Engine Owners Club Bulletin."

So there, too.

Giles' 1922 Frick, 2-cylinder 7x10, 60 HP at 150 pounds, 11 tons. Made at Waynesboro, Pa. Paul, its 4th owner, is re-fluing it.

Many a brave engineer was crushed against his firebox when a wooden bridge collapsed. The engine and separator jackknifed together, the feeder invariably smashing the crew against the boiler. If death were not instantaneous, it came slowly in steam and fire. Engineers hated stingy county commissioners for building buggy bridges. Thrifty road commissioners hated the engineers for smashing their 1-ton bridges with 12-ton engines. This Peerless engine died with its baler on. Jim Rathert, Forman, N.D., says, "I know nothing about this tragedy. It's an old post card I picked up someplace."

The Death of an Engineer

Separator on sleds was common in the early north when threshing went deep into Winter. This is George Hubert's 1912 outfit in the Badlands north of Medora, N.D.—Rathert

Left—Samuel Osborne, New Oxford, Pa., left, is a real old-time blacksmith who travels around to several steam engine shows, setting up a complete shop and drawing much attention.—Rhoden

306

Bellows Falls*

Vermont

STEAMTOWN USA
Bellows Falls, Vt.
Open All Summer

"Steamtown USA is owned and operated by the Steamtown Foundation for the Preservation of American and Steam Americana, and toward this goal is trying to assemble all manner of steam devices," says Edgar T. Mead Jr., chairman. Steamtown USA was founded by the late F. Nelson Blount (1918-1967).

Continues Mead, "A major portion of the collection deals with steam railroading, which enabled farm products to reach their markets and farm machinery to reach the rural areas. Steam shovels and rollers made the roads which brought farms figuratively closer to towns and markets. Steam tractors, of which Steamtown has two fine examples, were used on some farms in New England but were most of all used by the farmer in woodlot and lumber sawing. The examples seen at Steamtown are rather typical of average-sized tractors which were maneuverable enough to clamber up the steep hills and ravines found in the upper regions.

"In its extensive collection are flat bed and vertical steam mill engines which powered the more permanent mills to be found in Vermont and New Hampshire, some of which cut lumber and others ground grain into flour and feed. Steamtown has some 50 different steam engines covering an extremely wide range of old-time American uses, and the Trustees of the Foundation are on the lookout for additions which will complete the collection and better tell the story of steam on America's railroads, factories and farms."

Steamtown has a Case engine and this one, unidentified. Prof. Joe Habeger, Madison, S. D., opined this is a "made-up" engine cobbled together out of bits and pieces. Anybody else— —?

Wisconsin

* Eau Claire

Fond du Lac *

*Baraboo

*Boscobel

*Sussex

*Janesville

Threshing in the Dane, Wis., area around 1914. Engine is a 18-HP Nichols & Shepard; separator, 36-inch Red River Special. At the throttle is John N. Johnson, father of club member Jim. The other man on the engine is Ted Knutson, father of clubber Russell.—Badger Steam photos.

BADGER STEAM & GAS ENGINE CLUB
Sauk County Fairgrounds
Baraboo, Wis.
Fourth Weekend of August

A big whistle-blowing opens each day's show at noon and a parade at 2. Continuous activities include baling straw with horse power; steam threshing and sawing; shredding corn with gas engines, and steamers on the Baker fan.

The late Roy Raschein, implement dealer, "got a few men interested and got a few meetings started in 1964," reports Al Stieber, Baraboo, Wis. They incorporated with 17 members and staged a show that Fall after just a few meetings.

Campers are welcome. Electricity and water supplied.

And while you're here, visit the nearby Circus World Museum (Baraboo claims to be the mother of the Big Top) and the railway museum.

Ray Klinger's 9-HP Case came from New Mexico. Contractor's tanks are unusual. Separator is a 24-inch Belle City slat stacker from about 1860.

2-horse sweep powers IHC hand-tie wire baler with hand-inserted batter boards. Elmer Hehenberger, Baraboo.

1860 Belle City slat stacker does good work. "This old separator is very rare and always a big attraction," say the Badger boys.

The Wisconsin 16-32 was built in Sauk City from 1917 to 1923. It was ahead of its time with totally-enclosed gears, and evolved from Earl McFarlane's dissatisfaction with the 2-cylinder models then predominating. Of the 600 built, most used a 4-cylinder Climax KU 5x6½ engine and a Foote Model D transmission. A few other sizes were built. At 6,000 pounds, this was an unusually light tractor for its day. *McFarlane's sons still build drag harrows in the same factory.*

The Original Wheel Barrow Grass Seeder, O.F. Thompson & Sons, Pat. Oct. 3 1880, owned by Bill Riddle, Rio, Wis.

Left—James Leffel 6-HP 1893, owned by the late Roy Raschein, came out of a cheese factory. Has suffered some alterations, but extent of change is not known.

DRAWBAR H.P. 25
BELT H.P. 45
R.P.M. 375
PLOWING SPEED 1-2
FUEL KEROSENE

Old Number One

The Latest Oil Pull—The 12-20

"Old Number One" proves the dependability and long life built into every OilPull

What will your tractor be like in 1929—ten years from now?

Will it show as good a record of performance as has "Old Number One"?

After ten years of the hardest kind of work that a tractor can be put to, "Old Number One"—the first OilPull—was brought to the National Tractor Demonstration at Wichita, and put right to work plowing in public demonstrations alongside tractors that were not even dreamed of until years after this machine had been turning the sod of the Dakota prairies.

"Old Number One" was a pioneer tractor in the Northwest. To date it has broken 1,750 acres of tough, virgin prairie sod, has plowed 5,600 acres of stubble land, and in 321 days of threshing—during which it operated a 40 x 62-inch separator —it has threshed over 750,000 bushels of grain. Besides all this, it has done road work and miscellaneous power jobs.

As a proof that it is still a good example of OilPull dependability, its work at Wichita was excelled by no other tractor. And, mind you, "Old Number One" was sent direct from its owner's farm to the demonstration and was not sent into the factory to be built over. And just as important, this old OilPull is now back in the hands of its owner and out on its usual Fall threshing run.

Now this proves an extremely important point—a question that is today uppermost in the mind of every prospective tractor buyer—namely, that a tractor *can* be built to give dependable service day after day and year after year.

And the same dependability and long life, shown by "Old Number One," is built into every OilPull that goes out of the Rumely shops. "Old Number One" does not enjoy its record alone. It is known that many others of the first OilPulls built are still working; Numbers Six and Eight are in North Dakota —Number Nine in Kansas—Number Eleven in Michigan.

And with this proof of dependability and long life, you can add one other extremely important point—economy. The OilPull is the only tractor made with which is given a written guarantee that it will burn kerosene under all conditions, at all loads, at all times.

Dependability—Economy—Long Life. These are three vitally essential points that you want to be sure are possessed by the tractor you buy.

There is a size OilPull to fit your farm—four sizes—12-20, 16-30, 20-40 and 30-60 H. P., each possessing 20% reserve power over its rating.

Ask for the OilPull catalog.

ADVANCE-RUMELY THRESHER CO. *Inc.*, **LA PORTE, INDIANA**

BACKED BY WRITTEN GUARANTEE
ADVANCE-RUMELY

ADVANCE-RUMELY

CHIPPEWA VALLEY ANTIQUE ENGINE & MODEL CLUB
Eau Claire, Wis.
Show Date & Place Vary
Check IRON-MEN ALBUM Ads

A group of men in the Chippewa Valley had been collecting old machinery for years but not many of them knew each other by name. And it was known there were some very fine model makers of various types of machinery, relates Ernest Freid, treasurer.

Came 1963 and George Freid called some collectors and model-makers together. They formed Chip Valley and elected George president. Some months later they decided to show their stuff in August.

"The show was arranged with not much in the treasury," recalls the treasurer. "We had buttons made, sold for 50 cents for two-day admission and the show showed a large profit."

Everything shown is in working order. They thresh grain and saw lumber and shingles and run the Baker fan. They usually have five to eight big steam engines with several half- and third-scale steam models, a team of horses on the water tank and between 30 and 50 gas engines from ¾ to 25 HP.

Club members—37 at last count—live within a 60-mile radius of Eau Claire, but they all pitch in on the hard work involved in arranging the show.

Kermit Holcomb feeds McCormick-Deering.—ChipVal Photos.

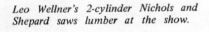

Leo Wellner's 2-cylinder Nichols and Shepard saws lumber at the show.

Declares E. Freid, "The club members have some of the most interesting old equipment and models in show business."

Claude Garton, Eau Claire, has many splendid models he built himself——steam traction engines, threshing machines, sawmill and many others. Leo Wellner, Stanley, has a large collection of steam engines, tractors, gas engines and many other implements. Lawrence Michelson, Cadott, has a fine collection of old cars, steam engines, gas engines and "anything that is old." Albert Martenson, Eau Claire, has a large collection of gas engines which he skillfully restores.

Model-maker George Wilson, Rice Lake, makes excellent models. Nyle Kurth, Eau Claire, shows a well-restored Case 65-HP and other unusual equipment. Fred Mueller, Fall Creek, has the sawmill. Jim Thill, Eau Claire, brings a 25-HP Mogul and other old pieces.

"The club does not have a set show date. We try not to have the show the same date as the other fine showings in the area. We advertise in THE IRON-MEN ALBUM Magazine along with posters and local radio stations." Check with Ernest O. Freid, 2313 Crescent Av., Eau Claire, Wis. 54701.

Rolling log into sawmill; nearest cant-hook run by Al Fried. Sawyer is Fred Mueller.

Clarence Jackson and his steam corn popper.

Sheep on treadmill runs cream separator. George & Ernest Freid.

Claude Garton's models.

Some engines and a labor-saving hand-cranked washing machine.

313

EARLY DAY GAS ENGINE & TRACTOR ASSN. Br. No. 2
"The Sussex Show"
Village Park
Sussex, Wis.
Third Weekend of August

Organized July 11, 1959, with 25 members, Branch 2 held its first few shows on the Adolph Nettesheim farm. Since moving to the village park, the group has become known as "The Sussex Show" and has nearly 200 members.

Show features Baker fans, steam and gas tractors, model steam engines and tractors, feed mill, clover huller, shredder and silo filler along with old gas engines, sawmill, teeter-totter and antique firearms.

Gilbert Lund, North Lake, Wis., restored 1931 Case C321429 to perfection. — Early Day.

OLD TIME ANTIQUE FESTIVAL
5 Mi S. Fond du Lac, Wis.
Late August or Early September

Unique in being a free-enterprise, free-admission show (most charge $1 or $1.50), the Old Time Antique Festival is staged by Bernard and Dorothea Kleinschmidt. A homemade steam engine runs a thresher and sawmill. Show feature is the 10-pony-power sweep driving a hand-fed, web-stacked separator.

Nearby classic car clubs drive over in droves to share the fun. Anyone who wants to display old guns, crockery and/or postage stamps sets up a table under a tree somewhere.

Among the models is a Hershall-Spielman merry-go-round of the 1880s operating at 7 PSI. There are 11 half-inch flues in her little insides, fired by charcoal fed by a shovel made from a tablespoon.

"Come who wants to come and display and also have fun. That's mostly what it's for," says Bernard. He doesn't live on the farm, so if you write to him, try 196 S. Seymour St., Fond du Lac, Wis. 54935.

Self-rake reaper owned by the Robert Grolapp family, VanDyne, Wis., "Was practically brought to us in a basket," says Kleinschmidt. "We've restored it this far."—Kleinschmidt.

Ponies on sweep power hand-fed thresher.—Gary Topp

Restored drag saw of uncertain origin powered by homemade steamer.—Ray Thornton.

315

ROCK RIVER THRESHEREE
Between Janesville
& Edgerton, Wis.
On Hiway 51
Date Unknown

Steam threshing, sawing, plowing, daily parade and a real live steam train——the Rock River Cannon Ball——are yours to behold.

They have some real classic engines: 1894 Harrison Jumbo 16 HP; the only existing one of the 8 GMC tractors General Motors built after taking over the Janesville Samson; Port Huron tandem compound; 1912 Townsend gas tractor that looks like a steam engine, boiler and all, built to side-step farmers' resistance to change; sawmill and cider press.

Jim Horton in 1955 asked some friends to help him thresh by steam. Not only his friends, but 400 strangers showed up! Jim and friends staged their first thresheree in 1957, organized in '60, bought their own farm a year later.

Walt Durst, foundry and machine works owner of Shopiere, Wis., fell in love with a little-bitty 75-HP saddle-tank dockside steam railroad locomotive when vacationing in Germany. He bought it and shipped it home. The Henschel, built in 1943 in Kassel, straddles a 600-millimeter track (23.65-inch)——a gauge for which no rolling stock is available in the U. S. So, starting with an empty track, he built rolling stock to fit.

Reconstructed as a Civil War engine, the Cannon Ball shoots around a 1½-mile track.

Write for show date to Glenn D. Beedy, Sec., Rt. 1, Waunakee, Wis. 53597.

6-HP Leffel portable, 1895, owned by Roy Roschein, Sauk City, Wis.—Edgerton Camera.

Boscobel engineers put on a pretty respectable show, as proved by their row of engines.
—Club photos

SOUTHWEST WISCONSIN ANTIQUE POWER CLUB
Boscobel, Wis.
Kronshage Park
First Weekend in August

The Boscobel weekly DIAL and the Boscobel State Bank in 1963 offered a $50 prize to one suggesting the best annual event.

Robert Jones, Boscobel, an officer in the newly-formed Southwest Wisconsin Antique Power Club, suggested an antique power show. He won. The first show was held the next year.

"A success from the start," reports Sec. V. L. Beeman, "the show attracted more than 10,000 persons at its fifth anniversary."

"The last three years the local women's club put on an open-air art fair and the two events complemented each other wonderfully. While the menfolk watched the big steam engines, wives wandered under the big elms in scenic Kronshage park on the Wisconsin River, viewing the rural art. Of course, the women also enjoyed the old engines."

The chamber of commerce co-sponsored the show and helped get it into orbit. Now the show earns a profit, with which it is hoped eventually to buy its own grounds and buildings.

Joe Pendleton, Boscobel, an old-time steam man, is president. Bob Jones and his engines were sadly missed at the 1968 show. He had died untimely of a bee sting.

Leon Vandervoort, Tomah, built this exact 1/3 scale Case 32-54.

"No automatic transmission," says Lawrence Huffman.   *Lorance Smith, Mt. Ida, Wis., is fascinated by gas engines.*

Women's club sponsors rural art show in Boscobel's Kronshage park on the Wisconsin River.

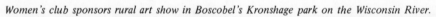

318

Harry Schell, Blue River, put Old Faithful together out of bits and chunks.

M. J. Rumely built in 1888 and still in service. Used to be horse-steered. Edward Washa, Muscoda, Wis.—SWW & DIAL photos.

Unnamed engine, 20-62 HP, bought new for $1,850 in 1908 by Andy Munyon, West Prairie, Wis. Has single 9x11 cylinder, weighs 10 tons, holds 12 bbl water. Leward A. Cook, Dodgeville, paid $2,200 for it.

ONTARIO

Wetaskiwin
*

* Saskatoon

Canada

*Collingwood

*Burford

Brigden *

ALBERTA   SASKATCHEWAN

GEORGIAN BAY STEAM, AUTOMOTIVE, GAS, ANTIQUE ASSOCIATION
Collingwood, Ontario
First Weekend in August

Georgian Bay show features a steam parade. First comes a 20-22 Waterloo followed by two 28-86 HP Sawyer-Massey engines. Owners are Hutchinson Bros. and Stewart Muir, Paisley, Ont. Bicycles are estimated at 10-toepower.—Club photos.

Among the steamers shown here are Sawyer-Massey, Waterloo, George White, MacDonald, Robert Bell, John Goodison, Case, John Abell Portable.

The last show presented over 15 steam engines, an equal number of gas tractors and 80 gas engines.

Organized in March, 1966, with 15 members, the club elected Barret Muir president. At last count it had 140 members.

Sawmill makes big noise about Georgian Bay show.

Dragsaw really pulls for the boys, too.

10-HP Case portable drives small edger. Vincent Riddell, Newmarket, Ont.

20-22 HP 1927 Waterloo. Jim Adams, Collingwood.

Bill Currie, Collingwood, Ont., built this model American-Abell plowing engine. You don't see many tricycle steamers about.

Sawyer-Massey 1911 sidemount, 100-HP compound.

321

28-86 HP Sawyer-Massey rear mount, 1919, 120 pounds working pressure. Hutchinson Bros., Kilworthy, Ont.

6-HP IHC.

30-50 Rumely owned by Murray McCabe, Tottenham, Ont.

"Victor" clover huller was built long ago by American-Abell Co., Toronto. Murray McCabe, owner.

JOHNSON & HOLT BOILERS
"Have Boiler Will Travel"
Burford, Ontario

Not a show, but a going business that buys, sells and rents steam equipment, Johnson & Holt have some real classic gems in their herd of steamers.

These are not showpieces (although many a collector would sell his wife and kids to get some of these, I betcha) but are working machines, out on the job. Among the slogans on the firm's letterheads are:

"You require a boiler——we have it" and "We buy, sell, rent and procure."

Stock includes steam pile drivers, portable space heaters, portable locomotive boilers mounted on rubber-tired truck wheels with folding stack for towing any place, and portable packaged boilers.

Ask where a given item is and genial Bill Johnson may tell you, "It's leased out by the year on a tobacco farm" or "Out on a construction job."

Two Sawyer-Massey (forerunner of Massey-Ferguson) Canadian-built tractors. The steamer is a 1915 25-HP side mount single simple 9½x11 western type engine. Gas tractor is also a 1915, rated 20-40 HP, 4-cylinder vertical, used for threshing, sawmilling, stone crushing, etc. "It runs well but is totally unrestored," says Bill Johnson.

1920 Waterloo 20-HP has a 9x10 side-mounted cylinder and is termed a "common eastern threshing engine." It ran a sawmill in northern Ontario. Note 2-speed gearing.—J & H photos.

Commonly mistaken for a Westinghouse, this 2-drum hoisting engine, 17 HP, 2-cylinder 7x8, 4,000 pound line pull, manufactured about 1925 by M. Beatty & Sons Ltd. in Welland, Ont., is constantly leased out, still on the job.

16-HP Norsworthy portable return-flue engine manufactured in St. Thomas, Ont., around 1895. Single 8x10 simple cylinder. Used for threshing and other farm belt power and sawing. This is the Scotch marine "wet back" boiler, still hard at work on a Canadian tobacco farm.

SASKATCHEWAN PION-ERA

The WORLD'S LARGEST PIONEER SHOW

"History in motion" is what folks around Saskatoon call their rootin-tootin six-day horse and machine extravaganza.

It's complete with grandstand shows, early steam and gas engines at their thunderous best, chuckwagon race, chariot race and light horse performance.

There's steam-engine hill-climb, Baker fan, shingle mill, Prony brake, stone crusher and sawmill.

They even have steam threshing. And a setting-up contest between steam and gas rigs, then threshing competition.

Threshing
Competition

Steam and gas boys pit their comparative skills. World championships are gained and lost in this setting-up and threshing competition. —Sask

Chuck
Wagon
Race

. . . and pony-powered chariot races make the ancient Romans look like paraplegics. —Delmar Studios

. . . a net feat, since 35 degree slope kills the draft and the engineer is in trouble if he kills his engine. There's no brakes on this rig so he's got to be nimble on throttle and reversing bar. —Sask

Hill
Climb

1825 groundhog, even though cranked by hand, was a huge improvement over Biblical flail (above). When some farm genius attached a fanning mill to the groundhog, the thresher was born. First combine was patented three years later, in 1828.—Sask

Acme stook (shock) loader saved a lot of bundle-pitching. Pione-Era threshing demonstrations take you from cradle, flail and winnowing basket through groundhog and steam thresher to combine, treadmill and sweep to modern engines.—Sask

Engine, separator and cookcar made quite a train.—Delmar

Wooden 20-foot self-propelled 24x36 combine was built in 1918, $5,000 FOB, Stockton, Cal. Hillside model has wheel that gears up and down to keep separator level on steep slopes while header reaches up or down. Was used by Mahr Bros., Milk River, Alberta, until 1944. Has crawler track on right. Cut up to 7½ A/hr. at 1½–2½ MPH.—Western Development Museum

Undermounted Avery and wooden thresher. High-clearance engine was favored on the prairies for turning under tall saplings.—Delmar

Welcomest time of the day at threshing was when the ladies brought out mid-morning and mid-afternoon lunch, as portrayed by famous artist Larry Green on our cover. — Sask

330

An acre a day was good plowing for two horses and one greatgranpa.—Sask

75-HP rear-mounted Sawyer-Massey 1-cylinder simple cost $3,500 new during World War I. Weight 28,000 pounds.—WDM

Next page: Northwest 36–60 thresher was right up to date in '02–'04, having both self-feeder and windstacker. Used by Kenneth May in the Oberon, Man. district until 1915. Windstacker fan shows an early arrangement, being mounted across the rear of the machine and gear-driven. 25-HP New Giant return-flue engine.—Francis J. S. Holmes

World's biggest plow: 20 bottoms; pulled by giant Reeves engine. Breaks up to 6 A/hr. See it at Pion–Era.—Murray Gibson

Just some of the steam traction engines in action at Pion-Era.— Gibson

It took 40 years for this maple tree to grow through the spokes of 1883 return-flue portable Whitelaw steamer, built at Woodstock, Ont. First used at Hamiota, Man., it came to Creelman, Sask. in '03. Retired in 1912, it rusted behind a blacksmith shop on the Andrew Allan farm. Donated by Allan; restored to running condition in Museum workshop.—Sask

333

Meet Pion-Era Pete

Reeves 1912 32–120 Canadian Special cross-compound No. 6819 was acquired from Kjellander and Son, Pense, Sask. Pulled 12–14 bottoms at 2½ MPH, weighs 38,000 pounds.—Delmar

1912 Case 40-HP steam engine, 22x37 Case thresher and 1936 C. Case tractor.—Johnson

25-HP NorthWest return flue was built between '02 and '04 as a straw burner. Used in the Oberon, Man., district until 1915. Note independent pump to supply feed water whilst working; can be operated by steam or by hand.—WDM

337

You'll see demonstrations of plowing and other field work, pioneer railway construction, a real ladies' sewing circle complete with guaranteed scandalous gossip, gymkhana, real live Indian pow-wow.

Then you'll see husband-calling contest, tugs-of-war, horseshoe pitching, pie-eating contests and all that. Old-time fiddler contest, sing-out, special children's activities.

One of the first houses built in Saskatoon is open for your inspection——the historic Temperance Colony house, right on the grounds. Watch the Doukhobor Society bake 30 loaves at a time in huge clay ovens they pre-heat with wood fires. Sample their wares on the spot with homemade jammmmmgood!

You'll watch the complete evolution of threshing over 5,000 years from the flail on up including horse-treadmill. Pioneer logging. You can even get behind the wheel of an ancient engine and make it go——and make it go toot!

Bartenders, sheriffs and honky-tonk girls are on duty at the 32-foot Blue Garter bar in the Sourdough Saloon. The bartenders twirl their whiskers and dish out root beer to 40 tables. The can-can girls twirl their little short skirts and the sheriff keeps jealous wives from a hair-pulling contest with them. The sheriff also helps keep fellas from getting trompled when one of the girls tosses her garter into the crowd. Those girls go through a heap of garters during the week.

There are vaudeville acts galore and top-name performers in song and dance.

Better go early——else there'll be 64,718 head ahead of you.

Next page: You ladies will enjoy the restored pioneer homes and the hostesses in authentic dress.—Pion-Era

Girls' International Rodeo contestants gather points at Pion-Era.—Pion-Era

Whoopie! Ride 'em Cowgirl

Why Pion-Era?

During WWII's scrap drives, some people became alarmed at the way old tractors and implements were disappearing. "A Saskatchewan culture and way of life and vanishing," says the Pion-Era program book. From this alarm grew the Western Development Museum. Machinery was collected into vacated air force hangars. Now the Western Development Museums at Saskatoon, North Battleford and Yorkton own some 250 early gas tractors, billed as the most complete line in North America.

States the booklet, ". . . the project spread like a prairie fire. Wagons, democrats (a once-popular light horse-drawn vehicle), buckboards and buggies of every description tell the story of the horse and buggy days . . . The Museum now has close to 250 (old autos) dating back to . . . 1902 . . . many in show room operating condition, as are the steam and gas engines.

"The Museum activities then spread to pioneer furniture and clothing protraying the more intimate side of pioneer life . . . cook stoves . . . hanging lamps, churns, sewing machines, spinning wheels, parlor games, dishes . . . mail order catalogs back to 1903."

The North Battleford branch boasts a complete pioneer village. And don't overlook the Yorkton branch.

Pion-Era got its start in 1954 when the province was planning its golden jubilee. The Western Development Museum was scheduled as the focal point. These big plans kind of shook some people because nothing like this had ever been tried in Canada so they thought they'd better wet their feet before they jumped in whole-hog over their heads. They decided to try like first a thresher's reunion such as were increasing in the States.

People pitched in with such vibratory enthusiasm that, much to everybody's surprise, the thing came off with great success. The mechanics from the Museum workshop refurbished some of the old steamers that hadn't moved for 40 years. Where one team of horses was anticipated to participate, 200 head showed up. Now Saskatoon is the world champion headquarters for ponies under 48 inches. As one visitor said, "Pion-Era is a world's fair."

Since the show date varies year to year, check with Box 1303, Saskatoon, Sask.

OPERATION BOOTSTRAP: Few tractors can pull their own weight but 1918 Hart-Parr 30 shines on the boot jack. Tractor was donated to the Museum by the Oliver Corp., Hart-Parr descendant. Operator is Bert Greenwalt, lifetime Hart-Parr and Oliver blockman and dealer.—Sask

Pion-Era Has Big Gas Show Too

1916 4-cylinder opposed 30–60 10-plow Pioneer gas tractor has 8-foot drive wheels, 7-inch bore, 8-inch stroke, cost $4,500 new, weighs 11½ tons, has 3 speeds up to 5 MPH. Last used in 1928.—WDM

1918 Rumely 4-cylinder 8–16 HP carried 3 mounted plows, cost $1,250. Can be run either direction—seat and pedals reversible. Single speed—2 MPH. 5,600 pounds.—Sask

30–60 Rumely Oil-Pull ran on mixture of kerosene and water. Cost $350 in 1948 (used).—WDM

345

Best 75-HP tracklayer had first hydraulic power steering.—Sask

"Most powerful gas tractor for farm use," was Twin City's claim for its 1919 6-cylinder 60–90. This one was bought new by Hand County, S. D., in Miller. First used in opening up of settlement on the Ft. Berthold Reservation in North Dakota pulling 12 bottom breaking plow and a packer.—WDM

IHC 1910 Auto Wagon was advertised to make business a pleasure and pleasure more of a pleasure—use it as a farm truck and as a family car. You cranked the 2-cylinder engine from the side; note chain drive, gas tank in front. Available with 1, 2 or 3 seats, with or without top, and choice of air- or water-cooled engine.—WDM

Early Days in the Prairie Provinces

Long-gone familiar scenes such as these are brought back to thundering life by Pion-Era.—Saskatchewan Wheat Pool

WESTERN CANADIAN PIONEER MUSEUM
Wetaskiwin, Alberta
May 1 to Oct. 1

Seven hundred antique cars, trucks, steam engines, tractors, gas engines, fire engines, airplanes, horse-drawn vehicles——these are yours to see every day all summer.

A very partial list of steam traction engines: '03 Avery & Rausch 16-HP, 1910 Nichols & Shepard 30-98 double simple; '04 Huber 20-60 return flue; '94 Minneapolis 18-22 HP return flue; 1895 Watrous 8-HP. Straight flues include the '02 American Abell 15-45; '09 American Abell 120-HP cross compound weighing over 48,000 pounds; an 1890 Canton Monitor upright, 1886 Westinghouse upright portable, '05 Advance 120-HP, 110-HP cross-compound and double simple and many makes and models of stationaries from popcorn engines to a 300-HP Corliss with 8-ton flywheel.

In the early gas engine line are Happy Farmer, Moguls, Holts, Averys, Titans, A-Ts, Gilsons, Marshalls, Minnies, Cases, Big 4s, the Multiped walking tractor with six feet instead of wheels,

'07 International with friction drive, 1914 two-cylinder Moline with front wheel drive, and makes you might not have heard of: Bower City, Emerson Brantingham, Eagle, Galloway, Heinrich Lanz, Lauson, Nilson, Parrett, Rock Island, Reliance, Turner, Yuba.

Stationary and portable gas engines too numerous to mention. There are WWI vintage airplanes and earlier, autos from early to late, trucks, fire engines.

You'll see every imaginable kind of household item and pioneer artifact from early times, besides a 7,000-year-old buffalo skull, locomotives, combines, log house, halftracks.

There are 15 rows of tractors and steam traction engines; electric cars, air-cooled cars, horse-drawn hearses and sweeps, treadmills and clocks, guns and china, 36-foot wooden combine, 12-bottom plows, and an Alberta-built 1920 24-48 tractor with wooden frame and spokes.

Two-horse binder was familiar to many of us without a lot of gray on our heads yet. The farm job the author hated most was shocking grain—especially barley—behind this mechanism which he admired extravagantly for its complexity.—WDM

Famous Red River cart supplied pioneers before rails reached them—WDM

WESTERN ONTARIO STEAM THRESHERS REUNION
Fairgrounds
Brigden, Ont.
Third Friday & Saturday in August

Steam threshing engines——full-scale and model——operate among gas engines, antique cars, old tractors, shingle mill, sawmill and all that, etc. You see a parade each evening, a rope-making demonstration and do some trading in the swap shop. Thrill to steam engine races, too!

Remembers Stewart Hunter, treasurer, Courtright, Ont., "Charles Spires asked, in 1957, about threshing on my farm. He said he had three steam engines and if I would bind some grain and get a separator he would bring the engine out and have some fun. Carl West had an engine, so we invited the public to come and see the live steam demonstration. Our crowd was not so large. The expense was greater than we received.

"But we had a good time and a lot of hard work. A good many comments from the crowd kept the show alive."

They skipped '58 and picked the name while planning the '59 show. This was the first of its kind in the province. Held on the Stewart C. Hunter farm, "We threshed grain, wood-sawed and had a steam engine race. The crowd was getting larger.

"In 1960 we displayed a model engine made by Matt O'Brien, London, Ont., and five big engines, a Ricker thresher, Baker fan and antique cars. The Hon. Bryn L. Cathcart, minister of travel and publicity, addressed the crowd. The crowds were getting larger.

"In 1961 we had steam threshing and steam engine races. Cathcart and Atty. Gen. Kelo Roberts spoke. Our crowds were getting so large we could not accommodate them on the farm. In 1962 we went to the Petrolia fairgrounds. We had the most mammoth parade Petrolia ever had in the town's Front Street.

Type X 1928 25-40 Oil-Pull No. 2038 sold new in 1929 to a Mr. Delrimpel (Dalrympl?) of Smithville, $1,710 delivered. It was used for threshing and other belt work for many years until Hugh Clark of Haggersville bought it and restored it. Bill Johnson, Burford, bought it and sold it to MacKellar. That's Alex giving rides to kids against the show background.—MacKellar

"In 1962 WOST went to Petrolia again and had another good show with barbecued chicken and the whole bit."

The next year they moved to Petrolia's Greenwood Driving Park and drew 6,000 or 7,000 people.

The next four years the show was held at Brigden. The antique show keeps getting bigger.

W. Ontario members are real proud of their oldest member, Joseph C. Wilson, octogenarian and still active.

Mr. Wilson threshed since 1910, using one Port Huron and two White steam engines plus Rumely tractors. In 1944 he traded his thresher for a combine; he's had four self-propelleds. With the help of his grandsons, he demonstrates rope making at each reunion.

"Even the ladies are interested in our show," states Oliver Will, Corunna, Ont., who took this picture to prove it. Goodison separator is owned by Clarence and Arthur Parker, Corunna. Jim Hunter, Petrolia, Ont., is separator man. Lady with the fork is Mrs. Edgar Maguire, Corunna. Raised on a Saskatchewan farm, she threshed with her father for years.—Oliver Will

"Can't Swallow it nor Spit it Out"

Ever wonder what goes on inside a dedicated engineman? Alex MacKellar, Alvinston, Ont., reveals the secret:

"I've been very interested in steam and gas tractors all my life and as a small boy never missed a chance to see one and admire it for size and power. The first tractor I ever saw was a 10-20 International my father owned. It was one of the first in the community.

"I can just remember the last time they threshed with steam at our farm. It would be about 1936 and I can still see the engineer backing that big Goodison engine around to hitch up the separator.

"Next year they had a new gas tractor, but it didn't run very well and seemed very hard to start. It was a Waterloo, I think, as it was a gray-blue with big decals of a lion on the fenders that looked very frightening to a five-year-old boy. This tractor was replaced next season with a MM on rubber tires.

"There was always something about the Oil-Pull Rumely that kept me under its spell long after the show was over and everything was silent again. Just that exhaust's steady beat and the spinning of the big flywheel gave me a lump in my throat that I could neither swallow nor spit out. So there was only one thing to do, and in the Fall of 1966 I started out bright and early one day to buy an Oil-Pull. It had been sitting outside several years. We started it up and drove it to the truck and headed home.

"My boy, nine, is as fond of this hobby as I am."

MacKellar is fond of Western Ontario club members, too. "A friendly and hard-working group," he calls them, "who take good care of their equipment and operate it safely. All boilers are government-inspected every year.

"The Western Ontario Steam Threshers Assn. show the best of the past preserved in the present for the pleasure of the future."

"I found my John Goodison engine at Lake Erie," recalls Stewart Hunter, Courtright, Ont. "It was owned by 12 tobacco farmers. They were not going to grow tobacco that year and all agreed to sell the engine as it was getting badly in need of repairs. I had to clean it, retube the boiler and put on a new stack but my wife and daughters, Jeanne and Joanne, helped along with my dad and Uncle Robert Hunter. They had both threshed in their younger days. This engine was built in 1925 at Sarnia, Ont., a 20–22 HP. It's government-tested to carry 140 pounds. She's a nice one." –Hunter

MacDonald 1913 engine No. 117 20–22 HP built at Stratford, Ont. by the MacDonald Thresher Co. Tested by Ontario Dept. Labour at 150 pounds cold water pressure, allowing 90 pounds working steam pressure. Ed Ferguson, Owen Sound, Ont., owner.–Ben Scaman

Sawyer-Massey 1913 No. 3936. George's son Harley Searson operating the saw—Searson

Medical Case History of a Steam Traction Engine

Sawyer-Massey engine No. 3936 was built in Hamilton, Ont., in November, 1913. The late William Blacklock, Campbellville, Ont., bought it the following May and used it for threshing. He traded it in on a gas tractor in 1926 to the John Goodison Thresher Co., Sarnia, Ont. Goodison rebuilt it and sold it to the late James Searson and his son, George C., Watford, Ont., in July, 1928, "and it was the last steam engine to be unloaded off a flat railway car in Watford," says George.

"We used it for threshing, vining green peas for a cannery, cutting wood and sawing lumber."

He bought his father's share in 1938 and continued the same work. In 1943 he quit threshing but kept the engine busy in the sawmill. He retubed her in 1944; in 1949 he honed the cylinder, refitted the valve, installed new piston rings and rebabbitted the main bearings. In 1954 the inside of the firebox gave out.

"I purchased Sawyer-Massey engine No. 5295 in 1954 to power the sawmill and pushed the original engine up by the end of the shed. There

it sat until 1960 when I found a place in London, Ont., to repair the firebox and front tube sheet under the boiler inspector's supervision for 150 pound PSI.

"From 1960 to December, 1965, I kept it for a show engine, giving her a new paint job in 1961.

"In December, 1965, when the tubes gave out in No. 5295, old 3936 was again put to work in the sawmill and has remained there ever since, cutting lumber as it had for years before its restoration, averaging over 300,000 board feet per year and as high as 6,000 or 7,000 a day." He takes her out to steam shows and parades "at least twice a year." He also does some steam threshing with a 28x50 Goodison.

Says Searson, "Having operated this engine for over 40 years, I feel this is a record for nowadays."

Early steam engine experts and writers noted that the average farm steam traction engine lasted seven years but opined they were good for many more years if properly cared for and operated. George proves they were right.

353

George White & Sons 1925 20–24 was manufactured in London, Ont. It ran a sawmill north of Shakespeare, Ont. until about 1950 when it became a show engine.—Bert Barty, London, Ont., owner.

This 1928 Robert Bell has never been more than 20 miles away from Seaforth, Ont. where she was built. Tested for 100 pounds working pressure. Shingle saw is over 100 years old.—Fred Mate, Bayfield, Ont., owner of both machines.

Sawyer-Massey 1913 engine No. 3368 25-HP weighs 11 tons; was built in 1913 at Hamilton, Ont. Its first home was in the west, but its job is unknown. "Just what Sawyer-Massey classed it is hard to determine," says present owner J. W. Nichols, Woodstock, Ont. "It is not a rear mount but it has extra heavy differential and gears and drive wheels, the same as used on their rear-mount plowing engines. It was brought to Ontario in 1956 from the Western Development Museum at Saskatoon by Bill Johnson, who traded a Watrous Champion portable for it. (US readers might be interested to know that the Watrous Champion is a replica of the deJune engine. It seems the Watrous people were some relation to Mr. deJune and obtained the Canadian manufacturing rights and built them at Brantford, Ont.) I restored it and it is Ontario tested for 150 pounds w.p." Nichols shows it at many Canadian shows. "Sawyer-Massey was a popular name in the industry and this engine always commands much attention at the shows. It is definitely a collector's item. So far as we can learn it is the only one of its kind in Eastern Canada."—Nichols

Matt O'Brien, London, Ont., built ¼-scale Case in three years. It measures 27 inches wide, 23 inches to top of stack, 64 inches long, weighs 525 pounds, has 2½-inch bore and 2¾-inch stroke, puts out 1½ HP on the belt, 1¼ on the drawbar. Boiler is tested to 350 pounds, works at 100 pounds, burns wood or coal.—O'Brien

Stanley Mitchell, Strathroy, Ont., built this ¼-scale model of a 65-HP Case: boiler is 44'x10" ID. Rear wheels 18 inches, front 12 inches. Entire length 66 inches, height to top of stack 34 inches. Bore 2½ inches, stroke 2¾ inches. Seven tubes 1¼ inches. "Runs very easy. Fires very easy on coal or wood. Weighs approximately 500 pounds. Tested for 100 pounds steam."—Mitchell

Wallace Lowrie and son Gary, Forest, Ont., own this 1918 Waterloo Boy 12–20. It was bought new in November, 1918, by James Maidment, Forest, for $1,325 delivered on flat car.– Lowrie

A Mr. McCay, Kincardine, Ont. traded a horse-drawn steam engine for this 1919 Titan 10–20 and used it in a cedar swamp on a shingle saw.–Lowrie & Son

Leonard Will, Corunna, Ont., age 12 (at right in photo), owns this 1923 Fordson. Says his father, Oliver, "Leonard at age 9 always wanted me to get an old tractor for the show. Finally last spring a friend called, wanted to know if we wanted to buy an old Fordson. It wasn't long 'til the deal was made. The late Alex Creaves, Croton, Ont., was the first owner. This tractor did farm work and custom clover hulling. It was used up to 1965, stored to 1968. Leonard and his lawnmower made enough money in one summer to pay for his tractor." Shown powering a 22-inch White separator.–Leonard Will

356

Ray G. Harwood comes from Detroit every year to tape steam and gas engine and sawmill sounds.—Oliver Will

Waterloo cutting box is thought to have been built between 1850 and 1860. Says owner Oliver Will, "I found it north of Wiarton, in the Bruce Peninsula. It was in an old log barn which had fallen down. First owner was William Tucker, Lion's Head. His daughter, Mrs. Alex Butchart, gave it to me. The wood frame had rotted out, but none of the iron was broken. She said it had not been used for over 35 years. With the help of my two sons, Burvel 14 and Leonard 10, we made a new frame, with all wooden parts painted a bright red with yellow trim. The wheel and knives run in the open. There is a place in the center of the hub for horse power, or a wooden handle on the spoke on the large wheel can be turned by hand. You can see a large cast iron ball, about 20 pounds, used to hold tension on the rollers. This is proof of age: weights were used before springs." This was Greatgranpa's silage-cutter. As Will describes its use: "Before you could use that Waterloo cutting box there was a lot of hard work. The corn had to be cut by hand with a short-handled hoe or scythe, then stooked till winter when it was needed to feed the cattle. Then it was hauled from the field each day and cut up as needed. The knives were about 18 inches long and real dangerous to the fingers. Back in the '20s I can remember several men who lost fingers, part of a hand, even some lost an arm."—Oliver Will photo

The Gilson Co., Guelph, Ont., built this 1910 "Johnny on the Spot" 1½-HP gas engine. Harry Penfound, Oil Springs, Ont., bought it for pumping water and running farm tools. In 1920, George Gaul and son Blake bought it for pumping water and running tools. They used it until 1953 when they installed Hydro electric power. Stored until 1968, when Oliver Will bought it. Has original rings and valves and battery box (dry cell and coil ignition). In restoring gas engines, Will is often unable to find parts, so he makes his own with welder, lathe, drill press and grinder. "Burvell Will, my eldest son, since the age of 12 spends his summer holidays working at these old engines. He does all the painting, striping and putting the names back in their original places. He is the youngest member of our steam show. How times have changed! I have changed from steam and gas to electric, employed by Ontario Hydro as customer serviceman," says Oliver.—Burvell Will photo

Where your groceries come from

Ask city folks where their food comes from and likely they'll say, "From the store."

And there's the chap who'd rather drink milk from a clean carton than from a dirty cow. And probably someone, somewhere, knows not the chicken is blood kin to the egg.

America was an agricultural nation from the first. Indian corn pulled the Pilgrims through the first winter. Indians showed them how to raise their own, though the colonists had no plow and for 12 years tore out bushes with their bare hands.

America remained an agrarian nation until about 1900, when industrialization overtook tillage. Economists ascribe part of our phenomenal industrial development to our no-less phenomenal agricultural progress which enabled one man to do the work of many, releasing more hands for manufacturing, teaching, research, service.

American agriculture produced surplus food to keep prices down, surplus labor to keep wages down. "A successful farm policy," it has been termed.

Spacemen today eat food grown on Earth. Space crews and lunar and planetary colonies will live on organisms "farmed" in lighted space-borne water tanks. (The meal-in-a-pill, scientists tell us, must ever remain what it is today——science fiction.) As long as men eat, farming will be vital.

Man progressed little while he lived by chasing game and grubbing grubs and roots. It was only when he learned a seed poked into a stick-made hole meant food for winter. Then he had to stay in one place to guard his crop and to prune back the invading jungle. Then villages formed, and towns and cities. Food stored up gave man time to think, to invent and to worship gentler gods.

Archeologists think holes poked in the ground were followed by a pointed stick pulled by wives or slaves, later by beasts of burden, scratching a groove. The crooked stick is still the major farm machine in undeveloped countries.

From the crooked stick developed the wooden plow with a curved wooden moldboard which actually turned a layer of soil over, sort of, burying weeds. And some forgotten genius tied an iron point to it with rawhide.

Centuries later a medieval Einstein reasoned out the iron edge.

From the invention of the wooden plow in antiquity and the yoking of oxen, buffalo and camels to it, agriculture progressed little until the horse collar was invented just a few centuries ago. Heretofore the horse pulled against a chest strap which, in a heavy pull, cut off his wind. Thus, though he could trot with a light buggy, he could not even walk far pulling a heavy plow or cart against his windpipe. The Collar, by distributing the load on his broad, firm shoulders, enabled him to pull the plow and wagon. At that time the latest farm technology was fast-stepping horses to replace slow-plodding oxen. An Englishman wrote a book, "Horse-Hoeing Husbandry," pushing this big new technological breakthrough.

Next time you're in a museum, look over the wooden spades, scoopshovels and pitchforks, plows and planters our forefathers used. One wonders how they got anything done at all.

The colonial plow was a massive thing of wood requiring "...a strong team, a stout man to bear on, another to hold, and a third to drive," wrote Charles L. Flint, Secretary, Massachusetts Board of Agriculture, 1872. He described a plow popular in 18th-century America as requiring "...a strong man to hold it,

Left: It took two men and a team of oxen to scratch a shallow groove in the ground of ancient Egypt.—J. I. Case Co.

Center: Wooden corn planter was technologically advanced when it was built in the early 1800's.—Photo courtesy John J. Menchhofer

Bottom: Wood beam walking plow pulled by one or two oxen, horses or mules was the pioneer's chief tool. Following in the furrow gave farmers the name of clodhoppers.—J. I. Case Co.

and about double that strength of team now required to do the same amount of work."

Then came plows of which the entire moldboard was cast iron, or cast or chilled steel. These met great resistance. "Iron poisons the soil," farmers believed. But some courageous——or foolish——folk tried it and through better tillage as much as doubled their yields. Folk-reasoning did a flip-flop: "Strong iron, strong soil," the village wisemen pronounced.

The iron plow conquered the East and Appalachia and the Piedmont. And it broke the prairie sod.

Trouble came the second year. Once the sod was broken, the iron plow wouldn't scour: moist prairie sod clung to it, causing a drag that exhausted man and beast and kept the furrow slice from turning neat and clean.

Mud on the moldboard stopped our Manifest Destiny westward.

Then a frontier blacksmith in Grand Detour, Ill., John Deere, beat a broken sawblade into a moldboard, 1837. The steel plow scoured in the black prairie soil, spearheading modern agriculture. Our western march continued as a broken and bent sawblade turned the prairie sod so corn and wheat could spring up in its track.

Cast-iron plow wouldn't scour in prairie soil.

People thought only a lazy man would ride a plow.

Every westbound wagon carried a breaking plow.

Foot lift: great back-saver. Note rolling coulter.

From flail to freedom

flail

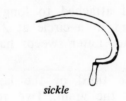

sickle

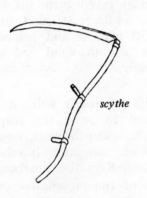

scythe

cradle

As the 1960 USDA Yearbook of Agriculture, "Power to Produce," says, "The progress men have made during the past century in methods of harvesting crops is the progress from flail to freedom."

We know from archeologists that a stone knife first tore heads from stalk. The bronze knife worked better. The Egyptians in 3000 BC used the notched sickle, a small improvement.

They and the Romans threshed by spreading the cut straw on the ground and driving livestock over it, rolling wheels over it or dragging sleds or stone—or iron-knobbed planks across it. Else they pounded it with the flail—a whip-like leather-hinged stick.

A strong man in 10 hours of flailing could knock 7 or 8 bushels out of the heads (and yet not get it all, by far).

The only improvements in the next 4,800 years were the scythe (a "stand-up" sickle), and then the cradle: wooden fingers attached to the scythe which laid the cut grain straws in a row or in bunches for easier garnering. While the men cradled the grain, women gathered it up and, with twists of its own straw, tied the bundles or sheaves.

So incomplete was the harvesting that the village poor survived by gleaning what the harvesters missed.

Thus crudely and incompletely threshed out on the floor, the grain had to be winnowed: the straw raked away and the residue scooped up in baskets and sprinkled out so the wind could carry away the chaff. Our colonists threshed and winnowed just as the ancients.

Plowing and planting and hoeing were work, but a man and his family could take care of enough land to feed themselves through the winter and a smidgen over to sell and trade so city folk could eat, too. It took 13 Revoluntionary farmers to support one city dweller. Today the average farmer produces enough food for some 30-plus people—a figure that will rise 'twixt writing and reading.

With steam power and gang plows and marvelous new binders and threshers, by 1910 a farmer needed only 135 hours of labor to raise 100 bushels of corn, 106 hours for 100 bushels of wheat, and 276 hours for a bale of cotton.

These 1960 averages for the U. S. were about 23, 17 and 77, respectively.

The big bottleneck came in harvest. A man could raise far more grain than he, his family and his neighbors could gather into barns. "...but it (grain) stood so long on the ground before it was reaped it was most shaken...." as the Virginia colony governor reported in 1617.

Groundhog Thresher

Hand-cranked spiked cylinder beat some of the grain out of the heads in mid-1800's.

Then Meickel, a Scotchman, invented the groundhog threshing machine in 1787: a simple toothed cylinder cranked by hand that beat the grain out of the heads. Someone had to rake away the straw, and the grain was basket-winnowed from the chaff as in 3000 BC.

A patent was issued in 1837 on a "combination thresher" which mated the groundhog to a fanning mill. EUREKA! A real threshing machine! Somebody still had to rake away the straw and winnow, but now animal power could be applied: dogs, goats and even horses on treadmills.

"Models made in 1850 could thresh several bushels of wheat an hour with a four-man crew and 6 to 8 horses on the sweep power...." recalls the 1960 Yearbook. "A larger model 10 years later was operated by 8 horses and had a capacity of 300 bushels a day."

The sweep power was a horizontal wheel attached to long poles like wagon tongues which horses pulled around in a circle at 2½ RPM. It was geared to a tumble-rod at 101:1 ratio. Later sweeps harnessed 14 horses.

As the thresher developed in the middle third of the last century, thoughts turned to a better way to cut the grain. Two reaping machines were invented in the early 1830's. Cyrus McCormick's reaper, pulled by one horse, cut the stalks. A man raked them off the platform in bundle-size bunches, as did the cradle, just right for hand-tying. The reaper reduced harvest labor 50 percent and helped insure a more timely harvest so less grain was lost to wind and weather. Later models bunched the stalks mechanically.

Soon after the reaper appeared, a Michigan farmer's wife, it is said, had a dream which impelled her husband to unite the reaper and thresher into one machine: the combined harvester-thresher, now called the combine (pronounced COMbine) which cut and threshed and separated and winnowed all in one operation. Says the Yearbook:

"The machine had all the major features of the present-day combine, but the idea was almost a century ahead of the technological progress necessary to make the machine a success." Even so, for 10 seasons it cut and threshed up to 25 acres a day but its inventors gave up for lack of power and too much moisture in the grain.

Shipped around Cape Horn, the Michigan combine harvested several hundred California acres in 1854 where the fields were bigger and the air dryer, spawning teeming generations of ever-bigger combines. Factory production began in 1880.

Early California combines, weighing up to 15 tons and pulled by 40 horses, cut a 35-foot swath. A ground-driven cleated bull wheel turned the mechanism. As steam developed, in 1890 a steam engine was mounted to turn the works while horses merely pulled the combine. When steam tractors came along, they replaced the horses. Gasoline engines began displacing steam about 1912.

Adding fanning mill and treadmill power to the groundhog boosted production to 300 bu./day in good going by 1855.--J. I. Case Co.

Horse sweep applied power of 6 to 14 horses to the thresher--a great advance.--J. I. Case Co.

The self-binder was first patented in 1850. It not only cut the stalks but tied the bundles with wire, later supplanted by twine, and survived into the 1940's.

Even family-farm-size combines, cutting 10 or 12 feet, required an operator in additon to the tractor driver. The one-man pull-type combine appeared in 1935, cutting a 5 or 6-foot swath, pulled by a 2-plow tractor and powered from its power takeoff, a rotating shaft that transmitted engine power to an external machine. The first machine adapted to the PTO was the binder——in 1919.

Self-propelled grain combines appeared on American farms for keeps in 1938 and steadily gained favor. WW II pressures made their place secure, supplanting pull-types on all but the smaller farms. Self-propelleds are most maneuverable and open a field with less waste, nor do they keep a tractor tied up.

Ideas die if their time has not come. In the late 1920's the Gleaner combine folks built a combine around a Fordson tractor. Farmers laughed, "I've got one tractor. I don't need two. And I sure don't need one I can only use two weeks a year."

Today you can buy self-propelled just about anything: windrowers, hay balers, forage choppers, corn pickers. Some manufacturers make the non-tractor: a three-wheeled power unit which pulls nothing. It forms the power base carrying and powering a combine, etc.

Thus we have seen that muscle ache and the taste of sweat were the farmer's lot——and his wife's——until steam left the factory and the rails to squat, motionless, in the farmer's barnyard to turn the few crude machines available. Putting wheels under it was the next step. A horse-drawn steam engine, the Forty-Niner, was built in 1849 in 4, 10, and 30-HP sizes. The 4-HP jobby weighed 1,000 pounds per HP.

Plowing, the heaviest farm work, got steam attention first. A self-propelled traction steam engine appeared in 1855. In 1859, Abraham Lincoln encouraged steam power on the farm.

Old woodcut shows horse-steered self-propelled steamer and web-stacked, hand-sacked separator. Notice gleaners with wooden rakes working the fields in this late-19th century scene.——J. I. Case Co.

Threshing from the stack near Ramona, S. D., in 1888 with a 14-horse sweep. Separator is hand-fed. To convert this machine to steam drive, the Cheney family took the side gear off and put on a belt pulley. Cheney tried to buy a self-feeder but couldn't get one. A neighbor named Woodmanse took a cardboard pattern off another machine and had the parts cast in Watertown, S. D.--Cheney collection.

Above: The self-binding reaper not only cut the grain and formed the bundles, as did the reaper, but it tied them--first with wire, later with twine--for curing out in the shocks before threshing. Albert and brother Chester Cheney posed on their binders in 1903. Droves of itinerant laborers "followed the harvest" from Texas into Canada. Did the farm term "bundle stiff" father the hobo's appellation "bindle stiff"? Photo is marked HARVESTING THE GOLDEN GRAIN--RAMONA, S. D.--A. B. Cheney collection.

Left: The web stacker was a chain raddle rake that elevated the straw--a big improvement over pitching it away by hand. This 1876 Farquar hand-fed hand-sacked wooden thresher belongs to the Pioneer Club of Indiana. --Photo courtesy John J. Menchhofer.

One man in the radio-equipped air-conditioned cab of a self-propelled combine can "make" as much grain in a day as a whole crew of his fathers.——J. I. Case Co.

Self-propelled steam engines were simply portable power plants built to move themselves about, still steered by horses (that's why you'll see a seat on the smokestack of some early engines). This experience ruined many a good team. The horses expected every load after that to pull itself. All they consented to do was steer.

English tractors had steering gears by 1863 but the first American steering gear was patented in 1880. Eventually the grander steam tractors had power steering.

Then the idea of hauling loads and pulling plows beefed up engines' motive gears and they became land locomotives, or true steam traction engines.

Every year, hundreds of wooden threshing machines burned when an overheated bearing set straw on fire. This danger speeded steel thresher development in 1906.

Stacking bundles to "go through the sweat" prior to threshing.

366

Specifications of the 14-28
OilPull Tractor

Draw Bar Horsepower	14
Brake Horsepower	28
Number of cylinders	2
Diameter of Bore	7"
Stroke of Piston	8½"
Belt Pulley—Speed R. P. M.	530
Diameter	23"
Face	8½"
Diameter of Crank Shaft	3¼"
Master Gear—Width of face	4"
Rear Axle, Diameter	3¼"
Crank Shaft Bearings—Length R. H.	8"
Crank Shaft Bearings—Length L. H.	7"
Connecting Rod Bearings Crank Shaft	3¼"
Piston end	3⅜ x 2⅛" Dia.
Front Wheels—Diameter	40"
Front Wheels—Width	7"
Rear Wheels—Diameter	56"
Rear Wheels—Width	18"
Speed—Miles per hour	2⅒ and 3
Reverse Speed per hour	2⅝"
Fuel Tank capacity—kerosene	31 gal.
Gasoline	3½ gal.
Capacity of radiator and cooling system	18 gal.
Width over all (without extensions)	6' 8¼"
Height over all	8' 3"
Length over all	13' 2"
Weight with tanks filled	8,700 lbs.

How the 14-28 is Equipped

The 14-28 is completely equipped with canopy top as shown, attractively painted and well finished. With each tractor is packed a complete set of tools, with an extra set of spark plugs, a set of spuds and two sets of angle iron cleats included.

When specified and at an extra cost, we supply extra rims and a self steering device.

ADVANCE-RUMELY THRESHER CO.
Incorporated
LaPorte, - Indiana

BRANCHES

Aberdeen, S. D.	Crowley, La.	Indianapolis, Ind.	Minneapolis, Minn.
Battle Creek, Mich.	Dallas, Texas	Kansas City, Mo.	Nashville, Tenn.
Billings, Mont.	Des Moines, Iowa	Lincoln, Neb.	Peoria, Ill.
Columbus, Ohio	Fargo, N. D.	Madison, Wis.	Portland, Ore.
San Francisco, Cal.		Spokane, Wash.	Wichita, Kans.

CANADA

Calgary, Alta.	Saskatoon, Sask.	Regina, Sask.	Winnipeg, Man

AD 851-878

(F. HAL HIGGINS Agricultural Engineering Research Collection, University of California at Davis)

Agriculture's Big Mystery

The sower went out to sow well into the 19th century.—Woodcuts and data courtesy Massey-Ferguson Co., Toronto.

Sickle or reaping-hook.

Scythe

Why were science and mechanization so long in coming to the farm?

Farming methods and equipment in 1830 were little different from Bible Times. Yet architecture flourished——great temples of fabulous design had stood for thousands of years. Sailing ships circled the globe in a breathtaking few months. Steam-powered industry poured forth a torrent of goods and steam sent them hurtling along the rails. Firearms and gunpowder were miracles of death.

Yet for 4,000 years science, as one author put it, "failed to contrive the moldboard of a plow or to flatten the sickle's awkward hook into the scythe's graceful and efficient curve." Fully 95 per cent of the world's people were engaged in agriculture, yet there was practically no progress.

The first effort toward farm mechanization was made about 1700 when Jethro Tull of England won the later title of "father of modern farming" by developing his theory of intensive cultivation and inventing the horse cultivator. His book, HORSE-HOEING HUSBANDRY, is almost the first significant work in agricultural literature. Inspired by the pipes of the organ he played at Oxford university, he also invented the seed drill.

Joseph Foljambe in 1720 patented a plow, introducing in one brilliant stroke the conical iron point, the clevis and, most important to the future of the world, the moldboard——". . . that exquisitely-curved surface which lifts the top soil, sheared by the point and landside, and turns it gently over upon itself in a continuous ribbon," as Merrill Denison wrote in HARVEST TRIMPHANT*.

Then came an attempt to mechanize threshing, when a canny Scot named Michael Menzies hooked a water wheel to mechanical flails. Nothing came of it. In 1758, his countryman known to me only as Leckie patented the rotary cylinder, basic to all threshing designs since. And in 1786 still another Scot, Andrew Meikle, combined beating cylinder and strawwalkers.

*(c) Canada 1949 by Massey-Harris Co., Collins White Circle Edition, 53 Ave. Rd., Toronto, PP 24-25.

It took thousands of years for the awkward reaping hook to evolve into the vastly more efficient and comfortable scythe, releasing the primary producer from the stoop of serfdom. Suddenly, in the late 1700's, the scythe became the vastly-improved cradle—simultaneously in many places.—Photos and data courtesy International Harvester Co., Chicago.

THE CRADLE

The farmer's toil became more productive but no less weary.

Wood's Patent Self-Rake Reaper.

Flailing.

The scythe suddenly evolved from the sickle at about the same time in various parts of Europe and the British Isles and was perfected in America. For the first time the reaper was liberated from the stoop of serfdom and could stand erect, cutting four or five times as much grain in a day as the sicklewielder. The cradle was the first combination of agricultural implements, coming in the late 1700s in Europe, which immigrants brought to America about 1800. Says Denison, "The cradle marked a great advance in agricultural practice and the apex of hand-tool development. With it one man and a helper could reap and bind from three to five acres of grain between sunup and sundown of a long summer day." He points out the farmer's labor had now been made more productive, but the drudgery and exertion in no way lessened: food production was still a narrow race with famine, requiring the hardest kind of unremitting hand labor.

The real beginning of farm mechanization occurred in 1783 when the Royal Society of Arts, Manufactures and Commerce translated and published Pliny's (Roman c 100 AD) description of a Gallic headstripper: a square box mounted on wheels or runners with a row of lance-shaped points in front was pushed by oxen into the standing grain, stripping the heads into the box.

Other inventors tried to imitate, mechanically, the swinging scythe. They set saw-toothed disks to rotating. An Englishman named Salmon hit upon the principle which all cutting equipment has followed since: the cutter bar (his had two sets of saw-tooth knives working reciprocally one over the other) driven by pitman shafts from the axle.

The first practical reaper appeared 15 years later, invented by Schoolmaster Henry Ogle, Rennington, England, who added the horizontal reel to bring the stalks back against the knives. This machine by 1823 could cut 14 acres a day, four and one-half times better than a man with a scythe. Farmers objected to the cost, and laborers, in fear of their jobs, threatened to kill the manufacturer.

Bandsters still had to gather the gavels and tie them with twisted straw.

Winnowing.

Pliny's Gallic Stripper about 100 AD.

A 27-year-old divinity student, Patrick Bell, in 1827 came up with the device which his supporters today claim was the forerunner of the McCormick reaper: a horizontal cutter bar, adjustable reel and canvas apron. An 1832 report has it that his machine swathed up to 12 acres a day at a cost of 3 shillings 10½ pence, against 11 to 13 shillings for hand labor. He was ahead of his time. Human sweat and blood was still too cheap to permit mechanization.

Adds Denison, "The first American invention worthy of note was that of Wm. Manning, Plainfield, N. J., in 1831 . . . a push-header, similar . . . to the Gallic stripper, but with a reciprocal horizontal cutter bar and a grain divider" (invented by Salmon). He reports a sailor, Obed Hussey, patented the first commercially-successful reaper and introduced the open guard, fundamental to all mowing-harvesting machines since.

Patrick Bell's Reaping Machine–1826.

Massey Toronto Light Binder.–1882.

John P. Manney's Hand-Rake Reaper–1851.

JOHN P. MANNY'S HAND-RAKE REAPER — 1851

Hussey's Reaping Machine–1833.

Harris Brantford Open-End Binder–1890.

According to an International Harvester Company publication, "With the cradle . . . a strong man trained in its use could cut two acres of grain a day. A second man could gather up and bind this grain into bundles.

"Harvesting was a thing of pitiless toil for pitiful results. Ninety per cent of the population lived on farms and toiled for their daily bread."

Cyrus Hall McCormick was born in 1809 in the valley of Walnut Grove, Rockbridge County, Va. "Even as a boy he showed a bent for things mechanical," says IHC. At age 15, Cyrus invented a lightweight grain cradle which enabled him to keep up with the older men in reaping wheat.

At 22 he continued his father's experiments toward a reaper and demonstrated one in 1831. Dissatisfied, he continued experimenting, and did not patent his machine until 1834.

He sold seven reapers in 1842, 29 the next year and 50 the next. In 1847 he moved his works to Chicago to be nearer the great grain-growing region. He introduced his self-rake reaper, which raked the cut grain off the platform, thus eliminating one man's labor in 1862. He developed the wire binder in 1874 and followed this with the twine self-tie binder in 1881.

Reported SCIENTIFIC AMERICAN, September, 1867: "Mr. McCormick having accepted an invitation from Emperor Napoleon to give a private exhibition of the working of his reaping machine, a trial was made a short time since on the Imperial farm near Chalons. The trial was a complete success and gave so much satisfaction to the Emperor that he immediately gave orders for the purchase of three of the machines for use on his private farms and earnestly expressed the intention of encouraging the adoption of the invention throughout France, on account of its great labor-saving properties."

The McCormick Reaper Works and several other companies combined to form today's IHC.

McCormick's 1831 reaper: Note the wooden bull wheel. Only the gears, cutter bar shafts and some fasteners are iron. It embodied the seven basic principles of grain-cutting machines: reciprocal knife, fingers or guards, revolving reel, platform, master (bull) wheel, forward draft and divider.

Artist's idea of young McCormick's first successful trial of his new reaper. We don't know who the boy riding the horse is, but the raker is McCormick's slave Jo Anderson.

The reaper and two men could cut as much grain in a day as four or five men with cradles or 12 to 16 men with sickles.

McCORMICK'S
PATENT
VIRGINIA REAPER.

The above cut represents one of M'CORMICK'S PATENT VIRGINIA REAPERS, as built for the harvest of 1848. It has been greatly improved since that time, by the addition of a seat for the driver; by a change in the position of the crank, so as to effect a direct connection between it and the sickle, (thereby very much lessening the friction and wear of the machinery, by dispensing altogether with the lever and its fixtures;) by board ribs on the reel, (which operates more gently on the grain than the round ones;) by a sheet of zinc on the platform, (which very much lessens the labor of raking;) by an increase of the size, weight and strength of the wheels of the machine, and by improvement made on the cutting apparatus

D. W. BROWN,
OF ASHLAND, OHIO,

Having been duly appointed Agent for the sale of the above valuable labor-saving machine (manufactured by C. H. McCormick & Co., in Chicago, Ill.,) for the Counties of Seneca, Sandusky, Erie, Huron, Richland, Ashland and Wayne, would respectfully inform the farmers of those counties, that he is prepared to furnish them with the above Reapers on very liberal terms.

The Wheat portions of the above territory will be visited, and the Agent will be ready to give any information relative to said Reaper, by addressing him at Ashland, Ashland County, Ohio.

Ashland, March, 1850.

I'll bet this is he first reaper handbill.—Courtesy IHC.

The Marsh harvester, 1875-83, carried two bandsters, who could thus do the work of the four or five who followed the earlier machines.

Curiously, the hay mowing machine was not invented until 1851, although it would seem to be a logical ancestor of the reaper.

As Denison describes the reaper, originally it deposited the bundle-sized bunches of grain in the path of the next round so the bandster had to keep up with the machine. The reel-rake reaper deposited the gavels, as they were called, out of the way.

Says he, "In place of the horizontal reel used on all earlier reapers, the reel-rake had four rakes or elongated paddles mounted eccentrically on a vertical shaft through which power was transmitted from a single main drive wheel. In operation the rakes rotated in a curious, jerky rhythm produced by a series of cams and automatic switches in the head of the shaft. Implement engineers still speak in lyric terms of the ingenious arrangement, but in its progress through the field the reel-rake looked like a tipsy, peripatetic windmill." Five or six bandsters were required to keep up with it. It sold for $125 in Canada, $50 more in the U. S. Canadian factory wages at this time were $5 to $9 a week for 10 hours a day, nine on Saturday.

One of the knottiest problems ever solved was the invention of the binder knotter. This was accomplished after many failures by John F. Appleby, an American inventor. According to FARM IMPLEMENT NEWS in the 1890s, "The clue came to him while watching the daughter of a neighbor at play with her Boston terrier pup. The youngster had a skipping rope at which the pup was jumping and once, when the rope fell loosely over the dog's neck and he shook his head and backed away to free himself, the rope slipped off his nose knotted."

374

The forerunner of the Massey-Harris combines was a header built in Australia in 1843 from the diagram of Pliny's Gallic stripper published 60 years before. John Ridley's wheat ripened so rapidly he could not possibly harvest it with sickle or scythe. He happened to have a copy of the 1783 report on Pliny's Gallic stripper——and he built one, adding a beater which threshed the grain which he later winnowed. Forty-one years later, another Australian added the separating feature.

Alert to new developments, M-H representatives brought them home to Canada. M-H began building the stripper-harvester, which evolved into a true reaper-thresher-separator, bull-wheel-powered. It proved itself in 1909, the first of the commercial combines. Says Denison, "The advance over the binder was as great as that of the binder over the reaper or the reaper over the manual harvesting. For the third time in agricultural history the cost and labor of producing man's basic food was drastically reduced."

Andrew Y. Moore reported that in 1843 he pulled a combine with 16 horses two abreast and harvested 25 acres a day. Shipped around the Horn to California, the machine spawned herds of its kind and enabled four men to do the work of 20 or 30. Combining cut costs to $1.75 an acre compared to $3 for steam threshing. A popular picture post card in Washington late in the last century showed 165 horses pulling five combines. In the early '90s, Holt and Best had 110-HP engines pulling 42-foot combines that cut costs to 25 cents an acre. A separate engine mounted on the combine got steam through a hose from the traction engine boiler. Because coal was scarce in the west, many of these engines were adapted to burning straw, and later to oil.

MASSEY HARVESTER — 1878

Massey's self-rake harvester—1878.

Meanwhile, back at the factory, ball and roller bearings reduced the draft of binders. "This machine reduced the human labor needed for the harvesting of cereals by more than two-thirds," opines Denison. With the commercialization of the one-man 16-foot self-propelled combine in 1938, the labor required to produce and thresh a bushel of wheat had been reduced from the 40 hours required with sickle and flail to less than a minute: a reduction of 2,400 plus. The cost of self-propelled combining was one-eighth that of binding-threshing, and it saved more grain.

When farmers got tractors, they soon pulled their ground-driven binders with mechanical power. Then some forgotten genius unhooked the bull wheel and hooked up the PTO.

The Massey-Harris 1901 experimental stripper-harvester counts the Gallic stripper in its pedigree, looked like a street-sweeping machine. Bull-wheel-powered.

The prairie combine (above) and the hillside combine (below—has reciprocally-raising/lowering right and left main wheels that keep the separator level on steep hillsides) relieved Mom of her biggest job—feeding threshers—and destroyed one of the best neighborin' traditions on the American farm. Steam threshing bees are bringing back the old neighborliness so that City Cousin can share it.

Rest for Milady

Another effect of the combine, says Denison, was upon farm women, "for whom mechanization had done little or nothing up to now," for they were at long last freed from their biggest annual job: feeding threshers. Says he, "At one stroke . . . combining made harvesting one of the speediest and least difficult of farming operations instead of one of the most laborious and time-consuming, and it did this at half the cost." He points out that by lessening manpower demands on the farm, more workers were released for the production and service industries so important to modern life.

Denison ranks the first, forgotten hitching of a binder to a tractor PTO with the invention of fire and the wheel.

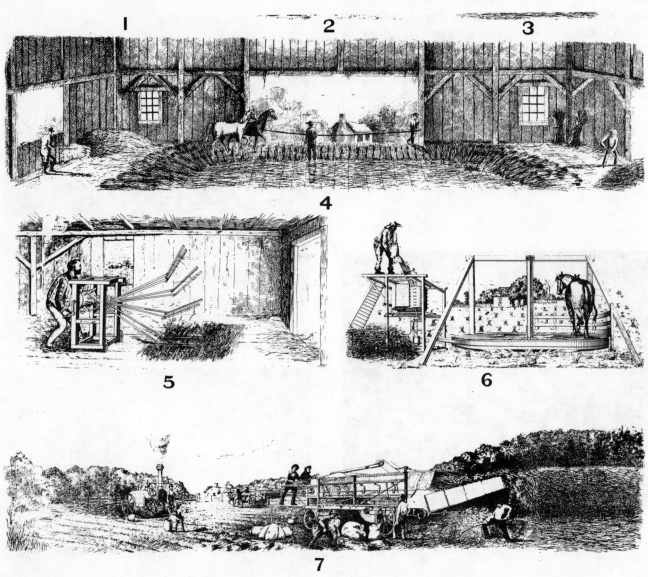

THRASHING AND CLEANING GRAIN.

AGRICULTURAL IMPLEMENTS.

1,943 Manufactories in the United States.

THRASHING AND CLEANING GRAIN.

No. 1. Egyptian—1500 B. C.
2. Roman Tribulum—100 B. C.
3. Hand Flail.
4. Horse Thrashing.
5. Flail Thrashing Machine.
6. U. S. Patent, Horse Power, A. D. 1834.
7. " " Steam Power, A. D. 1883.

Oxen were anciently employed in thrashing corn, and the same custom is still retained in Egypt and the east. This operation is effected by trampling upon the sheaves, and by dragging a clumsy machine, furnished with three rollers. A wooden chair is attached to the machine, and on this a driver seats himself, urging his oxen backwards and forwards among the sheaves, which have previously been thrown into a heap of about eight feet wide and two in height. The grain thus beaten out is collected in an open place, and shaken against the wind by an attendant with a small shovel, or, as it is termed, a winnowing fan, which disperses the chaff and leaves the grain uninjured.

Horace further tells us that the thrashing floor was mostly a smooth space, surrounded with mud walls, having a barn or garner on one side; occasionally an open field, outside the walls, was selected for this pur-

pose, yet uniformly before the town or city gates. Such was the void place wherein the "King of Israel, and Jehoshaphat, King of Judah sat, each of them on his throne, clothed in his robes, at the entering in of the gate of Samaria, and all the prophets prophesied before them."

In the marginal reading we are informed that this void space was no other than a thrashing floor; and truly the area was well adapted for such an assemblage, being equally suited to accommodate the two kings and their attendants, and to separate them from the populace.

A four-horse power portable engine with six-inch cylinder, pressure of steam 45 pounds per square inch, revolutions, 140 per minute, has thrashed, under favorable surroundings, 320 bushels per day of ten hours; coal consumed 3 cwt. Another engine, of five-

horse power, thrashed 400 bushels; coal consumed 4 cwt. Another, of six-horse power, thrashed 480 bushels; coal consumed 5 cwt. Another, of seven-horse power, thrashed 560 bushels; coal consumed 6 cwt. Another, of eight-horse power, thrashed 640 bushels; coal consumed 7 cwt. Another of ten-horse power, thrashed 800 bushels per day; coal consumed 9 cwt.

The economy of these performances is evident at a glance, and even if much less work than the above was effected, such an engine would, if mounted on wheels, prove a most valuable acquisition to any neighborhood composed of thrifty farmers, who might, by an equitable arrangement, become both the owners and beneficiaries of the same.

	1860	1880
Capital Invested.	$11,477,239.00	$62,109,668.00
Value of Productions.	17,829,940.00	68,640,486.00
Wages Paid.	5,080,549.00	15,359,910.00
Hands Employed.	14,814	39,480

SUB CLASS.

THRASHING AND CLEANING GRAIN.

18,527 Machines Manufactured in 1880.

CAPACITY—	Primitive Made	Present Machine
Bushels Wheat per day,	20	1,000
" Oats "	40	2,000
Hands Employed per day,	4	4

Grain Thrashed, 1882, 1,540,000,000 Bushels.

2,615 Patents Granted by the United States.

THRASHING AND CLEANING GRAIN.

No. 1 Egyptian—15 B. C.
2. Roman Tribulum—100 B. C.
3. Hand Flail.
4. Horse Thrashing.
5. Flail Thrashing Machine.
6. U. S. Patent, Horse Power, A. D. 1834.
7. U. S. Patent, Steam Power, A. D. 1883.

We here enlarge a portion of the preceding page for your easier reading. Material provided courtesy G. B. Gunlogson.

5

Thrashing and Cleaning Grain

Oxen were anciently employed in thrashing corn, and the same custom is still retained in Egypt and the east. This operation is effected by trampling upon the sheaves, and by dragging a clumsy machine furnished with three rollers. A wooden chair is attached to the machine, and on this a driver seats himself, urging his oxen backwards and forwards among the sheaves, which have previously been thrown into a heap of about eight feet wide and two in height. The grain thus beaten out is collected in an open place and shaken against the wind by an attendant with a small shovel, or, as it is termed, a winnowing fan, which disperses the chaff and leaves the grain uninjured.

Horace further tells us that the thrashing floor was mostly a smooth space, surrounded with mud walls, having a barn or garner on one side;

occasionally an open field, outside the walls, was selected for this purpose, yet uniformly before the town or city gates. Such was the void place wherein the "King of Israel and Jehoshaphat, King of Judah sat, each of them on his throne, clothed in his robes, at the entering in of the gate of Samaria, and all the prophets prophesied before them."

In the marginal reading we are informed that this void space was no other than a thrashing floor; and truly the area was well adapted for such an assemblage, being equally suited to accommodate the two kings and their attendants, and to separate them from the populace.

A four horse power portable engine with six-inch cylinder, pressure of steam 45 pounds per square inch, revolutions 140 per minute, has thrashed, under favorable surroundings.

320 bushels per day of ten hours; coal consumed 3 cwt. Another engine of five horse power, thrashed 400 bushels; coal consumed 4 cwt. Another of six horse power, thrashed 480 bushels; coal consumed 5 cwt. Another of seven horse power, thrashed 560 bushels; coal consumed 6 cwt. Another eight horse power, thrashed 640 bushels; coal consumed 7 cwt. Another of ten horse power, thrashed 800 bushels per day; coal consumed 9 cwt.

The economy of these performances is evident at a glance, and even if much less work than the above was effected, such an engine would, if mounted on wheels, prove a most valuable acquisition to any neighborhood composed of thrifty farmers, who might by an equitable arrangement, become both the owners and beneficiaries of the same.

Sticky Soils vs. Steel Plows

While the sandy and gravelly soils of the East gave little trouble to the cast iron and even wooden plows the pioneers carried westward with them into Illinois, the rich prairie soils seemed to raise an insurmountable barrier.

Once the sod was broken and the grass-roots decayed, the prairie soils refused to scour, making plowing almost impossible. (For an explanation of scouring and other technical stuff, see the accompanying note.)

It has been said that prairie mud would have stopped the westward march of America's Manifest Destiny had not someone invented a plow that would scour.

A frontier blacksmith, John Déere, in 1837 solved the prairie soil-scouring problem by hammering a plow out of a broken saw blade. And ever after, we're led to believe by careless farm writers, all plows were of steel and therefore scoured well.

I often wondered what kind of a saw blade: no handsaw seemed big enough. And I wondered why steel plows scoured in the prairie soil where cast-iron ones didn't.

My researches turned up more assumptions than facts. It is assumed by some that Deere hammer- ed his 1837 plow out of a broken sawmill blade of the long up-and-down type. While the circular saw had been patented in England in 1777, there were few of these in America and almost certain- ly none in the little frontier town of Grand Detour, Ill., although Major Leonard Andrus, Deere's sometime partner, had a sawmill there. The standard 12-inch width of the reciprocating millsaw blade would explain the curious diamond shape Deere's first plow is thought to have had——a shape to which he would not have been confined had he had a bigger piece of metal. His first plow has disappeared.

Extant is a plow Deere built a year later. It seems to have a wrought-iron moldboard and a steel share. Historians are not certain if his first plow's moldboard was of steel or of iron, but they are certain the share was steel. Edward C. Kendall of the Smithsonian believes that even if the first plow were all-steel, and he's not sure that it was, Deere used wrought-iron moldboards with steel shares well into the 1850s. He quotes a news- paper ad Deere published in 1843:

"The Moldboard of this well, and so favorably known PLOUGH, is made of wrought iron, and the share of steel, 5/16 of an inch thick, which carries a fine sharp edge. The whole face of the moldboard and share is ground smooth, so that it scours perfectly bright in any soil, and will not choke in the foulest of ground. It will do more

"Hmmmp! Upside down!" the Indian is reputed to have said when he saw a plow turn a furrow slice. Naturalist John Muir (1838-1914) describes the work of a bull plow in the prairie sod in the 1850's:
"They were used only for the first ploughing, in breaking up the wild sod woven into a tough mass, chiefly by the cord-like roots of perennial grasses, reinforced by the tap roots of oak and hickory bushes, called 'grubs,' some of which were more than a century old and four or five inches in diameter . . . If in good trim, the plough cut through and turned over these grubs as if the century-old wood were soft like the flesh of carrots and turnips; but if not in good trim the grubs promptly tossed the plough out of the ground." And as an old-time ploughman can tell you, being tossed by those handles was like being tossed by a bull.—Illustrations courtesy Deere & Co.

work in a day, and do it much better and with less labor, to both team and holder, than the ordinary ploughs that do not scour, and in consequence of the ground being better prepared, the agriculturalist obtains a much heavier crop."

Note the wrought-iron moldboard and steel share. It is thought the importance of the steel share caused these plows to be called steel plows even though only the share was steel. It is also thought the secret of scouring was not in the steel but in the smoothness and polishing.

Even before leaving his native Vermont, young Deere the blacksmith had built local demand for his high-polished hay forks and shovels. A smooth, polished surface resists sticky soil less than a wooden moldboard, or even than a wooden one overlain with iron strips nailed on, which offers many cracks, holes and nail heads to soil movement. Even the cast-iron moldboard, I presume, has a texture to which prairie soil can more easily stick.

Farmers know too well that even today's steel moldboards won't scour if rusty.

(Source: Paper 2, pp 15-25, "John Deere's Steel Plow" by Edward C. Kendall, from Contributions from the Museum of History and Technology, US National Museum Bulletin 218, Smithsonian Institution 1959.)

Pulled by four yoke of oxen, this large wooden-beam breaking plow, sometimes equipped with wooden wheels, broke the sod in the mid 19th century. Large wheel runs in furrow, small wheel on land, thus regulating depth of cut.

Artist's conception of young frontier blacksmith John Deere pondering the farmer's plight in 1837. Note paddle in farmer's right hand with which he repeatedly had to scrape the muck off his plow.

When he broke away from the curious diamond shape imposed by broken saw blades, Deere was able to form more sophisticated moldboards. Hardly a wagon went west that didn't carry a long breaking plow. Often its first job was to cut sod blocks with which to build the family's first home.

Polished steel scours. One horse and one man replace eight oxen and two men.

Advertisers loved to show slim-boned, prancing race horses gaily dancing along with whatever product. The first farmers to ride their plows, requiring a third horse, were considered lazy by their clod-hopping neighbors.

Blacksmith Deere shapes an unconventional moldboard out of the biggest piece of steel he can find—a 12-inch wide reciprocating saw blade, broken at Major Leonard Andrus' sawmill—bending it over a log.

Some Definitions and Other Stuff

Our discussion of plows and plowing is intelligible to other farmers, but city folks may be bemused by our shoptalk.

It is thought man first farmed by poking holes in the ground with a stick and dropping in a seed. (Shades of cavemen!—Agricultural engineers predict that before 2000, farmers will be shooting seed into the ground with compressed-air injectors!) Then he learned to scratch a furrow with a stick, and later to pull the stick with wives, slaves or beasts. The crooked stick is still used to scratch the soil in some backward nations.

The plow has been basic to agriculture since before the dawn of history. Practically all land is plowed each year before a crop is sown. Today a few farmers believe there are better first steps, but their number is minuscule.

The crooked-stick plow changed but little until 1720 when, in a single inspired leap, it blossomed into the cutting-and-turning instrument we know today.

Joseph Foljambe patented a plow which introduced not only the conical iron point and the first clevis, but, most important, ". . . the idea of the moldboard, that exquisitely-curved surface which lifts the topsoil, sheared by the point and the landside, and turns it gently over upon itself in a continuous ribbon," writes Merrill Denison.

To the non-farmer we should explain it is important to turn the furrowslice upside-down cleanly and smartly to bury and thus kill weeds, and also to bury stalks from the previous crop so they won't interfere with subsequent operations. Unless the plowshare and moldboard scour bright and shiny, the soil clings and the plow mushes along, pulls hard, and fails to turn the furrowslice upside-down. Then the farmer has to stop frequently, pull his plow out of the ground and scrape off the clinging soil with a paddle or scraper, vastly multiplying the time and effort required to get his plowing done, and doing an inferior job withal.

While modern plows designed for tractor speeds——5 or 6 MPH compared to 1½ or 2 MPH for horses——have been refined, ganged, mounted and hydraulically controlled, their essential cutting-turning form and function are the same as Foljambe's.

More on the All-Wheel Drive

Deere & Co. was a relative latecomer to the tractive power field, though long a force in tillage and other implements. The company never built steam engines, and apparently did not enter the tractor field until about 1918, when it marketed the three-wheel All-Wheel-Drive and the Waterloo Boy simultaneously.

Capt. Francis Hansen's souvenir booklet, "The Old West's Mystery Tractor," (see Rollingstone, Minn., section) states:

"If you have never heard of the John Deere All-Wheel-Drive Tractor, you are just one of several million other Americans (including historical societies and implement dealers) who are not aware that Deere and Company designed and sold a gasoline-burning tractor more than six years before the introduction of the famous Model D.

This fact has apparently been obscured by the long-held belief that the Waterloo Boy, the forerunner of the Model D, was Deere's first farm tractor.

"Deere and Company's tractor development actually began on March 5, 1912. Recognizing the inevitable future use of the tractor as a source of farm power, Deere's executive committee directed their experimental department to produce a tractor plow. Mr. C. H. Melvin was in charge of this project, and he soon developed an experimental tractor that closely resembles the Hackney Motor Plow. This single machine . . . was soon abandoned, and, in May, 1914, another company engineer, Mr. Joseph Dain, founder of the Dain Manufacturing Company, was asked if he could design a small tractor that would sell for about $700. Within two weeks he submitted a positive reply and in February, 1915, his first All-Wheel-Drive tractor was completed. By the end of that year, two more of these machines were assembled."

Extensive tests with the 'Dain' tractors were conducted at locations ranging from Winnebago, Minn., to San Antonio, Tex. On March 13, 1916, Mr. Dain dispatched the following telegram from his Texas location:

"HAVE FOLLOWED TRACTOR CLOSELY FOR TWO WEEKS. CONDITIONS EXTREMELY HARD AND ROUGH. ABSOLUTELY NO WEAKNESS IN CONSTRUCTION. GEARS, CHAINS, UNIVERSALS, IN FACT ALL PARTS IN GOOD CONDITION. TRACTOR HAS TRAVELED NEAR FIVE HUNDRED MILES UNDER EXTREME LOAD. CHANGE SPEED GEAR A WONDER. I RECOMMEND TO THE BOARD THAT WE BUILD TEN MACHINES AT ONCE."

Hansen reports the ten were built, followed by 100 in 1918 and 100 in 1919, despite Dain's death November 1, 1917. "By now, maximum effort was being directed toward the production of the Waterloo Boy tractor and the manufacture of the 'Dain' tractor ended."

My researches indicate that the Waterloo Boy kerosene tractor, a two-cylinder three-plow job of more conventional design, was manufactured by the Waterloo (Iowa) Gasoline Engine Company and marketed simultaneously by that company and by Deere. Deere acquired the Waterloo company (still manufactures tractors there) and introduced the Model D in 1923, still of two-cylinder design. Deere pointed to many advantages for two cylinders: simplicity, big and there-fore rugged parts——all adding up to long life and economy.

The D was rated at 44.8 belt HP and 40.6 drawbar HP. It was built until 1953. Early models sold for under $1,000.

Deere continued the two-cylinder design until about 1960, when farmers' demands for more and ever more power presented a problem: to get more power out of two cylinders on a transverse crankshaft would make the tractor too wide to go down the corn rows. With the passing of the Old Guard in the Deere company, young engineers turned the engine in line with the tractor and added two more cylinders, producing a four-cylinder in-line engine like everybody else.

Taylor Manufacturing Company, Westminster, Maryland, exhibited at the 1878 Paris Exposition. This illustration from their special catalog shows their big engine at that show. Prof. George Davidson of the University of California went over to act as a judge of the steam engines and brought back catalogs now in collection of F. Hal Higgins.

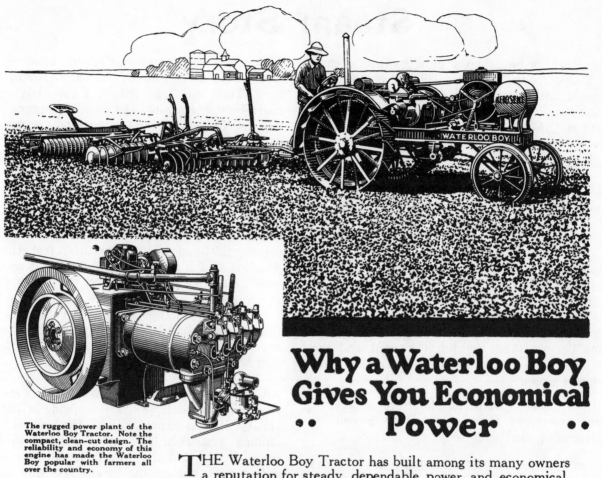

The rugged power plant of the Waterloo Boy Tractor. Note the compact, clean-cut design. The reliability and economy of this engine has made the Waterloo Boy popular with farmers all over the country.

Why a Waterloo Boy Gives You Economical ·· Power ··

THE Waterloo Boy Tractor has built among its many owners a reputation for steady, dependable power, and economical, money-making service. Back of this power and service stands its sturdy two-cylinder engine.

WATERLOO BOY
BURNS KEROSENE COMPLETELY

The 25 H. P. Waterloo Boy twin-cylinder engine is of the heavy-duty type, designed and built especially for hard, continuous service. Two-cylinder design means fewer moving parts, and allows increased size and strength of every part throughout the engine. The engine is horizontal, and placed crosswise on the tractor frame. This eliminates bevel gears. Bevel gears cause friction and wear rapidly. Waterloo Boy drive is direct through straight gears.

John Deere Implements and Waterloo Boy tractors and kerosene engines are distributed from all important trade centers. Sold by John Deere dealers everywhere.

The engine burns kerosene completely. A patented manifold superheats this low-priced fuel, converting it into a highly-combustible gas. The compact construction of the engine permits the gas to enter the cylinders without condensing. The motor turns every particle of this gas into positive power.

Simplicity is an outstanding feature of Waterloo Boy design. You don't have to be an expert to care for it. There are a number of inspection plates. Each one is conveniently placed. Every part is easy to get at from a standing position. Any adjustment easily made.

The positive spray Oiling System is simple and reliable. Fewer moving parts mean fewer parts to oil, and every part is kept in a constant bath of lubricant.

The twin-cylinder Waterloo Boy Engine develops its maximum power at low speeds. Its perfect balance eliminates vibration. Low speed without vibration lengthens the life of the engine and reduces the upkeep.

The real test of a tractor is field performance. The Waterloo Boy engine has high field efficiency. It is giving thousands of satisfied owners dependable, economical power.

JOHN DEERE
JOHN DEERE
MOLINE, ILL.

THE TRADE MARK OF QUALITY MADE FAMOUS BY GOOD IMPLEMENTS

Steam Story

The Romans brought the plow to Britain, says the Encyclopedia Brittanica. Some plows were equipped with wheels and designed to be pulled by the horse's tail. This custom existed in Ireland as late as 1634 when a law was passed prohibiting "plowing by the tayle."

The first steam engine of record was made about 130 BC by Hero of Alexandria, the aerophile, a primitive steam reaction turbine. (See model of Hero's engine in New York Steam Engine Assn. section, page 208.)

Greek priests used a heat engine of sorts, although not really a steam engine, to make the faithful believe the gods obeyed the priests: The altar fire heated the hollow altar, pushing water into buckets which, by their weight, opened the shrine doors. When the fire went out and the altar cooled, the buckets were thus emptied, and the doors closed.

In 1663 Edward Somerset described a way of raising water, as from a mine, by a pair of displacement chambers.

The earliest practical steam engine was Thomas Savery's, patented in 1698: a pair of displacement vessels lifted water to drain mines, supply municipalities, and even to run water over waterwheels to operate mills and looms. Pressures used were 100 to 150 PSI, and without a safety valve hard to handle. This method was extremely extravagant of fuel because of heat waste through cooling the vessels: steam displaced the water, then cooled, producing a vacuum to fill the chamber again. Savery measured performance with a strange new term, "horse power."

Already, however, Denis Papin had suggested raising a piston with steam pressure, then condensing the steam so that atmospheric pressure would again depress it––the earliest piston-and-cylinder engine. He heard of Savery's engine in 1705 and improved it by putting a floating diaphragm atop the water to keep water and steam separate. It has been described as a noncondensing single-action steam pump, with steam cylinder and pump cylinder in one.

This same year, Thomas Newcomen introduced the atmospheric engine: steam raised the piston; a water jet condensed the steam, forming a partial vacuum which pushed the piston down and moved the walking-beam which raised the pump piston. His 15 PSI was easier to handle.

The valves were manipulated by hand––a job boys could do as well as, and more cheaply than, men. Then one lazy fellow, a valve-boy named Humphrey Potter, in 1713 decided flipping valves was too much like work and rigged up cords and catches so the engine valved itself. History does not say, but I imagine he was fired for his indolence.

Thus we see the happy little tale we were taught in school about little Jimmy Watt watching the lid bounce on his mother's teakettle, and deciding that if steam could lift a lid it could do work, and thereupon inventing the steam engine as soon as he got big, doesn't quite fit the facts. Long before Jim was born, Newcomen's atmospheric engine had been draining mines. It reigned supreme for three or four generations before Watt ever scalded his first finger.

An instrument-maker in Glasgow, Watt was repairing a model Newcomen engine at the University. He was impressed with the heat wasted in chilling and re-heating the cylinder on every cycle. He decided the remedy lay in keeping the cylinder as hot as the steam. To this end he added an external condenser and a vacuum chamber which greatly increased both speed and efficiency in 1763. It was still single-acting.

Another inventor had already imparted rotary motion through the connecting rod and crank, common on the treadle-powered lathes of the day. Watt devised sun-and-planet wheels and other methods of making the reciprocating motion rotary until the rod-and-crank patents expired. He added the flywheel to keep 'er turning. By making the up-and-down piston turn a shaft, vast new worlds of work were opened to the steam engine. The reciprocating action could do little but pump.

In 1782 Watt patented two improvements: double action, and the cutoff to use steam expansively. His pressures were seldom over seven PSI. He assigned to horsepower the figure we use today: 33,000 ft/lb/min. (A man is rated @1/10 HP.)

1910 Orbit

If you're interested in steam engines, don't ever pass up a chance to look at Prof. P. S. Rhodes' STEAM ENGINE GUIDE (1910).

Unidentified photo. Experts believe engine is a pre-1900 Huber return flue. This design, bringing the smoke and flame back to the firebox end into the stack, was hellishly hot for summer threshing, but warmly appreciated for fall corn shelling and wood sawing. Unjacketed boilers baked a man who had to get out and get under.

"Old No. 1" was built in 1869, now stands in Smithsonian. It was simply a skid engine on wheels moved around by horses. Stack folded back, driver sat on that.—J. I. Case Co.

Early skid engines.——J. I. Case Co.

He was concerned that operators had no conception of the incredible power at their fingertips, nor of the appalling havoc it could work if it got loose:

"When properly handled and cared for, it (the steam boiler) is perfectly safe, but the fact must never be lost sight of that it may if neglected be one of the most terribly destructive agents that man has to deal with," he wrote.

The enormous energy in steam and superheated water under pressure is hard to comprehend. Even after seeing the figures, they are so large the mind boggles. To put this energy into visible terms, Prof. Rhodes cited a 25-HP boiler containing 52 cubic feet water and 26 cubic feet steam @ 150 PSIG.

Under these conditions, he says, the boiler contains 9.73 pounds steam which, at this temperature and pressure, holds 1.3 million foot-pounds of energy. When a boiler explodes, we think only of the steam as releasing energy. But the water @ 150 pounds and 365.7 degrees F. contains 20 times as much energy as the steam and actually explodes——the water itself at this temperature is explosive——if pressure is suddenly released, as in event of boiler rupture. In the ton and a half of water in there, at this temperature, are 38 million foot-pounds of energy added to the 1.3 million in the steam. (A foot-pound of energy, you'll remember, is what it takes to lift one pound one foot.)

If all this energy could be put into a gun, Rhodes wrote, it would shoot a one-pound bullet 7,500 miles straight up. He thought that was sufficient to put it into orbit——and this half a century before Sputnik! All this energy applied to the 11½-ton engine would blast it into the air a third of a mile, he said!

Reynold L. M. Wik writes that Thomas Jefferson wrote from a visit to England in 1786 after seeing a steam engine work, "The power in this age in steam though known is but now beginning to be applied to various purposes to which it is acceptable . . ."

Wik reports an Englishman, Richard Trevithick, built a 4-HP threshing engine in 1812 which threshed 1,500 sheaves of barley in four hours. Observers agreed it was better than horse power. It weighed 1,500 pounds and cost 63 pounds.

Trevithick communicated "a few wild ideas" to the board of agriculture: "It is my opinion that every part of agriculture might be performed by steam. Carrying manure for the land, plowing, harrowing, sawing, reaping, threshing and grinding and all by the same machine, however large the estate. Even extensive commons might be tilled effectively . . . and without the use of cattle. I think a machine that would be equal to the power of 100 horses would cost about 500 pounds. It would double the population of this Kingdom, for a great part of man's food now goes to horses which would then be dispensed with, and so prevent importation of corn, and at a trifling expense make our markets the cheapest in the world . . ."

It was estimated that in England by 1820 there were enough steam engines to build the Egyptian pyramids in 18 hours. They totaled 325,000 HP, little of which was used on farms.

A mechanic, Oliver Adams, a Delaware millwright, in 1786 applied to the Pennsylvania legislature for exclusive rights to build a steam carriage to move over common roads. The committee considered him insane. Wik lists him as the first American manufacturer of stationary portable engines for farm use in 1812.

By 1838 a survey showed 1,860 stationary steam engines in the U. S. totaling 36,319 HP or about six times the total of all the railroad locomotives. The few in agriculture were mostly driving saws and grist mills. On southern plantations, 585 were crushing sugar cane, grinding grain, sawing lumber and ginning and baling cotton.

A typical plantation engine in 1823 was of the low-pressure condensing type averaging 16 HP and costing about $7,000. Wik estimates that by 1849 farms employed about one-fourth per cent of all the 10 million steam HP used in the U. S.

In 1850, engines still cost about $1,000 and even the wealthiest farmer paused and pondered before unpocketing that sum. Horace Greeley in 1850 opined the steam engine could find many jobs on the farm. ". . . we have hardly begun to use steam yet. . ."

Hiram and John Pitts, brothers, Winthrop, Maine, in 1834 made the first practical threshing

Sawmill woodcut dates from about 1882.—J. I. Case Co.

First The Belt

machines which separated the chaff from the grain. Their principles have been followed by all. In 1856 DeBow's REVIEW thanked Divine Providence that horse-drawn machinery had enabled man to work out his salvation from the primal curse, "By the sweat of thy brow thou shalt eat bread," and suggested even further improvements were possible.

The steam engines of the 1840s were the long-john type requiring masonry support and complicated connections to the machines driven. One farmer bitterly complained to COUNTRY GENTLEMAN in 1858, "There never were and in all probability never will be a suitable force or power for the use of cultivators of the soil." Then someone mounted the engine and flywheel directly on the boiler and mounted the boiler on wheels so it could be pulled by oxen from job to job. The portable steam engine was born! Note the date well: 1849. This was the Forty-Niner described earlier. Prices ranged from $625 for the 4-HP to $2,300 for the 30-HP.

Then arose debates about the relative merits of horses and steam engines, as later were to come

arguments about gas vs. steam, two-cylinder gas vs. four-cylinder and biplanes vs. monoplanes. I can remember hot horse/tractor arguments as late as 1937. I suppose soon we'll be arguing LOX vs. atoms for rockets.

As early as 1832 an Englishman named Heathcote tried to plow with a stationary steam engine using ropes and pulleys to pull the plow back and forth across the field at Tiverton. "But the machinery was too complex to merit adoption," wrote an observer.

A self-propelled engine plowed an acre in 70 minutes near Louth in 1857, the ILLUSTRATED LONDON NEWS reported, but "required an army of mechanics."

About this same time, John Fowler and Frederick Howard, deciding steam engines were too heavy to travel on the fields, revived the stationary engine idea, with the cable wound on a windlass to pull gang plow back and forth. Within eight years (of what date our source does not say) over a thousand of them were in use.

In the United States before the Civil War, breaking was done with huge, cumbersome bull plows pulled by three to seven yoke of oxen lumbering along at a bovine one MPH.

A Louisiana planter said it took $12,000 worth of slaves, teams and plows to turn 10 acres a day.

Many a village blacksmith turned his brawny hand and hammer to building a steam engine that would plow. One of the most nearly successful American engines was built by Joseph W. Fawkes of Lancaster, Pa., about 1856 or '7. His 30-HP engine had a vertical boiler and rolled on a 6-foot wide drum. The WISCONSIN FARMER pronounced his steam plow successful and himself immortal. Two months later the engine buried itself and Fawkes found mortality again. In 1858 a Californian, Warren P. Miller, demonstrated a track-laying steam wagon, forerunner of the crawler tractor of today.

Wik offers an explanation of the many early failures of farm steam power: "Each engine was built by an individual . . . Lacking capital and financial reserves, the inventor could not carry out experiments to improve his engineering models." The first one not only had to work but pay off——without the research, development and testing that goes even into a new hairpin today. He was shot down on the ground. None of them worked. Makers of stationary and railroad engines, unable to fill all their orders anyway, preferred to stick with much birds in hand rather than to chase after one in bush.

Wik also points out the excess ambition of the early designers: they tried to build the biggest machines ever that could turn over the whole outdoors in one round. And instead of taking a successful steam engine and adapting it, they, without experience, tried to build a wholly new engine.

The goat, sheep, dog and later the horse treadmill and sweep accustomed farmers to labor-saving belt power The steam engine took over first as a stationary belt drive. Sawing cordwood and lumber made much use of steamers, which could be fueled free on sawdust, edgings, bark and scraps.

Then...

...Wheels Under the Belt

He reports that James Waters, Detroit, in 1860 plowed 70 acres with an engine 37 feet long on drive wheels 10 feet high pulling 13 plows turning a 19-foot swath.

In 1870, the commissioner of agriculture noted that only two patent applications for steam plows had been filed that year. "It requires time . . ." he said. And even inventions that were reasonably successful died on the vine of financial starvation. (See Sageng Self-Propelled Thresher story, page 191.)

After the Civil War, some British engines were imported. A Louisiana sugar planter used the cable plow on his 1,000-acre estate, insisting that crop production could be increased one-third and the number of mules reduced the same proportion.

Col. Wm. Patterson, a Philadelphia merchant, paid $13,000 for two 14-HP British stationary engines with plows and cables. But cable-plowing——like a tenement wife reeling her diapers out to dry——was not adapted to big Western fields.

The smithies and machine shops had enough success, however, to scare the old-line engine makers into experimenting at long last with running gears under their proved stationary steam engines. Acceptance was instantaneous even though gears broke and chains and belts jumped off going downhill, leaving the engineer to ride 'er in or jump off himself. Whereas six horses struggled to move an engine, $150 worth of gearing enabled two horses to steer it. By 1883,

Stack folded for low bridges, for storing in shed. This 1885 straw burner was self-propelled and had a steering gear, but could also be horse-drawn.—J. I. Case

two-thirds of the threshing engine orders were for self-propelleds, reported the Cooper Company. The first self-propelled put out on a business-like basis was built by Merrit and Kellogg in 1873. Although their spur-gear design was widely copied later, they went broke in three years. Cooper sold 100 bevel-gear-drive engines in 1876.

Steering with horses had two more advantages: they comprised a reservoir of reserve power to help the engine out of a hole, and their presence helped allay the fears of horses met on the road. Even after steering gears came in and steering horses were no longer needed, some state laws required their presence for its psychological effect on passing teams.

A 60-HP Russell here pulls 8 John Deere 14-inch bottoms at Prairie Village. It didn't take this many men and boys to operate the plow, either––one man could do it alone while the engineer and fireman handled the engine. Today a modern farm tractor pulling 4 plows can plow as much in a day with only one man. Plow was built about 1911. Engine is owned and operated by Lloyd Hinker, Woonsocket, S. D.

Then . . . . . draw bar power

Ere the turn of the century, the steam traction engine was well enough developed it could not only power the thresher on the belt but could pull thresher and tender to the next job, and plow between threshing seasons.—J. I. Case Co.

At least one case is reported in which oxen got thirsty and pulled their steam engine over a steep bank into the river. The hot smokebox was known to enthuse a balky horse who tried to fly by the seat of his pants.

A 1909 encyclopedia attributed to machinery the 86 percent increase in per-worker farm production from 1870 to 1900.

When steam first took to the fields about 1850, the nation had about seven million horses. Power represented by horses increased faster than steam to 1910, near-peak year for steam, when we had 21 million horses and about four million steam horsepower plus about one and one-half million gas HP. Animal power increased to 22 million by 1920; although steam had begun to slip, it hit five million HP. Steam and horse both plummeted by 1930, when gas HP hit 22 million.

As Wik points out, horsepower measured in the number of horses is illusory. Whereas a farm might have 50 horses, they couldn't all be hitch-ed to a plow, or all set to turning a belt. Nor could you work a horse all day and all night, too.

Reeves built a 40-HP cross-compound plowing engine with a 9x15 and a 14x15 cylinder. Wheels were seven feet high and almost five feet wide. The rear axle was 7 inches in diameter. The engineer rode in the top story of the cab while the fireman sweated below his feet.

Case built a few freight engines that weighed, wet, 46,000 pounds, put 216 HP on the belt, pulled 25 14-inch plows or, on the highway, 50 tons of freight.

Steam power displaced wind and water for running looms, forges and their bellows, mills and pumps and transformed industry from cottage crafts to factories, spawning the hive of sociological ills which Dickens and his kind fought to correct. Thereupon poets switched from the Song of the Shirt to the satirical rhyme about wasn't it nice that the factory was so near the golfcourse: the little children at their work could watch the big men at their play.

392

Nebraska's
Steam wagons

By 1868 the 60-HP Standish steam plow and a 4- or 5-man crew could hack up to 5 acres an hours, compared to the acre a day of a man walking behind a 2-horse plow. Two years later a six-bottom gang plow was hailed as a great labor-saver because it required but a single operator, and he could double as fireman.

Village handymen of the '70's started hooking up chains and belts to the wheels of portable steam engines that they might propel themselves. Pity the poor engineer whose chain jumped off on a hill (even store-bought jobs did that). He had to jump off, too, to save himself while his engine cartwheeled or rolled or smashed.

Bridges were another hazard: full many a brave engineer went down with his engine when it crashed through a horse-and-buggy bridge. Few engineers appreciated the power of steam; hundreds were killed when they let their boilers boil dry and blow up.

Doubtless the dangers, however unnecessary, added to the engineman's heroic halo and, in the eyes of farmers' sons and farmers' daughters, embellished his steamy day of glory.

By 1900, 5,000 steam traction engines were built annually.

A steam wagon train——no rails——stuck out across the unmarked prairie in July, 1862, from Nebraska City, Neb., for Denver, 600 miles away, hauling 20 passengers. Invented by a Minnesota legislator, Maj. Joseph Renshaw Brown, it was powered by four 12-hp steam engines with 12-inch oscillating cylinders driving wheels 12 feet high. It was steered by little 6-foot wheels attached to the front axle by a ball-and-socket joint. The vertical tube boiler was fed from a water tank integral with the body.

The "Prairie Motor" ascended a grade of 60 feet to the mile hauling 20 tons in cars behind it. Brown envisioned a vast network of Prairie Motor roads across the Great Plains beating the railroads to the business.

Headed for Denver at a larrupin' 5 MPH, the "beast of the prairies," as some called it, negotiated two steep hills west of town and broke a crank at Mile 12.

His New York foundry having turned to "top secret" Union military work (which turned out to be the "Monitor"), Maj. Brown didn't get back onto his project until after he'd fought the Civil War. By then the railroads had beaten him to the prairie business.

The two front wheels and a cylinder, and a Nebraska City street named Steam Wagon Road, are all that remain of the Major's major opus.

The beast carried wood and water for 32 miles. One question was never answered: where, on the arid, treeless plains, was he going to get more?

Steaming up

We would not presume to tell an old hand how to fire up——you fellows were experts ere we were even a gleam in Daddy's eye. Nor are we trying to give the city slicker a short course in steam engineering. But we thought folks who've never fired a steamer might like to know there's more to it than just turning a key. Our mentor here is an experienced engine man who wishes to remain anonymous lest the neighbors think he's trying to tell them what to do.

Biggest day in the spring for a hooked steam man is the day he first fires up. It's an impatient wait during the lengthening days as winter reluctantly wanes. He watches the weather reports and goes to bed with one eye on the sky, hoping for a mild day tomorrow. If the air's below 22 degrees, the water will freeze before he can get it hot.

Meanwhile, out in the shed he's looked the boiler over for wet seams and flue tubes. [Most farm steam engines had fire-tube boilers: the 36 to 76 flues (depending on the size of the engine) are 2-inch seamless ductile steel pipes carrying hot gases and smoke from the firebox forward, through the water, to the smokebox and out the stack. This design is called a fire-tube boiler: the tubes carry the fire. This design was characteristic of the railroad steam locomotive. (Indeed, the old steamers today are repaired with used flues removed from railroad engines.) Big power plants, steamships, etc., have water-tube boilers: the tubes carry water, surrounded by fire. (See diagram, p. 44)

A white crust around the tube at the endplate indicates she's leaking where the flue fits into the endplate (a rolled fit, not welded). A few simple minutes with roller and hammer snugs them up. If the white is inside the flue, this indicates a leaking flue which must be cut out and replaced. When the trouble is at the end, the tube can be tipped——a new end section welded on.

In cleaning flues with his spiral-steel reamer on the end of a 12-foot rod, any extra resistance the cleaner meets indicates the possibility of a split.

Contrary to what you might expect, a leaking flue does not explode. It just leaks. Water drips out the smokebox and, if the leak is real bad, out the firebox.

Flues aren't too hard to find. New ones are kind of expensive but for $5 you can pick up used flues from locomotive, school and apartment house boilers. Replaced in routine maintenance, these used tubes have got 20 or 30 years left in them for an engine that's seldom used except at annual shows.

A white crust around a flue tube indicates a leak.

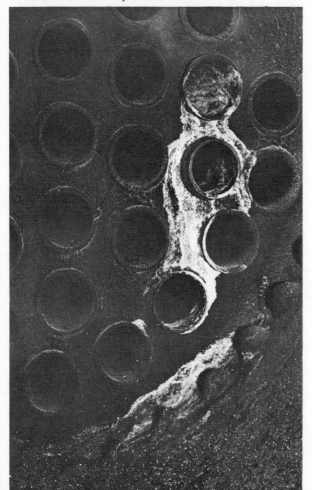

If the cleaner meets resistance inside the flue, that may indicate a split.

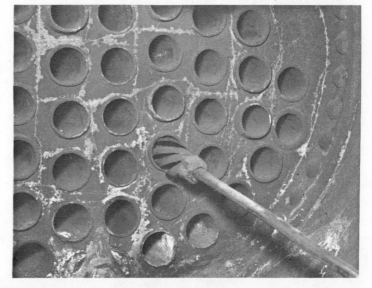

ns the flues--a job that has to be done several times a day, especially if the load is light. Heavy going blows some of the soot out.

Bottom left: Long-handled tube cutter reaches through smokebox, cuts end off defective flue. Shorthandled cutter is used in firebox.

Upper left: Split flue is pulled out through front flue plate, new tube inserted. Firebox end is beaded over to keep fire from burning ends off; bot ends are rolled tight.

Upper right: Tubes are roll-fitted into the endplates or flue plates... no welding, no gasketry, no cement here. This is the tube roller: hit it and turn it and hit it again.

Lower right: Rolling tubes is a dirty job if there's a fire in her.

396

To replace a flue, you cut off both ends, pull her out through the smokebox, push the new one in. You crawl into the smokebox and bell over the flue end so the fire won't burn it off, then roll it tight. Roll the smokebox end. It isn't too much of a job when you know how and have the special tools, but hard on the ear drums. A potbelly is no advantage in the firebox.

Be sure the fire's out.

Father and son, heads wrapped to keep soot out of hair, make a tight pair while rolling tubes inside firebox, which in this engine is 42 inches long, 30½ wide, 27 high. Dad's showing son how to "Roll Them Tubes." Camera is looking through inspection hole with Dad holding flashgun inside firebox.

While waiting for the weather to warm up he's caulked the seams by beating them tight with a cold chisel.

Our engineer friend checked the grates and chipped off any clinkers building on them. Clinkers slow the airflow, producing a smoky, poky fire and burning out the grates because the incoming draft keeps the grates from overheating.

It takes 250 gallons to fill a 60-hp boiler——a ton of it. He's careful to keep oil, detergents and soaps out of the tanks he hauls water in, for they may promote foaming and priming.

"If you won't drink it, don't put it in your boiler," is one old engineer's counsel. In fact, the human stomach is far better equipped to handle impure water than is the boiler. Mineral from hard water forms scale (like in your tea-kettle) which not only insulates the tubes and cuts engine efficiency——when the engine cools, the scale shrinks more than the tubes and squeezes them loose from the endplates.

Our engineer prefers rainwater from a cistern. If he can't get it, he bails it out of a dugout or pond. He's even been seen hauling it from the water softener company in town.

He doesn't believe in boiler compounds to reduce scale. As an engineer on a steam-powered seagoing tug during WW II he learned, "The more junk you put into a boiler, the easier it will prime and foam."

Two levels in the water glass are of life-and-death importance to the engineer. One is the level at which water just comes over the crown sheet (the "roof" of the firebox), and the other is an inch of water over the crown sheet. When he's firing a boiler he's never fired before, he takes out the wash-out plug or hand hole plug above or in the back of the boiler so he can see the crown sheet. While filling the boiler he keeps a close watch through the hole and notes the water column level when water first wets the crown sheet.

The crown sheet is his life insurance: if he lets it get dry, it gets red hot and can blow out, killing him and everybody in sight.

He fills the boiler until the water glass is half full.

Into the firebox he throws oily wiping rags, then straw, cobs or kindling-wood. He may

"If you wouldn't drink the water, don't put it in your engine," say the Old Hose comes from barrel pump on tankwagon. Takes 250 gallons to fill this boi.

throw in a little kerosene or diesel fuel (NOT gasoline!!!). When he gets a thin, even bed of red-hot coals he starts putting in coal. Engineers used to buy egg-size nut coal, but nowadays it's hard enough to find coal of any kind and you have to unload it yourself.

He has his fireman or flunky break the big chunks into fist-, egg-, and nut-size pieces: by holding the chunk in one gloved hand and hitting it with a hammer...not just for firing up but for the whole run. Uniform small-size coal makes easier firing.

If he can't buy egg or nut coal, he has to break it in his hands––one lump at a time.

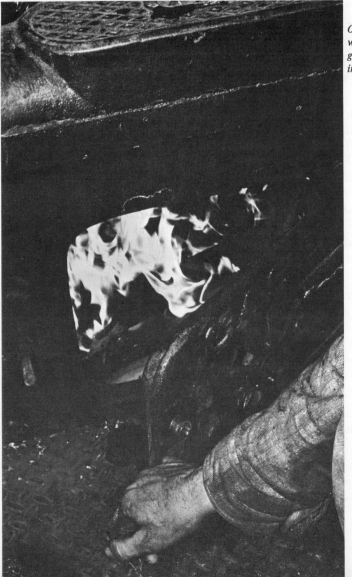

Oily rags, straw, cobs and/or kindling wood start the fire. When he has a good bed of red-hot embers, he lays in a thin layer of egg-size coal.

Getting up steam

He keeps the fire even and spread to all corners of the firebox, level all the way across——not heaped in the middle. He keeps the fire door closed except for throwing in fuel. Occasionally he pokes the coal with the shovel turned over. This is all the stirring his fire needs while building pressure.

The boiler goes through a sweat: water vapor in the combustion gases condenses on the water-cooled tubes until it drips out fore and aft. You can't tell a leaking tube from sweat at this point. The sweat will dry up as the boiler heats; the leak will get worse as pressure builds.

When she starts to boil she sings like a teakettle. While the boiler is warming up, the engineer and his crew thoroughly oil the engine and fill the hard oilers with hardoil (what I always thought was filling the grease cups with grease).

He watches the hand hole and wash-out hole filler plugs, snugging them up a little if they leak.

First-steamed water may make 15 pounds pressure in a surprisingly short time. This is just air driven out of the water. The stack blower soon bleeds this off.

The stack of a farm steam traction engine, compared to the powerhouse smokestack or even your house chimney, is relatively short and therefore doesn't produce much draft. A steam jet in the stack creates more draft on the venturi principle. A good engineer, however, doesn't need the blower much to raise steam. "He'll get up early enough to get his fire hot in time for threshing right after breakfast," says an experienced threshing engineer.

When steam gets up to 25 pounds, he checks all the hand holes and draws them up snug. "Don't use brute force on the hand hole bolts," he warns, "because it isn't needed and you'll only ruin the frog. The same applies to the brass wash-out plugs. Brute force here a few times and they'll have to be replaced because they cut away. You may strip the filler plug in time.

Installing A Never Leak Gasket

"If the hand holes weep, they'll quit as more pressure builds. If they leak, the leak will get worse with pressure. Then you'll have to cool and drain the boiler and replace that hand hole gasket."

If a hand hole gasket leaks, he cools and drains the boiler, takes out the hand hole plugs (holes for washing the inside of the boiler) and cleans the holes thoroughly, removing all the old gasket and any scale. He does the same with the hand hole plate.

He oils the bolt and runs the nut up and down the bolt with his fingers until the nut goes on easily.

Using an old gasket for a pattern, he cuts a new one out of good gray or red rubber low-pressure gasket material, making the outside just a little larger than the hand hole plate. He cuts the inside hole just large enough to fit snugly on the hand hole plate.

After getting the hand hole plate and gasket back into the hand hole, he straightens it up square with the hole. He puts the frog on the bolt and runs the nut up finger-tight. Now he eyeballs hole, plate and gasket.

"You should be able to see a small amount of gasket between the plate and the hand hole. If you see the plate is going to touch the hole, move it slightly so it won't touch when you draw it up. Don't be mean——just tight enough so it won't leak. When you've got 25 pounds of steam, tighten it again. It'll never leak, although it may weep a little."

But an engine's tears, like a woman's, with tender loving care are soon dried.

After he gets the leaks stopped and the boiler stops sweating and starts singing, he opens the smokebox door at the front of the boiler and pokes the flues again.

"Do a good job fast," cautions our engineer. "You're wasting heat and cooling off the boiler. When I was small I could never do it fast enough for Dad. He always finished it when I was half through."

Closing the smokebox door, he goes back to the platform and opens the draft halfway and opens the blower. "Watch the soot come out!" he chortles. "But don t do this with a crowd of well-dressed people around. They won't like the color of their clothes. Then shut off the blower and begin to warm up your engine. This isn't easy, either. Be careful."

While the boiler's warming up, he fills the oilers   *...and fills the hardoil cups with hard oil.*

s...   *Crosshead slide...*

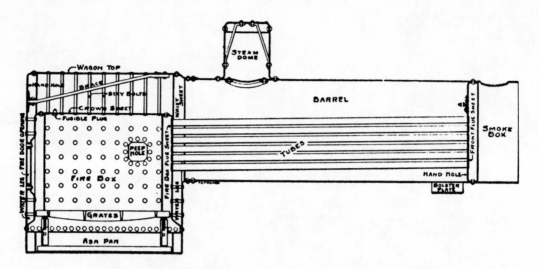

SECTIONAL VIEW OF BOILER--COAL AND WOOD BURNER

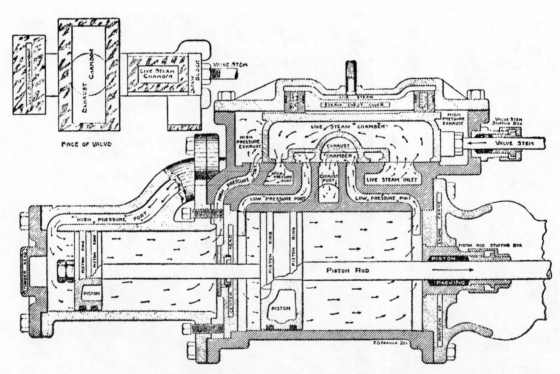

SECTIONAL VIEW OF WOOLF COMPOUND CYLINDER

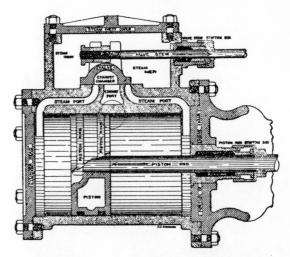

SECTIONAL VIEW OF SIMPLE CYLINDER

E ngine" sometimes refers to the entire machine, sometimes to the boiler alone, but properly to the engine proper: the cylinder, piston, flywheel and attachments.

Most farm steam traction engines were single-cylinder "simple" engines, although a few were two-cylinder and some were "compounded." In a simple engine, steam expands once in the cylinder and then exhausts through the stack. In a compounded engine, steam expands first in a small cylinder, then again into a larger cylinder (both on the same push rod), where it does another batch of work before escaping into the stack.

The J. I. Case Threshing Machine Co., leading steam engine maker, didn't think much of compounded engines, apparently, although its 1908 catalog offered them in 27, 36, 45, 60 and 75-HP. The catalog commented, "In some sections and for some lines of work, the 'compounded' has a slight advantage over the 'simple'."

In the 60-HP engine, for example, the simple engine had a 10-inch bore and a 10-inch stroke; the compounded had a 7-3/4-inch high-pressure cylinder bore and 11-inch low-pressure bore and a 10-inch stroke. It cost $100 more. Both operated at 130 pounds.

The engine posing for the photos in this section is a 60-HP 1917 Case simple single cylinder, 10-inch bore, 10-inch stroke, 250 rpm, 40x12-inch flywheel,, 30½-inch barrel (boiler) diameter, 46 flues 2x90½ inches, firebox 42x27x30½ inches, grate area 7.88 square feet. It had 216.9 square feet heating surface above the grates, carried 1,540 pounds of water at working level, a ton including feed water in the tender. Working pressure is 140 pounds per square inch. It had one speed forward, 2.61 mph, and the same in reverse. Cost $1,700 new. This engine will run on wood, coal or straw; for burning straw, a straw chute and firebrick arch were added, as well as a wood jacket. It is equipped with the jacket.

It is owned by George Klinkner, farmer, Artesian, S. D., whose father, Frederick, bought it new in 1919.

Starting the engine

At about 50 pounds steam, he very carefully opens the main valve on the steam dome, then the valve to the steam chest

When pressure hits 30 to 60 pounds, depending on the size and make of the engine, our engineer opens the main valve on the steam dome very slowly. If he gave it a whirl, a sudden steam blast could carry a slug of water that would hit the pipes like a shot shell and bust them. Valve open, he just barely cracks the throttle

With the throttle opened slightly, he opens the water bleed-off on the steam chest—the box-like affair just above the cylinder which houses the valve and where the steam is shunted to one end of the cylinder and then the other. When steam comes through the bleed-off and has warmed up the steam chest, he opens the cylinder cocks and starts rocking the engine with the reversing lever, rocking it until the cylinder is thoroughly warmed and all the water is worked out of it before he allows a complete revolution. Water won't compress, you know, and if there's enough condensate in the cylinder to fill the space between the piston and the cylinder head, a complete revolution would break a piston or blow the head. For this reason, whenever he stops the engine, he opens the cylinder cocks to let the water out before starting it again. (Some engines have automatic cylinder cocks, similar to steam traps.)

The first engineer who gets up enough steam to blow the whistle in the morning scores a point on all his neighbors. In the old days, engineers put as much store by this as the housewife did in being the first to hang out Monday's wash. As each engine man got up pressure, he tooted to let the neighbors know he was in business. Shrill shrieks wafting across the prairie made the sun come up most musically. Whistles were a status symbol: everybody wanted a bigger one than everybody else.

He caresses the throttle with a lover's hand so as not to jar the gears. These are cast iron, brittle as glass. Open, they're lubricated with axle grease and dust.

The engineman watches the sight feed to make sure the steam chest oiler is working, never taking it for granted.

He keeps an even, thin fire, not a large lumpy one. He keeps ashes in the ash pan from piling up to touch the grates, for this will burn the grates——again, by blocking off the cooling draft.

He keeps the grates well-covered with a thin layer of hot coals. Whenever he throws in coal he checks his fire for holes and fills them. "You can easily see the holes in your fire: the grates show up. Gray smoke indicates holes in your fire." He spreads his coal as he scoops it in. "Don't keep the firebox door open too long as this lets cold air in and cools the boiler fast."

Engineers and photographers live at opposite ends of the universe. They've forever got a running battle going on. The good engineer works for a clean exhaust, "Just a whisper of smoke," but the photographer wants vast billows, the blackest possible. Most engineers will, however, as a special favor, throw in a big splash of coal, some straw or even an old tire to make smoke for a picture, even though it hurts the engineer's pride, his flues, and——worst of all——his reputation.

"Sorry about that," says the photographer. "Toss in another tire."

He cautiously cracks the throttle.

With the reversing lever, cylinder cocks open, he rocks the engine forward and back, working the water out of the cylinder.

Warming up is touchy business. Note intense concentration.

Injecting cold water cools off boiler, wastes fuel. Pre-heater (cylinder ejecting steam) warms feed water with exhaust.

Engineer watches water glass as if his life depends upon it——which it does!

The engineer keeps an eyeball peeled on that water glass. He trie to keep water at least an inch above the crown sheet for safety.

"The best firing is when the water is between one inch above the crown sheet to half a glass, depending on the load. In easy going yo don't need so much water," says our engineer.

The engine carries a 350-gallon tender to replace water evaporate into steam and blown out the exhaust. When there's pressure in th boiler, the engineer turns on the steam-powered injector which force water in against steam pressure. Since the injector is not automatic it's the engineer's skilled hand that keeps the injector working at jus the right speed to keep water high enough for safety and low enoug that she won't prime.

Pulling the engine hard, demanding more steam than the boiler i producing with more than half a glass of water, may make the boile prime: water goes over with the steam. This will make the engin knock and can, as we described, ruin the engine. When she starts t clank, he opens those cylinder cocks before you can say steam trac tion engine. "Closing down the throttle will usually stop the boile from priming."

When he gets the water worked out of the cylinder, he closes th throttle until the priming stops. He then checks the fire for holes an breaks up any large lumps, fast. If he has a lot of unburned coal i the firebox after the engine has primed, he stirs the fire a little. I he's been using too much draft, he closes it down half, throttle down the water injector or shuts it off.

"The engineer watches the water column as he works back to hi load, working the water a half to an inch-and-a-half below its previou level," reveals our engineer.

Cutting the pressure and opening the throttle wide increases the ten dency to prime. An even, hot fire without holes and a controlle draft help control priming. "With a hot fire and just enough water opening the throttle only a fourth to half an inch more than neede for governor control is safest," says the engineer.

Foaming is different from priming. Foaming produces bubbles no only on top of the water but all through it, raising the foam-and water level maybe into the steam dome, which is there to let wate fall out of the steam so it won't be carried over into the engine Modern dish and laundry detergents are getting back into our wate supply and increasing its foaming tendency.

Takes a quick hand on the throttle (center lever) if she begins to prime. Right-hand lever is clutch; left-hand, reversing gear.

Maybe she's got a lumpy fire. He stirs with his shovel turned over.

406

He's working with 100 to 155 pounds per square inch steam pressure here. (Most farm steam engines were designed to work at 125 to 135 pounds; some state laws limit this to 100.) While the boiler was built with a safety factor of five and factory-tested at 225 pounds, that was 50 or 60 years ago. And that safety factor is figured on a boiler that isn't red-hot. When water gets below the crown sheet all rules are off: a red-hot crown sheet will buckle or blow at working pressure.

Water drops fast as it gets close to the one-inch above the crown sheet. This isn't much of a margin on rough land, for on a downgrade the water rolls to the front of the boiler, leaving the crown sheet high and dry. Should the engine head downhill long enough for the crown sheet to overheat, then start uphill, cascading water onto this thick chunk of red-hot steel, the gunpowder workers' wives' prophetic song would come instantly true for the engineman's widow:

Someday there'll be a thunder sound
And scattered far and near
O'er hill and dale and all around
Will be my husband dear.

If his pressure is high and he's dangerously low on water, he stops and takes on water.

"It's better to stop than to ruin a boiler."

"To use your injector, open the steam valve on the injector wide and throttle the water side until the water doesn't go out the overflow. Sometimes an injector gets hot and won't draw water. Cool it by pouring water on it and take off the suction hose and let the hot water out. Keep a cool head and don't get excited. Good injectors do work."

Some state laws required two injectors or water pumps.

If water drops below the wet crown level, the engineer "Is going to be a busy man. He throws the belt if he's threshing, pulls the pin if he's plowing, and gets those front wheels up on some bundles or backs the drive wheels into a deadfurrow. Then he goes to work on that water."

There's a fusible plug in the crown sheet that melts before the crown sheet gets dangerously hot, letting steam into the firebox to smother the fire. But sometimes the plug scales over so heavily that, even though the plug melts, the steam can't blow through and smother the fire like it's supposed to.

Even if the crown sheet doesn't blow, overheating can warp it so it tears loose of the staybolts and ruins the boiler.

"If the fusible plug melts, there's nothing for it but to pull your fire, cool down the boiler, crawl into the firebox and replace the plug."

The surest way to a short life is to inject water onto a red-hot crown sheet. This five-eights-inch-thick steel holds a lot of heat, makes flash steam. Flash steam is uncontrollable and makes that thunder sound, carrying to your widow news of her late husband.

"If you have any doubts about the crown sheet temperature, just stick your shovel into the firebox. A red-hot crown sheet will throw a bright red glow on the shovel." Red signals danger. When you see red, here's your Standard Operating Procedure:

"Open the safety valve and hang the poker on the handle to keep it open. Close your draft and dump your fire. Stay there and try to cool off your boiler. Don't run, or a hunk of boiler will catch you."

Many operators today run at lower pressures because, after all, these boilers aren't as young as they were 60 years ago. Rust and corrosion could have eaten a thin spot. And since steamers are used just for show these days, they don't have to work so hard. The less hard they pull the longer they last. One operator refuses to plow with his steamer because the heavy drawbar load cuts out the gears. And when the gears are gone, there ain't no more nohow. Today's farm implement dealer is fresh out of steamer parts.

If the crown sheet gets red, he hangs the poker on the safety valve and starts pulling his fire. To run is to die.

Shutting her down

When his day's work is done the engineer isn't through yet. There's more to shutting off a steam engine than just flipping the ignition switch.

He dumps his fire and cleans the ash pan, scraping the ashes out of the corners. Ashes are hard on the water leg and water bottom. Ash draws moisture; moisture activates the sulfuric and other acids in the ash, causing severe corrosion.

When he shuts her down for the night, he closes off the main steam valve by hand. "A wrench will damage the seat." If the engine will run again tomorrow, he takes on enough water to have at least half a column (in summer; if there's the least chance of freezing, he drains her all over).

He lets the fire burn out, but he closes the drafts so the boiler will cool slowly. Although it takes two hours to get up steam in the morning, he doesn't try to bank the fire to keep steam up because this is hard on that part of the boiler and will cause the grates to heave under the fire. He just gets up a couple of hours earlier.

If the engine isn't going to be used again for a while, and ESPECIALLY if there's freezing weather in prospect, he drains her completely——opening not only the main drain but also the cylinder cocks, steam chest bleed-off, tender drain and disconnecting all pipe unions.

The most important thing about shutting down the engine is forecasting the wind's direction on the day he'll fire up again, whether tomorrow or next Spring: the wind must blow right into the firebox door. If it doesn't, the draft will be slow, the fire balky, and it may take four hours instead of two to get steam up. And you don't move a cold engine around very handily——takes a whole herd of gas tractors to budge it.

Then when the fire is out, he caps the stack.

You have to pull the fire, too, if a leak develops, and to shut her down for the night.

If he forgets to drain anything, it'll freeze up and bust. Here he drains the throttle.

line gets its plug pulled, too. Here you get a good view of the primitive d-chain steering gear.

Main drain empties boiler for winter. Engineer can also blow out sludge here.

He caps his work by capping the stack.

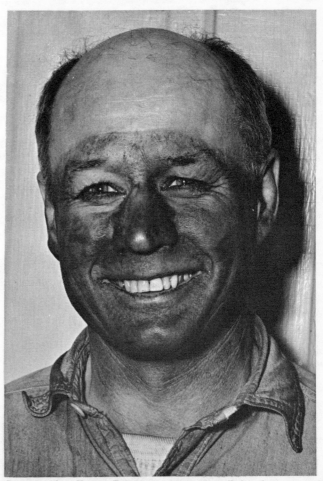

Portrait of a Happy Engineman (you can tell by the soot on his teeth). But Mom, strange creature, prefers gas tractors.

409

The steam engine man
a dying race? . . . . . .

The lusty steamer man of 1920 is gray today. When his breed is gone, there will never be another and his lore will be interred with his bones.

Or will it?

There's a new breed of engineers coming along. Though their chins are yet as bare as their elder's pates, their eager young minds are soaking up all the old-timers can tell them and show them on the care and operation of steam engines. The love is in their hearts unbidden.

One of these was a steam engine man at age 11. Today, at 14, he can bead flues, clean tubes, fire up, belt up to the thresher and keep the old brute singing a busy song right along with engineers of 50 years' seniority.

His grandfather Fred Klinkner paid $1,700 for a new 1917 60-HP Case steam traction engine and $695 for a 44-inch separator. He threshed for years around the home farm at Scotland, S. D. Granddad taught his son, George, 10 years younger than the engine, all he knew about steamers. But Granddad Fred passed on and George went to war. For a third of a century the old steamer sat in the shed, cold and silent. It's a wonder she didn't go overseas as shrapnel—the fate of many a brave engine.

A proud day—after months of crawling in and out of the firebox, rolling tubes, greasing bearings, oiling the cylinder, breaking coal, hauling water—Donald Klinkner at last graduated to the controls of Father George's 1917 60-HP Case steamer to become, at 12, the world's youngest steam engineer.

Don started learning the steam engine business at age 11. He helped his father restore the aged monster to mint condition.

. . . . noises from the grave

Then in the early '60's came noises from the grave: steam was reborn——not for getting farm work done any more——two hours steaming up isn't like turning the starter switch on a modern tractor——but as the biggest, lustiest, heaviest, dirtiest and, its disciples assure you, the funnest hobby going.

When the eastern South Dakota Threshermen's Association started staging annual steam threshing bees with a single borrowed steamer on Prof. Joe Habeger's farm near Madison in 1963, George yoked three modern farm tractors together and hauled his dad's old Case out of the barn. He was farming at Artesian, 60 miles west of Madison, by then, but distance and hiring a 20-ton lowboy was no matter. Here was a chance to bring the sleeping beauty to life, all 10½ tons of her muscle, whistle and affection!

He ransacked the attic for the owner's manual, scrounged around the archives of his brain for near-forgotten lore learned as a kid, reamed the flues and fired her up. The piston, that hadn't moved for a third of a century flashed. The dusty flywheel turned at last, throwing off clouds of chaff and spiders.

And 11-year-old Donald was right there, eyes big and bright. Before his next birthday he was the world's youngest steam engineer.

Ever since he was a little fella just big enough to clamber into the cab, Don had scrambled around over the boiler, explored the controls, rattled the shovel in the cold black firebox, going choochoochoo as he and the old girl conquered childish worlds. He didn't have to learn to love the monster. They'd been pals since before he could remember. And it wasn't much of a problem to learn to clean and fire and run her, either. With Dad as his teacher, his mind soaked in instructions like bread sops up milk.

While his city cousins are entranced by rockets and satellites, while some of their neighbor kids go on rumbles, young Donald is scouring flues, restoring the old beast, running it or is folded up inside the firebox beading-over flues.

By the time he was 12, Don was good enough to run the steamer in the Madison shows. Dad had no qualms about leaving him in charge despite the awesome responsibility. With a huge crowd gathered 'round like that, a careless engineer could kill not only himself but a hundred others.

Don likes it all. Even the dirty work.

Ask him, "What's your favorite sport?" and you get a quick answer:

"Steam threshing."

"Your favorite work?"

"Working on the Case."

"Your favorite music?"

"The steam whistle."

"Your favorite perfume?"

"Coal smoke and Mom's cookin'!"

An engine, protected from the weather and kept oiled and in repair, will last forever. Boiler plate can still be rolled. Tubes can be picked up in junkyards. Bearings can be poured from a ladle of molten Babbitt metal, a sheet of paper wrapped around the shaft for clearance. Worn-out gears can be rebuilt with the welding torch, or can provide the patterns for new castings.

Steam engines are immortal. And if each new generation of enginemen begets another, and if people continue to crave new experiences, crowding around these gentle giants from the past, the whistle's joyous shout will roll across many a prairie yet.

Long months of instruction preceded his laying a hand on the controls. Dad shows him what the levers are for. First thing he learned to operate was the whistle, and that's still his favorite, Mom says.

...mall part of the crowd that gathered to watch Don thresh wheat at the 1967 Madison, S. D., Prairie Village Steam Threshing Jamboree. The ...neer has a profound obligation with this many people around to keep anything from happening.

Nobody's down below except a Governor, a U. S. Senator, a Queen and some town leaders. Up above, the Engineer is King, Seer and Hob-Nobber with the gods!

You're a happy man when you get that throttle in y *hand, the engine throbbing, the stack barking, the r* *unwinding behind you at 2.61 MPH!*

Why a steamer is a dreamer

There's an air about a steam engine man.

I don't mean just the fragrance of coal smoke and crankpin oil that clings to him months after he's drained her for winter. I mean that far-away look of the prophet who sees things unseen by mortal eyes——the aura of mystery surrounding the great soul who hobnobs with gods and is privy to secrets closed to mere earthlings.

For the steam engineer is master of power such as turns the world, that unlocked Earth's cornucopia. Under his cunning hands this strength, equal to fourscore or more great horses, meekly serves humankind, issuing from a black tube as mysterious and potent, in its way, as the nuclear physicist's black box.

In that sooty head is lore the ancients never dreamed of——how to get steam up in hardly two hours——what black smoke means, what gray smoke means, how to prevent holes in your fire——how to keep the flues clean——when to set the cut-off for heavy load, how to slice it for light——and even how to keep the boiler from blowing up.

Engineers are a bold race, and proud, men the world has passed by, much to its loss.

The Day I Drove a Steamer

Speed Kills.

You can get into trouble at 1/8 MPH.

I asked our friendly neighborhood engineer if I could drive his 1917 60-HP Case. He said sure. (He'd already taught me how to blow the whistle.)

First of all, there's a trick to steering. The old worm-and-chain steering gear has a ratio of about 40:1. It's practically impossible for one man to turn the wheel when she's settin' still. But when she's moving, no matter how slowly, even I could spin the wheel with one hand.

I was under a bit of a handicap what with two cameras and a 10-pound flash powerpack around my neck and a camera in the other hand. But I soon discovered you have to anticipate your turns about a quarter of a block ere the corner and get that steering wheel to spinning. It takes two full turns just to crank the slack out.

Not knowing whether the throttle opened forward or back was a trouble. Not knowing whether the valve lever went whichaway to reverse the engine, and forgetting all about the clutch lever, I think I made the engineer's bald spot turn gray as I almost hooked a threshing machine, skinned by a 10-ton 1914 Minneapolis Farm Motor and rounded the corner on four wheels into the lane without quite hitting anybody. When you don't know what you're suppose to do nor how to do it, a snail's pace is the pace of fools.

But I'll tell you, man, when you get those 10½ tons zooming along at a full-throttle 2.61 MPH and feel that invincible surge of mighty power beneath your hand and the rhythmic heave of the steel deckplates under your feet and hear the bark of the exhaust in the stack and feel those cinders in your eyes and taste the soot upon your lips and suck in the heady, hot cylinder oil——man, you're hooked.

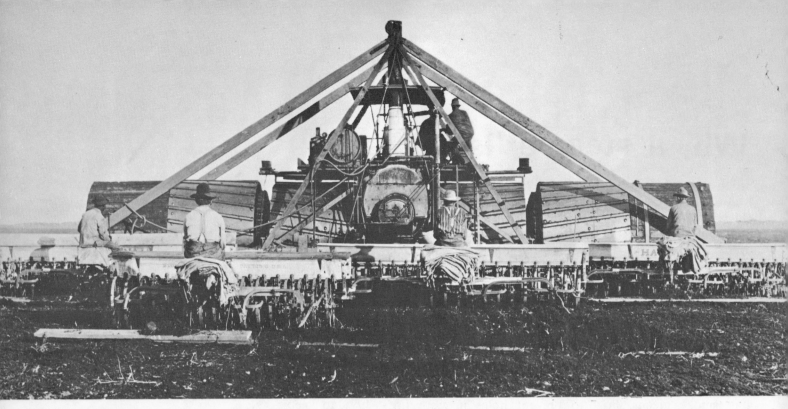

Stupendous, Tremendous, Colossal

Birth of the 20th Century saw the birth of giants such as the world has not seen before nor since.

In 1900 Holt built almost 45 feet of steam traction engine (above) for farming California's San Joaquin Valley. Each wheel was 7½ feet in diameter and 6 feet wide——and there were six——count 'em!——of 'em! to float it on the soft ground. It worked fine until you had to cross a road or a bridge, go through a gate——or just turn it!

At the same time, Daniel Best built the 20-ton toy (right) for the Middle River Farming Co., Stockton, Calif. Wood-covered wheels were 9 feet diameter and 15 feet wide!

Technical data on these steam engines is not available. The Holt machine seems to be a straight-flue job with the firebox at the rear and the drivers forward. Best's is obviously a return-flue.——Caterpillar Tractor Co. photos

The agriculture revolution builds steam

Just as the stationary steam engine powered the Industrial Revolution——just as the locomotive and steamboat powered the Transport Revolution——so the steam traction engine and the brood of machines and implements it begat spawned the Agricultural Revolution.

For the first time in history, the man on the land could accomplish more than the limit of muscles. The spectre of famine was banished from an entire nation——a miracle transcending anything the mind had conceived before——because now energy came from other than muscle——from long-stored fossil fuels rather than just from the energy a single summer's sun could store in grain, grass and fodder.

Still gathering speed, the Agricultural Revolution has gone fastest and farthest in the United States thanks to the farmer's readiness to try the new-fangles, his willingness to forget Granpap's ways. Never before in the experience of the human species——and even today only in America and those industrialized nations who have followed our example in mechanizing a free agriculture——has food outrun famine.

Bonanza boom and bust

While steam was King on the Great Plains, Steam was God in the Red River Valley of the North.

The railroad barons of the 70's and 80's—pushing their rails westward across the fabulously rich Red River Valley at Fargo between Minnesota and Dakota, toward the wide Missouri that slashes Dakota into East River and West River countries—needed something to haul.

Settlers and their chattels would make nice west-bound revenue. And what would be more profitable than hauling their wheat back East?

The railroaders came up with a flamboyant showmanship scheme which for sheer spectacularity and giganticism pales the most costly Hollywood extravaganza to half a spark.

They boomed the bonanzas.

Each bonanza they created was a huge farm of multi-thousand acres, exploiting herds of drifting laborers and the biggest equipment made. Big equipment, of course, meant steam traction engines of a size never before seen off the rails. While they used big steam equipment, "they were not big users of steam. They couldn't afford it," Hiram M. Drache, professor of history at Concordia College, Moorhead, Minn., told the author. Drache wrote "The Day of the Bonanza," from which the following material is borrowed, courtesy Dr. Drache and his publisher, North Dakota Institute for Regional Studies.

Steam traction engines pulling 14-bottom plows were seen. The little 12-ton toys popular among family-type farmers, capable of pulling only 8 plows, merited not even the barons' scorn. Some of the bonanza farms were so huge they even had their own railroads and line elevators.

The goal was profit, of course, but this was but a secondary goal. The first goal was publicity to lure hardscrabble New England farmers to the lush, stoneless Great Plains. Journalists then as now loved bigness and noise and statistics. Papers played up the huge farms—as the bonanza barons knew they would—the huge equipment, the huge crops. Settlers rose to the bait and the railroads fattened on their traffic, which was the whole idea of the bonanza farms in the first place.

Early photographs show 43 binders working in one field; 34 four-horse 8-foot binders in another; a horse barn holding 125 head.

Uncle Sam even issued a 2 cent postage stamp in 1898 showing 18 bonanza gang plows, each pulled by 4 horses or mules, in one lineup.

These were the biggest of the big farms and, by the standards of their day, the most efficient—compounded of the biggest and therefore most efficient steam equipment built; hired hands that need not be fed nor paid during the slack season, but cast to Winter's winds.

The bonanzas failed.

They failed although they bought land as cheap as 16 cents an acre when the family farmer had to pay $1.25. They failed though they avoided taxes for years. They failed although their land value jumped an average of 31 percent a year.

Observes a historian, "The natural rise of land prices was sufficient in most cases to make the bonanzas a financial success. An increase of $1 per acre each year multiplied by several thousand acres certainly gave a good book profit. This favorable speculative factor was a major reason for the financial durability of many of these bonanzas."

Uncle Sam issued an 1898 Two-cent postage stamp based on this Bonanza photo of 18 gang plows in one line up.

In 1879 one of the big land companies sold land, for which it had paid $3.75 an acre just a year earlier, for $10 and up. By 1920 this same land was selling for $90 to $115. Wheat ranged during this period from 75 cents per bushel to as high as $2; the bulk of it sold in the $1.10 to $1.40 range. (Today it is running from $1.57½ to $1.97½.)

In 1880 the Toronto Daily Globe editorialized, "Dakota and Minnesota will rue the day when the bonanza farms were introduced," reports Prof. Drache. He quotes William Dalrymple, son of a bonanza founder, in 1917, "It will be better for the state, for the towns and cities of the state...to have a great many small farms in place of one big farm."

Actually despite the much-shouted efficiency of the huge bonanzas, their profit per acre was so small that the smallest land tax wiped it out. As early as 1883 some of them began to break up. The longest-lived survived into the 1920's.

Drache quotes a 1900 writer, "The impression has been circulated far and wide that in agriculture, as in manufacturing, the big fish are eating up the little ones and that the independent small farm is a thing of the past." But after visiting the Red River Valley he concluded, "The great estates of that region are doomed to disintegration. The great wheat ranch cannot compete with the small diversified farm."

Commented our historian, "Labor on the family plan plus the ability of the family to take advantage of some hidden income which was not possible on the bonanzas eventually proved the superiority of the diversified family farm."

And wrote the Minneapolis Journal in 1893, "The bonanza farmer is not a social animal with his neighbors. He leaves the country early in the fall until spring. The silent and almost deserted farms are left in charge of the foreman; the proprietor spends his winter (and his money——dcj) somewhere else."

At this time seven families totaling 35 people were operating 28 sections (17,920 acres), which could have supported 100 families of 500 people.

Prof. Drache disagrees with my question in Catholic Rural Life magazine (3-67): "But in view of the history of ancient empires which rose on the production of their agricultural families and fell when these families were destroyed; in view of our contemporary observations of the failure of Chinese and Russian communes, in view of world history, which shows the large collectivized farm, whether communal or capitalistic, produces more famine than food; in view of these historically recent bonanza experiments here in our own country, why do we permit the present hell-bent race toward corporate collective farms which have never, ever worked?"

419

Fifty Years
a Machine Man

written about 1925 by Bascomb B. Clarke
editor, AMERICAN THRESHERMAN

There is no calling I can think of that has a wider range of experience than the machine business and especially the threshing machine business.

My first experience with a flail began in 1863 down in Arkansas, where an old coon-hunter from North Carolina had raised a patch of rye which we threshed with flails. I can almost feel the bumps on my head, now, that I received before I learned the simple twist of the wrist that brought down the flail in such a manner that it fell flat on the straw and did all the separating. Afterwards we cleaned this rye by one man on a bench pouring out the grain in a little stream and two others fanning the chaff away by walloping a sheet back and forth, thus creating a breeze that did the separating. Oh, you Old Terriers with your 36-inch cylinders, self-feeders, automatic weighers and windstackers of today, who back up to a 5,000 bushel job and clean it up in a few hours, what do you know about real threshing machinery——the flail? Do you think we performed this arduous labor for our health? Not so you could notice it.

My next experience was holding sacks for a ten-horsepower threshing outfit that showed symptoms of real work sometimes. Next I was advanced to a position of "band cutter," the fellow who stood beside the man who fed the machine and cut the bands, not twine bands, brother, but those made of straw, for there were no binders to tie the grain for 20 years after I had been dubbed and created a thresherman, made so in a just and lawfully-constituted manner and according to Hoosier ritual.

Some of you old timers remember how it was to stand up on a straw stack where mouldy ragweeds gave you a bad taste in your mouth and where you swallowed enough dust to fertilize a turnip patch. Well, that was my experience as soon as I was strong enough to manipulate a three-pronged fork. I well remember an old "sweepstake" horsepower threshing outfit 'way back in 1868. The inventor of this machine must have been inspired by Providence to help the fellows on the straw stack who were perishing for water to wash down the ragweeds and dust, for this old boy operated the straw carrier with a long chain running from the fan belt to the upper end of the carrier. I always preferred the "tail-end" of the machine on a straw stack, for there you had to keep the straw back, but you could stand still and let the other flunkies do the traveling around, pushing the straw back and patting it down, something after the fashion of a dog hunting the head of his bed.

On one particular occasion I remember the machine crew were crowding the mourners on the straw stack to the limit, not stopping to water us more than once an hour. It was during this hard run that it occurred to me that just a tiny twist of the tine of the fork under the drive chain might bring relief. You know that the feeder who knows his business keeps a close watch on the straw stack as well as every other part of the machine. It required fast work to move the previous question, so I gave the correct sign of distress and off went the chain. We all wondered how in thunder that chain ever happened to fly off that sprocket. What you don't know in this world of trials sometimes won't disturb your conscience, especially if you are a thresherman.

Well, when we finished there, I pulled out for the Indiana State Fair the next week. That was the week in which a "field trial" between two of the leading thresher builders of the state took place. It was agreed by both concerns (both being thoroughly honest and above suspicion) that they would clean up each other's waste. The machine that did the best work lost the prize because it was found to have the most waste grain. The honest old Quaker whose machine lost the premium said to the awarding committee: "I can understand why my competitor wins, because he has the least waste grain. But what I can't understand is how we both threshed only white wheat, while all excepting a few grains found in our waste is Mediterranean wheat."

The facts were, that the competitor's men, who cleaned up the old Quaker's wheat, had filled their pockets and then, having their jack knives opened, slit their pockets and allowed wheat to fall into the waste. Thus they won. But they forgot to use the same kind of wheat in their pockets that they had threshed with the two machines. All's fair in love and war, but this was unfair advantage over which we had a good laugh together fully 20 years later."--Provided by G. B. Gunlogson

(Author's note: competition between threshermen on the rings took such jolly forms as railroad spikes in bundles and dynamite under the rigs.)

A Thresherman's Memories

by G. B. Gunlogson
(1950)

Personal experiences and observations of 50 years ago are mostly forgotten except for those that made the deepest impressions.

Nothing that happened during the year stirred the family and the whole household quite so much as the approach of threshing time, and the final arrival of the threshing rig. The steam traction engine pulling the separator and frequently a tender was truly the giant of the grain fields. It had its own code and privileges which no farmer would dispute. It followed roads or trails only if it found the shortest distance to its destination; otherwise it went across fields and fences.

Every farm boy wanted a toy engine and thresher and these he made for himself. Anything from a cigar box to a longer wooden box on which were mounted some spools and sprockets would serve for the separator, while old stovepipes provided the usual material from which the engine was made.

The first "pay job" to which most farm boys aspired in the early days of threshing was balking straw. This was before the windstacker. A heavy wooden pole was used, a horse hitched to each end. The horses had to be guided separately, since the straw pile being pushed would be between them, and this was usually accomplished by a boy riding each horse. When a pile of straw had collected behind the thresher about the height of the horses, they would be driven up on either side and the straw pushed along by the pole to a desired distance from the rig.

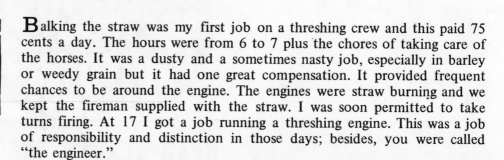
Balking the straw was my first job on a threshing crew and this paid 75 cents a day. The hours were from 6 to 7 plus the chores of taking care of the horses. It was a dusty and a sometimes nasty job, especially in barley or weedy grain but it had one great compensation. It provided frequent chances to be around the engine. The engines were straw burning and we kept the fireman supplied with the straw. I was soon permitted to take turns firing. At 17 I got a job running a threshing engine. This was a job of responsibility and distinction in those days; besides, you were called "the engineer."

The steam traction engine held a peculiar fascination for most men familiar with them. They exuded an atmosphere of friendliness. There was something strangely satisfying about the song and the hiss and the purr and many different kinds of noises, which expressed its moods and state of being. For example, in the morning when the engine was being fired up, one could tell at a distance, by the sounds, the progress of the firing. At first there would be a slow dribble of water from petcocks, pipe connections, etc. This occurred with the slight expansion of metals and the first change of pressure within. This would be accompanied by soft purring noises, then when steam appeared, the dribbling would be replaced with the soft hiss of steam. The pitch of the sound would go up as the steam pressure rose. Soon the blower would be turned on for more draft and provided a still new overture of music.

About 1911 I had to cross the Cannonball River in North Dakota with a steam threshing rig but the bridge wouldn't hold us. The water was about four feet deep. The fire was pulled with a full head of steam before the crossing. I calculated there was enough steam in the boiler to take us across. A volcano of steam erupted as the river water contacted the hot metal. Once across, a cable pulled the separator.

The reason you see so many Case steamers around yet today is that Case was the all-time champion steam engine builder, turning out 35,737, nearly three-times runner-up Huber, with 11,568 (figures from Maurice Kildare in RELICS magazine, Winter, 1967). He says Aultman-Taylor built 5,870; Geiser 15,801; Minneapolis 7,981; Port Huron 6,030, and Harrison 839. The grand total steam engine count when production stopped in 1925, adding up the above, hit 83,824.

However, Kildare neglects to count Russell, Reeves, Nichols & Shepard, Shay and others.

Mr. Gunlogson, who was closely associated with the J. I. Case Company for many years––first as engineer, later as head of Western Advertising Agency, Racine, Wis., which handled (and still handles) Case advertising–– presents larger figures.

Says he, "The history of the steam engine as an agricultural machine began shortly after 1870 and so far as its production is concerned, ended about 1923. In those 50 years, great changes were made in the steam engine as well as in threshers and other farm machinery. The steam engine is of course inseparably tied up with the grain thresher.

"Custom threshing grew as the size and efficiency of this machine advanced. Labor-saving attachments, particularly the self-feeder, wind-stacker and grain weigher were important developments.

"During the first 25 years of this history, about 40,000 engines were produced of which about one-half were traction. The 1900 census reports 6,569 steam engines manufactured of which 5,470 were traction engines. The peak in production was reached in 1911 and '12. From 1900 to the end of production nearly 100,000 engines were produced, mostly traction."

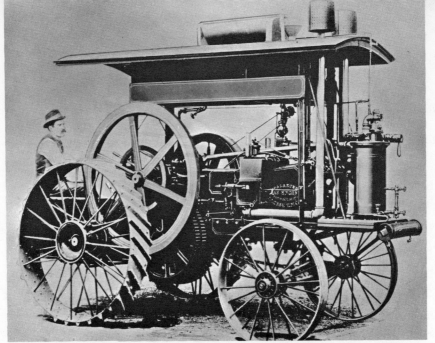

First gas tractor of record lacked carburetion and ignition equipment to make it a commercial success in 1892. Case got into the gas tractor business commercially in 1908 and in 1917 was still saying steam would always be preferred in some places for some farm jobs.--J. I. Case Co.

Sneaky · stinky · noisy ·

little upstart ·

As steam grew to supremacy, a slippery little infant was trying to grow up enough to challenge King Steam. A Frenchman tinkered in 1678 with an internal combustion engine fueled by gunpowder. Others, too, experimented with gunpowder as well as turpentine, natural gas, coal gas--even coal dust! Drake's 1859 oil well started the petroleum industry and gave the sputtering babe the nourishment it needed to grow up.

The Otto engine, developed in Germany on the 4-cycle principle we use today, was a factor by 1876. Rudolph Diesel, starting with coal dust, patented his compression-ignition engine in 1892.

Just as the first horseless carriages were built by hanging a gas engine under a de-shafted buggy, so some of the first gas tractors were simply steamers with a gas engine substituted for the steam. In fact, it's hard for the uninitiated to tell an early gas tractor from a prime steamer: they both have smokestacks in front, a big hunk of metal in the middle and a cab at the rear, with little wheels ahead and huge drivers behind.

The first gas tractors were built to LOOK like steam engines--even complete with whistle-- on the theory they wouldn't scare the horses so much.

This is the 1915 Case 20-40 that started Prairie Village. It still runs like a charm. If you can't tell the difference between this and a steamer, don't be discouraged. They fool a lot of people and horses on purpose.

if it would start

The first recorded use of the word "tractor" to replace "gasoline traction engine" is found in an 1890 patent. The 1908 Case catalog presents "steam traction engines," but the 1917 edition sells "steam tractors."

Case built the first recorded gasoline traction engine in 1892. It was not commercially practical, however, needing carburetion and ignition equipment not yet invented. Case offered their first commercial gas tractors in 1895, several sizes of 2-cylinder models.

Practically every major farm machine advance was made by a farmer. In his own shed he cobbled up some crackpot contraption which a manufacturer took over, developed, refined and promoted.

A well-driller and thresherman named John Froelich mounted a single-cylinder gas engine on a steam tractor chassis in 1892, building his own traction gears. His contraption threshed for 50 days and worked at temperatures from +100 to −3. The Froelich fathered the John Deere.

They were all self-starters

The war between gas and steam heated up between 1910 and 1921, when there were 168 tractor companies, of which 160 have died. Steam engine builders refused to load their wares on freight cars carrying gas tractors.

The 1917 Case catalog, while offering both steam and gas tractors, prophesied: "We know that in some localities steam has always been and always will be the most satisfactory power. Time will prove."

The same issue offered a 12-25 gas tractor with two speeds—an innovation: 1.75 MPH for plowing and 2.2 MPH for light work. Said the catalog, "Some light duty tractors we know are so designed as to operate up to 4 miles per hour. This policy we believe is wrong, as it is most extravagant and is unproductive of the best results." Now they'll top 20 MPH on the road, loaded.

Steam engines had been rated at 15-45 HP, 20-60 HP, etc., meaning they could deliver the lower power at the drawbar and the higher power on the belt...they used up 2/3 of their power just to move themselves. Notice how much more efficient were the gas tractors: they needed only half their power for themselves. Today's tractors are rated like 60 HP, period, although every farmer knows they'll struggle harder on plowed ground than on firm.

Case's largest gas tractor in the 1917 book was the 30-60 2-cyl. horizontal 4-cycle with a 10-inch bore and 12-inch stroke, operating at 365 RPM. The magneto was "...protected by a rain-and-dust-proof leather hood. The carburetor uses successfully and economically the various grades of naphtha, distillate, kerosene and gasoline."

The horse came under merciless corporate attack. No less an authority than Thomas Edison pointed out the tractor ate no hay on Sundays.

The same catalog went to bat for steam thus: "Tractor farming is a proven success. A farmer with a reliable tractor can farm at less cost, less time, and at a greater profit to himself than farming with horses. ....It is hardly necessary to comment on tractor plowing. Its success has been demonstrated and proved. Plowing the soil deep enough and at the right time is today reckoned as a factor that increases crop production in many cases as much as 100 percent." The plow that required but a single operator in addition to the engine crew was much extolled.

Horse-powered agriculture peaked in the U S. about 1920 when we had 25 million horses and mules, dropped to a 2-million postwar low. The resurgence of riding has brought them back to near the 3-million mark.

...you started 'em yourself! A. D. McCracken (right) had been cranking the 1920 Minneapolis 35-70 for half an hour by horsing up on the ratchet bar and never got a pop. As he stood gasping with his tongue hanging out to his belt buckle I asked him for "one more for a picture"--and as the shutter clicked, the old ogre took off! Prairie Village has an acre and a half of barrel engines of all sizes. Roger Garlick does the honors with his little jewel (left). Note the steamer-type water glass. And if you think that thing on the windmill looks like a Size 150 overhalls, you're right. They're 15 feet from strap to cuff, and as soon as we can find a feller to fit 'em, Joe will be out of office.

Below: Joe Habeger's 1-cylinder Rumely hitched to a 1906 Case 42-inch steel separator. "The tractor's too small for the thresher, but I just pull it around for effect," says Joe.

Steam threshermen found themselves losing out to more enterprising neighbors who bought gas engines and sold their services on a single competitive advantage to the farmer: "You don't have to haul coal."

Says USDA, "...the rate of technological progress had slowed down (1920). The availability of good new land had dwindled to insignificance. One-fourth of the harvested crop acreage was being used to produce feed for power animals.

"If methods had not been changed, many more horses, more men to work them, and much more land to grow feed for them would be required for today's net agricultural output. The American economy of the 1960's could not be supported by an animal-powered agriculture on our...slowly shrinking land base. National progress on all fronts would have been retarded seriously had not agriculture received new forms of power and sources of energy not restricted by biological limitations."

The first gas tractors were as big and heavy and cumbersome and slow as their steamy-breathed kissin' cousins. This iron-mountain type

tractor prevailed from 1910 to 1920, but, says USDA, "it could not accomplish the many tasks necessary to mechanize the farm." It could pull a plow in the field, a wagon on the road, or a machine on the belt. Period.

"Manufacturers began experimenting with light tractors suitable only for cultivation...," says the historian. But the farmer didn't want two tractors--a big one to plow and thresh, a little one to sow and cultivate and mow. Many farmers kept heavy tractors and heavy horses well into the '40's. What they wanted was a farming machine big enough to plow and thresh, small and nimble enough to cultivate and sow. They wanted an all-purpose tractor.

The first successful all-around tractor was the International Harvester 1924 Farmall, which established the tricycle "landing gear" as successful. It plowed and threshed as well as it sowed, etc.

The Minneapolis Farm Motor 35-70 HP was built in 1920 by the Minneapolis Threshing Machine Co. Its 4-cyl. crossmounted engine had a 7½ inch bore, a 9-inch stroke. The machine weighed 23,500 pounds sopping wet, cost about the same as a steamer of equivalent power. Belt and reverse clutch were built into the pulley; a separate clutch on yon side gave it its one speed of about 2¼ mph. This was a road special.

Belt had to be twisted on some engine-thresher combinations so the thresher would run the right direction and thresh instead of unthreshing. Where the engineer had a choice, as with a steam engine that would run equally well in either direction, he twisted the belt to make it run truer and more proof against the wind. Note the pleasure young and old are taking in Joe's monster. That's him in the pith helmet in the cab, left.

Welcome
to Iron Mountain

The 450-rpm engine was designed to cool with 60 gal. water and actually had a water-circulating pump. Joe uses drain oil for a coolant—finds it runs hotter so kerosene burns better—and oil doesn't freeze. Observes Prof. Joe: "Sixty gallons is a lot of water to put in every morning by the bucket."

The 'Big 4'

The 1911 Big 4 was built in Minneapolis, as were many gas traction engines of the time. Its drive wheels are 8 feet high and it was sold with an 8-bottom plow just like the one it's pulling. The radiator is a section of a fire-tube boiler, flues and all, almost half as big as that of a small steam engine, and holds 70 gallons of water. Cylinders were cast separately with the heads on: an integral or bonnet engine. You started it by jumping up and down on a torque bar hooked to the PTO shaft at the rear. Owned by Milton Ayers, Madison, S. D.

Agricultural engineers with a prophetic bent predict eventual once-over machines that will prepare the seedbed and plant and fertilize and apply one-shot pesticides in one operation. Following them will come the once-over harvesting machine that picks, cleans and processes, perhaps even canning and freezing and packaging the crop in one pass.

Whether you live in the highest-rise apartment or the plushiest suburb, what happens on the land affects you IF you eat, drink, pay taxes and/or wear clothes. And mostly what happens on the land is agriculture.

Despite one metropolitan daily editor's statement that "agriculture isn't important any more"——despite the fact that less than 8 percent of our people are farmers, despite your paying only 17 percent of your take-home pay to feed your family instead of the 33 percent in the '30's when food was "cheap" (compared to the 50 to 100 percent food costs people in hungry countries), this "unimportant" agriculture today produces 70 percent of our new wealth, 70 percent of our industrial raw materials, employs 4 out of 10 people farming, processing and distributing farm production or supplying farmers with the goods and services they need to produce. Farm exports produce a big chunk of our foreign exchange, holding down our deficit of payments, and keeps a brake on inflation.

Steam power first put farming into the big time——and now steam is being urged to replace gas engines in autos to hold down air pollution!

Full circle, anybody?

Nobody seems to know anything about this Hart-Parr, except that it looked like a steam engine after the fashion of the day and had the steering wheel on the right side.

Hart Parr

1913 Rumely Oil—Pull; 1 cyl. 10x12, 5 plow, 2-speed 1.9 or 2.75 MPH @ 425 RPM. It was oil-cooled to get a higher operating temperature for more efficient kerosene combustion. It weighs 14,000 pounds in its stocking feet, says Joe Habeger, its master.

Rumely

In 1920 the Rumely Oil-Pull had 2 8x10 cylinders and was rated at 20-40 HP, still 5-plow. It's still oil-cooled. Owner Roger Garlick is at the controls, getting 2 and 3.2 MPH out of her @ 450 RPM. Stark naked, the tractor weighs 13,000 lbs. Note the progression here to more complexity (double the number of cylinders), smaller cylinders, higher engine speeds and higher travel speeds and lighter weights, a trend continuing today.

His passenger is having a Big Time blowing the whistle: Garlick added a compressor and air tank just for kicks.

Today's tractors of the same plow-class have 4, 6 or 8 cylinders; engines operate at 1,250 to 4,000 rpm, deliver plowing speeds of 4 and 5 MPH and road speeds of 15, 20 and 30 MPH, and weigh 3,000 to 4,000 pounds.

Nebraska test records show that in 1920 the average wheel-type tractor tested delivered 5 drawbar horsepower hours per gallon of gasoline or distillate. The average wheel tractor tested in 1959 delivered 10 DBHPH (but the gasoline cost 4 or 5 times as much!). Diesel wheel-type tractors went from 10 DBHPH in 1935 to 13.5 in 1959.

An early attempt at "motor cultivation" is this 1919 Allis-Chalmers articulated machine that drives from the front wheels and steers by hinging in the middle. Rear unit carried cultivator, plow, drill, planter, etc. It was rated at 6-12 HP @ 800 RPM with a 4-cyl. vertical LeRoi engine. Speeds were 1.5 and 2.8 MPH.

We think we're so modern today with our electric starter and lights, articulated tractors, front-wheel drives and unit-type implements. The Moline Universal had these in 1919. Rated a 2-plow tractor, it had a 4-cyl. vertical en bloc engine, 3½-inch bore, 5-inch stroke. It delivered 9-18 HP @ 1,800 RPM, weighed 3,300 pounds, went ½ to 3½ MPH.

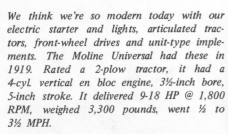

– 1927 18-36 Hart Parr 2-cyl. crossmounted 4-plow 2-speed 800 RPM kerosene or distillate. George Demary, Winfred, S. D., owner.

Only in the last couple of years have we turned from cursing our "surpluses" to blessing our abundance-and-to-spare.

We think today's marvelous machines are a vast improvement over the steam engine. But look at the improvement the steel plow marked over the iron one; the iron over the wood; the wooden plow over the pointed stick.

Here was tremendous power tamed to man's hand: a single steam operator could guide the power of not 40, but 60, 80, even 250 horses! And as so many kings before it, steam came to kingship through revolution——the Agricultural Revolution. For nearly half a century King Steam reigned supreme in all his smoky glory. Steam was big and powered big machines that inspired big ideas.

Remarkable for sheer size if nothing else was a 1900 Best steam traction engine built for a Stockton, Calif., farming company. Its wood-covered drive wheels were each 15 feet wide and 9 feet high. It weighed 82,000 pounds. See page 416.

man plants, covers, packs, fertilizes and pesticizes one trip. The ticket for this one man's pile of iron would have bought four or five steam ng rigs 60 years ago requiring 100 men to operate them. — *J. I. Case Co.*

Full Circle, Anybody?

Everything goes in circles. Tractor shape evolved from square to streamlined (for 4½ MPH!) and now is back square again. Now we've turned the full circle back to the iron mountains of yore, with behemoths showing up like the 15½-ton baby below.

Compared to the acre that great-granddad could plow in a long-hard day, this giant will turn, it is said, 18 acres an hour, or chisel 38 acres an hour. It has capacities like 13 16-inch plows or a 56-foot chisel plow (shown).

The V-8 two-stroke-cycle diesel puts out 350 HP at 2,300 RPM. A rather complicated gearbox gives 16 speeds from 2.68 to 22.65 MPH. She weighs 31,000 pounds day and night. Axles are rigid; she steers by center articulation (right).—Steiger Photo and chart

For comparison again, a 32-HP Reeves cross-compound steamer pulling 16 plows and two grain drills near Albion, Wyo., in 1911 turned out what was considered truly remarkable performance one day: plowed and seeded 65 acres. This outfit required one engineer, one fireman, one tank man, two blacksmiths, two plowmen and one cook.

Axles are rigid; she steers by center articulation.—Steiger photos

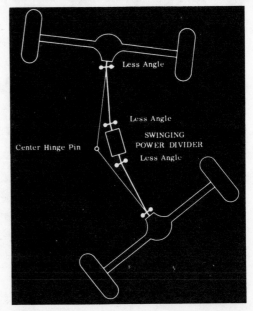

434

Top: The 4-plow 1925 Huber was rated for 4 plows. Its 4-cyl. engine had 5-1/8x6¼ bore and stroke, deliverd up to 3 MPH @ 1,150 RPM, 2 speed. It weighed 6,230 pounds. This one represents an early conversion from steel rims to rubber tires, probably done in the '30's when cutting down steel wheels and adding rims for tires was about all that paid the village blacksmith's rent. Operator comforts were nil.

Center: Gray 20-40 Canadian special built in 1918 didn't have rear wheels––it drove through a chain to a spiked drum that could be filled with water for more weight and traction. Water ballast, they called it. Today's tractors have cast-iron wheel weights plus water in the tires with calcium chloride as an antifreeze. The 4-cyl. crossmounted engine gave 2½ MPH @ 600 RPM, and a 20-40 HP rating.

Bottom: But farmers didn't want such small tractors. They wanted them big enough to plow, yet nimble and high enough for cultivating and other work. This 1930 Oliver Hart Parr row crop single front wheel was patterned after the 1924 Farmall row-crop all-around tractor which pattern is still followed today, although more usually with close-set dual front wheels.

435

Another modern Iron Mountain: no data—but the men standing nearby give you an idea of its size.

A more family-sized biggie of today is this 4-wheel-drive tractor and 7 semi-mounted plows.

The Ag Cat is especially designed for agriculture: spraying, dusting, seeding, etc., built for heavy loads, slow flight, short, rough fields, safe maneuverability at low altitudes. I'll bet my friend Roy Houck could really herd buffalo in 'er! (See my book WHERE THE BUFFALO ROAM AGAIN for the story of herding buffalo by air.)

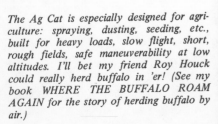

436

J. BOYDELL'S INVENTION. (Patented in 1846.)

Close-up of Boydell's tractor as pictured in the U.S. Agricultural Report of 1867. Its ancestry traces back beyond the Revolutionary war date almost to the first patent granted by the British. Boydell was a Canadian, but his steamer was used in war in 1856 and then in British farming trials in '57.

1713: The Caterpillar idea started early in Paris with "little goats" pulling these rollers under a body in which the kiddies rode around the Champs Elysees. The French Academy of Science gave credit to F. Hal Higgins for making them dig out the drawings to prove France was 57 years earlier than the English with the crawler. Edgeworth in England added steam power, however.

Now Comes Gas

The tractor age began in 1889 in the U. S. when a single-cylinder Charter engine was installed on a steam traction engine chassis in South Dakota. In that year, the Charter Gas Engine Co. built six units.

Wik says that following Froehlich's hybrid of 1892 (he mounted a stationary gas engine on steam running gears) came the 1894 Huber single-cylinder vertical engine of huge size and small power. He says, "The Hart-Parr engines built at Charles City, Ia., in 1902 and 1903, were the first really successful gasoline tractors built in the U. S. They ushered in the tractor era of farming."

Many of these tractors, Wik tells us, were so difficult to start that occasionally engineers let them run all night rather than face this baffling problem in the morning. The Hart-Parr manual listed 19 rules to start and 13 to stop.

How a Couple of College Kids Upset the Industry

The University of Wisconsin shops clattered and banged with unusual fervor. Couple of kids were building some gas engines. That's OK——they were studying mechanical engineering and design and were required to build an engine. But they didn't have to build FIVE! Build five they did, which was probably a fair percentage of the nation's total gas engine production in that year of 1898. C. W. Hart and C. H. Parr, students, not even graduated yet, had started a gas engine factory.

Graduate they did. They formed Hart-Parr to build stationary gas engines. They developed oil-cooling to get around the problem of evaporation and freezing and to achieve the higher temper-

"The Granddaddy of the Tractor Industry," a company caption says of Old No. 1——1901: two-cylinder horizontal four-cycle gasoline engine with 9-inch bore and 13-inch stroke sparked by low-tension generator. Oil cooling required five expansion bulbs. Rated a 4-5 plow unit. Note 1,000-pound flywheel and chain drive. One was built, ran 17 years.

ature needed for good kerosene combustion. The first year in business they lost $353.89. The second year they lost $491.17. Instead of getting mad and cashing in, the stockholders told the kids to keep going. The third year they showed a profit of $1,564.16. Madison didn't want industry, however, so they moved to Charles City, Ia., in 1901.

Both boys were farm boys and they saw the limitations of steam power on the farm. They thought it might be a good idea to provide something else. In 1902 they produced a gasoline traction engine. This was quite a mouthful, so they called it a tractor, and the name stuck. History is not clear whether they thought up the word themselves——but the first recorded use of the word "tractor" occurs in an 1890 patent. They sold one tractor in 1902 and 15 in 1903, oil-cooled.

A historian wrote that Hart and Parr ". . . had started experimental work on gasoline engines in 1895, and by 1905 had established the first business in the United States devoted exclusively to the manufacture of tractors. They designed their tractor for drawbar work rather than for belt work as evidenced by the ruggedness of its transmission which well withstood the heavy strains imposed when plowing."

The world's first gas tractor ad, in THE AMERICAN THRESHERMAN, Dec., 1902, for No. 2, drummed up enthusiasm for a two-cylinder horizontal oil-cooled gasoline engine operating @ 280 RPM. Ad emphasizes all the things the tractor hasn't got——doesn't mention it hasn't got a seat. Rated 22-45 HP. Only one was built. It was used 17 years.

With gasoline becoming scarce and high-priced, they developed engines for kerosene, distillate and fuel oil. Engine No. 3, 1903, had a two-cylinder horizontal four-cycle 10x13 kerosene engine with water injection to reduce knock. No spark plugs: dry-cell make and break had points inside combustion changer. Had two carburetors. Company built 15 that year.

Among the firsts credited to Hart-Parr are the first tractor plant, first successful production tractor, first tractor advertisement, first oil-cooled engine, first valve-in-head engine, first kerosene engine, first tricycle row-crop, first multi-speed transmission, first successful tractor diesel engine.

A happy customer reported tractor costs vs. horse-farming costs: He bought a 60-HP Hart-Parr; his letter carried in the 1917 catalog reads in part: ". . . as I had never handled an engine before, and had only about an hour with the expert, it is not surprising that I was more afraid of the engine than the engine was of me."

He itemizes horse-charges for seeding, harrowing, double-disking, plowing and cutting 4,795 acres totaling $2,947.35; his tractor costs, including 8 per cent interest and 10 per cent depreciation on the $4,500 tractor, totaled $1,912.50. "Deducting this from the earnings, it will be seen that I am the gainer by the use of the power outfit by the amount of $1,300.45. J. B. Musselman, Culpar, Sask."

The 1901 Hart-Parr tractor factory at Charles City, the first tractor plant, still builds Oliver and Cockshutt tractors. With 17 acres under roof and three shifts, the plant can produce 100 units a day. One historian sums it up: "In 1901, Hart-Parr, using a heavy-type, oil-cooled, twin-cylinder engine, built their first tractor, and the report is that it was sold in 1902 . . . worked at least 17 years . . . Hart-Parr Company deserves recognition as a founder of gasoline tractor activity."

Hart-Parr Tractor Company was one of the ancestors of the well-known Oliver Corporation, through whose corporate veins today flows the fiscal blood of other well-known farm machinery pioneers such as Oliver Chilled Plow Company, Nichols & Shepard, Cockshutt, Cletrac, Farquhar. Oliver today is a wholly-owned subsidiary of White Motor Corp.

Pretty good for a couple of college kids.

Maybe they were too busy to riot.

No. 3, 1903, has 2-cylinder horizontal 4-cycle 10x13 kerosene engine with water injection to reduce knock. No spark plugs: dry-cell make and break had points inside combustion chamber. Had two carburetors. Company built 15.

22–45 was built from 1903 to '06. Had induction magneto and pressure lubrication. An "auto-sparker" (dynamo) was optional but you still started it on 5 dry cells. Weighed 19,000 pounds. Planetary gears inside belt pulley reversed it.

RIGHT SIDE, 45 BRAKE, (22 TRACTIVE) HORSE POWER TRACTOR

The 40–80 was built from '08 to '14: 4-cylinder horizontal engine burned either kerosene or gas. Oil-cooled. Jump-spark ignition with dry cells and high-tension mag. 400 RPM. 2 speed. 36,000 pounds. 1913 price $3,200.

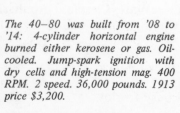

The 15-30, built from '09 to '12, started out with opposed cylinders, later had upright two-cylinder engine. A threshing model and a plowing model were offered. Two speeds up to 4¾ MPH.

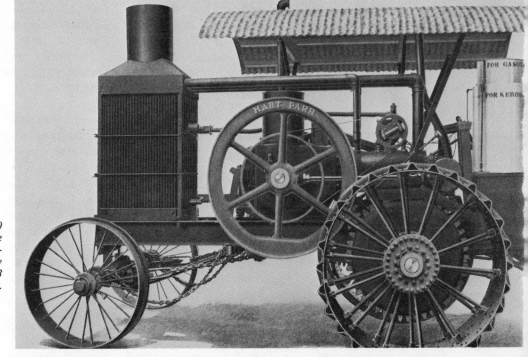

Old-reliable 30–60 was powered by a 300 RPM 2-cylinder kerosene horizontal engine using dual jump-spark ignition with low-tension magneto. Started with gas on 5 dry cells. Hit-miss governor. One speed—2.3 MPH. Flywheel weighed ½ ton, tractor 10. 1913 price $2,300.

Little Red Devil was Hart-Parr's answer to the demand for a light tractor. Had single drive wheel, 2-cylinder 2-cycle water-cooled engine, 600 RPM, no valves, no transmission, no differential. To back up, you reverse rotation of engine. 2-speed. 2-cycle engine required more skill and care in adjustment, gave trouble, and 3-wheel design tended to roll over and play dead on slopes.

The "Model T" Tractor

Henry Ford (1863-1947) said in his autobiography that one of his greatest boyhood experiences was his first sight, as a 12-year-old Michigan farm boy, of a steam engine coming down the road. It was simply a portable engine geared for transport——not even yet a traction engine.

"It was that engine which took me into automotive transportation . . . from the time I saw that road engine as a boy of 12 right forward to today, my great interest has been in making a machine to travel roads."

He elsewhere wrote that from that day his ambition was to develop practical power and "to lift farm drudgery off flesh and blood and lay it on steel and motors," according to a company publication. Young Henry was tinkering with farm tractors in the 1880s long before he turned his hand to automobiles.

Just as his mass-produced Model T car put the automobile in reach of the ordinary citizen, so his Fordson, the first mass-produced tractor, put the tractor in reach of the ordinary farmer. The Fordson was to other tractors and to agriculture what the Model T was to other cars and to transport.

Henry Ford actually built experimental tractors in his late teens or early 20s. His first homemade steam engine, made from the bones of a mowing machine, ran 40 feet. Later models ran farther. Then he decided there was no great trick to building a huge steam engine for a few wealthy farmers on big farms. That, he decided, "Did not seem worthwhile."

"I have walked many a weary mile behind a plow and I know all the drudgery of it," he said. "What a waste it is for a human being to spend hours and days behind a slowly-moving team of horses." (To plow his quarter-section farm with a 12-inch walking plow, a man and his horse would have to walk 1,320 miles; to plow a section, 5,280 miles, and to plow five square miles, their furrow would more than encircle the earth at the equator.)

Ford became interested in the internal combustion engine because it was lighter. He built one out of gas pipe and it sort of ran. As he studied the gas engine he concluded the farmer "would be more interested in something that would travel on the road than in something that would do work on the farm." Therefore he concentrated meanwhile upon getting his auto into production. "With the automobile on the farms, the tractor became a necessity, for then the farmers had been introduced to power," he said later.

May we deduce that his aim all along was to mechanize the farm——and that he became the world's leading auto maker merely to precondition farmers to accepting the tractor?

While getting his Model T car into production, he continued, although at a reduced pace, experiments on the tractor. In 1907 he produced a gasoline-powered "automobile plow" capable of pulling one bottom. In the next 10 years he built over 50 experimental tractors.

Came WWI and the U-boat blockade produced near-famine in England. British officials decided they'd have to grow more food at home, and for this they needed swarms of good tractors. They tested a couple of Ford's experimental models and asked him to build 7,000.

Ford demurred, opining his tractor was not yet perfected. The Britishers persuaded him they needed working tractors now, not perfect tractors later.

The Big Bull Tractor—1917. In the great Winnipeg and Nebraska field trials, steam triumphed over gasoline in 1908 and '09 but gas forged ahead in 1910. The Bull Tractor Co. in 1913 produced a 3,000-pound tractor for $395. Ford in 1917 started the Fordson under $300.

With all the Fordson's imperfections, 7,000 of them went to Britain and, from one point of view, won the war. The name derived from the firm name, Henry Ford & Son. Farmers now had their Model T cars and "Model T" tractors.

During some of the 1920s, 75 per cent of all tractors built in America were Fordsons. By the time their manufacture moved to Ireland in 1929, 739,977 Fordsons had been built.

Its four-cylinder 20-HP engine burned gasoline or kerosene and broke many an arm that cranked it. Farmers died when the stubby machine reared over backwards on them. With all its faults, the Fordson sold well and lasted long, being still active through the '30s and into the '40s. Specs listed for the Fordson "22" in 1919 were 22 BHP, two 14-inch plow capacity, 1,000 RPM, four vertical cylinders 4x5-inch, Holley carburetor, kerosene, Ford-built magneto ignition, splash lubrication, belt pulley extra, 1¼-8 MPH.

This was a high-speed tractor in a day when some manufacturers thought anything over four MPH was immoral.

In 1939 Ford again manufactured tractors in the U. S., introducing the Ford-Ferguson three-point hitch that enabled a farmer to attach a fully-mounted implement in one minute instead of half a day, and to control it with a little hydraulic lever instead of by main strength and oatmeal. The Ford-Ferguson system also introduced the geometric principle that transferred implement draft to the tractor wheels as tractive pressure. Heretofore the only way to increase traction was to build-in cast iron and to add weights. Other manufacturers, caught with their competitive britches off, scrambled to cover.

The improved model introduced in 1947 reached annual production of 100,000 units, said to be a record.

(——information courtesy Ford Motor Co.)

Troubleshooter's Diary

In the early gas tractor times, farmers accustomed to horses were sometimes perplexed by these balky, new-fangled gas contraptions. Manufacturers kept trouble-shooters on the road. Here are some observations C. DeSparks published in 1919:

He solemnly advises that, when you have tractor troubles, "removal of the cause is the cure."

Two men spent much time looking for stuck gears, lost compression and poor timing when a carburetor adjustment was necessary.

"We once drove 10 miles in severe weather to tighten a few nuts on dry cells for a bright, intelligent dairy farmer."

"We feel certain that most of the trouble experienced in the field is due to the lack of mechanical training of the operators. The same trouble bothered the binder in the early days. It will not be long till the gas tractor becomes much more complicated and efficient and yet will be handled with less trouble because men everywhere are rapidly learning how to operate and care for complicated machinery."

"We cannot too often repeat our great commandment, 'Keep the tractor lubricated and all parts in adjustment.' This is the Great Law for tractor health."

Case 107 — "A Remedy Not to Use"

"A valve stem began to stick while threshing. Rather than stop, the operator dusted the stem well with emery flour. Of course, the stem loosened, and before the emery ceased to cut, the stem was so badly damaged that the valve did not seat properly. Such treatment as this is never advisable."

It was the custom for a factory expert to accompany each new tractor to the farm to get the engine and the operator started and to train the operator. The factory man might spend over a week with the customer (especially if the Mrs. was a good cook).

"In case of breakage there is but one plan to pursue. Order your repair parts, get them in place as quickly as possible, and go ahead."

Engines ran on kerosene, were started on gasoline. Sometimes the operator, before stopping the engine, forgot to switch to gasoline so the carburetor bowl was still full of kerosene. Then he had trouble in store.

One method of starting: wrap a rope around the belt pulley and pull it with a horse.

A farmer sent to the factory for an expert, who found the water in the "cooler" frozen. Many farmers didn't realize a cold night would freeze the water. Antifreeze was still years in the future. Pumping, carrying and lifting 70 to 130 gallons of water every morning was a bit of a chore.

Observed DeSparks, "The directions for starting in summer are not adapted for winter work and the prevailing grades of fuel make heat of some sort necessary in severe weather." Few engines had chokes at this time. "We have tried starting a tractor standing out of doors in severe weather and find that it must be run several minutes by another motor before the heat of compression and friction is sufficient to produce an explosive vapor in the cylinders . . .

"Personally, we prefer a good torch though it may be permissible to use waste or cloth saturated with fuel for the heating . . . the spark plugs should be removed and thoroughly warmed to insure them against a short-circuit from moisture which might be condensed on them . . . It will be further necessary to heat the carburetor, air pipes and cylinders near the admission valves to warm the air sufficiently to vaporize the fuel as it passes through to the cylinders . . . we hold that extreme weather demands some heating regardless of the make, except as one may obtain a special winter fuel, which costs too much for the average tractor owner to use. In some exceptional and rare cases it may be necessary to warm only the spark plugs.

"With the advent of winter the gas tractor operator works under peculiar conditions."

Of plows and plowing, he said, "For years, plow designs has been shaped by the need of meeting horse speeds——2 to 2½ MPH. Higher speeds have been tried, but it has been found that, all things considered, horse speeds are the best and most economical for the largest variety of soils."

Peeking at the future, DeSparks predicted, "The 4-wheel-drive is rarely used . . . though it is very successful on motor trucks——and there may be something come of it in time."

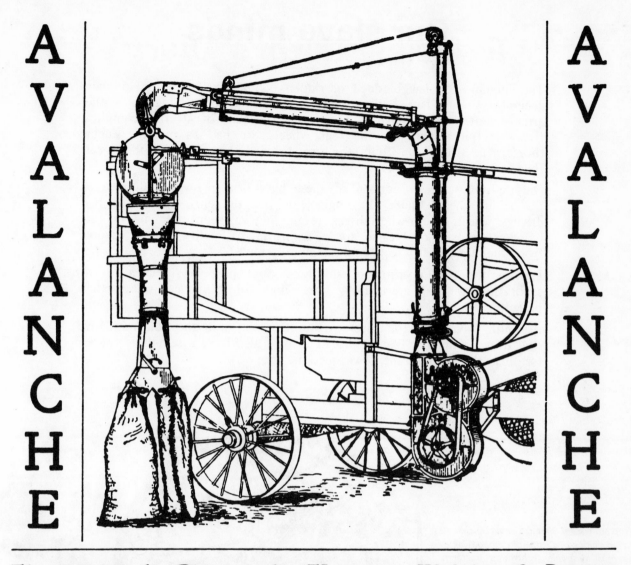

A V A L A N C H E (left margin, vertical)

A V A L A N C H E (right margin, vertical)

The Avalanche Pneumatic Elevator,, Weigher & Bagger

has a whole lot of good points not possessed by other similar machines.

It is stronger, more durable and much lighter than others.

It has no elevating cups or chains to cause you constant trouble

It has no buckets to catch and tear off.

May be raised, lowered, or turned in any diretion from ground or wagon.

Burnishes and improves the condition of damp or smutty grain.

CLEAN GRAIN brings more money than that which is not just right.

There are many other points worth investigating; do you want to know them? Circular tells all and i's free. Write one.

The Pneumatic Elevator and Weigher Co.,

2200 Shelby St., INDIANAPOLIS, IND.

445

Our slave minds

The human race has plodded or ridden behind the horse for so many generations that it is still almost incapable of conceiving any other arrangement. Even though it was easier (because of steering complications) to put power on the rear wheels, we had to put the engine (horse) in front on our tractors (plows), trucks (wagons), cars (buggies) and airplanes (!).

Only a minuscule proportion of these have broken away and powered the front wheels under the engine, or put the engine over the rear driving wheels. Four-wheel-drives (even they've been with us in rare brands for over 60 years) are a' facing-up to reality and a divorce from the horse. They're becoming more popular.

Perhaps the rear position of ship and boat propellers relates to the sailor having been pushed by the 'wind for centuries, rather than pulled.

A South Dakota tractor driver, Arthur D. Cole, built the Cole rein-Drive that drove with lines like a horse. LaCrosse also built a rein-drive tractor (see it in the Mt. Pleasant, Iowa, section, page 66).

"It would seem that....Arthur D. Cole has developed a tractor embodying the most desirable features in tractor construction," said MOTOR ME-CHANICS, June, 1917, "as well as to have combined a wheel tractor and crawler type tractor interchangeable on the one power unit." Technical data on the Cole Rein-Drive is unavailable, but an illustration shows it pulling three plows. Thanks to the Iron-Men Album Magazine.

The power plant of the Rein-Drive tractor is underslung between a pair of wheels which are six feet in diamete Control is obtained through reins.

We are still so wedded to the horse, mentally, that most corn, cotton, soybeans, sorghums, etc., are still planted in horse-wide 36 to 42-inch rows. When I was a kid I thought this was because corn wouldn't grow at any other spacing. Only lately it's been pointed out to me that this is the width of a horse. Our horse-farming forefathers planted the rows far enough apart for a horse to walk between. Tractor makers still largely make tractors and implements to fit the horse row! Only in late years have a few brave souls upped yields with rows twice as close.

The human mind is a slave.

John Deere came out with the first mechanical implement lift in 1928, freeing the farmer from the backbreaking chore of levering his implements out of the ground (although steam-lift plows had trailed the steamers). Harry Ferguson developed his three-point hitch in 1939.

Caterpillar introduced the first Diesel-powered farm tractor in the U. S. in 1931, the first year a radio-controlled tractor was tested.

Generations of tractor-farmers bumped along on their high-cleated steel wheels until the early 1930's when Firestone put air tires on a tractor. Farmers laughed and laughed until:

The famous race driver, Barney Oldfield, the first man to drive a car over 60 MPH (when he commented to the press, "I tell you, gentlemen, no man can travel faster and live!") was hired. At a farmer field day he plowed the infield with a rubber-tired tractor until a good crowd assembled. Then he unhitched the plow, shifted into a special high gear, and drove that air-tired tractor around the racetrack at 60 MPH!

Farmers stopped laughing and started buying.

A note from Miss Jean Sonnhalter, Firestone Tire & Rubber Co. PR dept., to the author says Harvey Firestone introduced the pneumatic tractor tire in 1932. "In time all types of farm implements were equipped with Pneumatic tires and Mr. Firestone's goal to put the farm on rubber was realized," she writes.

"We do find evidence in our archives that Barney Oldfield did stage a demonstration at the Indianapolis Speedway to popularize the farm tire. However, we do not have any photographs of this particular event."

Harvey Firestone and his son, Leonard, try out some new farm tires at the family's experimental farm at Columbiana, O. — Firestone photos

Famous racing driver Ab Jenkins, on tractor, set a tractor speed record of 65.45 MPH in 1934, helping to popularize the new-fangled air-tire developed by Harvey Firestone, leaning on wheel.

Future Farming
Like in 2000 A.D.

While pea-pods and carrot-tops make milk, a driverless contraption will plant, fertilize, spray, harvest and package the crop all in one pass.

No, we won't have instant crops yet: the machine will do these jobs in reverse order——harvesting and processing one crop and planting the next in one operation. The machine, watched by radar, will be electronically controlled by radio, by wire grids buried in the field or by computer tapes and sensing devices such as mechanical fingers that can feel the difference between a ripe and a green cherry, or electric eyes that can see an open cotton boll and pass over an unready one.

Thus sayeth the agricultural engineers.

These are some of the predictions of a Ford Tractor study. Other 21st-Century farm implements will include a control center equipped with electronic wizardry reducing farming to an almost-exact science by riding herd on 4- and 6-wheel-drive electric tractors powered by fuel cells* or efficient storage batteries. Manned machines will offer the operator all the comforts of home: air conditioning, food warmer, coffee maker, refrigerator, TV and——the kitchen sink! Combination hovercraft-helicopters will spray.

To eliminate field compaction, a traveling bridge will straddle fields like a shipyard crane, running on border roadways, tillage units dangling from the truss. Some farmers will shoot seed into the soil with air-gun planters. Chemical coatings on the seed will provide fertilizers and bug killers, and will enable farmers to plant in any slack season, holding seed dormant until traditional seedtime.

Chemical growth regulators will perform such odd chores as protecting Canadian citrus fruit from sub-zero temperatures! Others are already boosting soybean yields by causing more blossoms to set seed.

Also anticipated are solar energy applications (an auto has already been powered by solar cells on its roof, and solar batteries are powering satellites now); converting city sewage into fertilizer (Milwaukee has been doing this for years); irrigating with desalted sea water——and satellite surveillance.

One spin-off benefit from the space race is the discovery that satellites can detect, world-wide, crop diseases and insect threats in time that they may be halted. These eyes in the skies also report crop and moisture conditions. Changes in light and heat reflection are the key. This has already begun.

*Allis-Chalmers experimented with a fuel cell tractor in 1959: propane gas trickling through fuel cells produced electricity without flame, driving motors in the wheels—electric final drive!

Artist's view of a crop-surveying satellite that will warn of drouth, diseases and weevils before they get a head start.—Ford

Future turbine-powered tractors will be controlled by computer programs and by furrow-sensors. Turbines will give greater power without increasing weight.—IHC

448

Good bugs will be distributed to gobble up bad bugs.

Ford predicts high-rise apartment houses will dot the pastoral scene——environment-controlled luxury dwellings for super-cows giving four times today's milk-flow on a diet of cannery wastes and other crop residues. Each superior cow will leave a thousand calves to carry on her high-production genes (eggs will be transplanted from top cows to common incubator cows). The beef steer will reach 1,000 pounds at 10 months. Hormones will persuade sows and ewes to double their reproduction rate. Hogs, chickens and sheep will also be raised in these climate-controlled luxury apartments. Waste water will be purified and reused. Nor will suburban residential neighbors complain——cow hatcheries will be odor-free.

Plastic or glass domes will cover 10-acre fields and bigger. Ideally-controlled crop conditions therein will yield like 500 bushels corn per acre, 300 wheat, 175 soybeans, tenfold forage tonnage.

The sea will be farmed like the land and fish fenced and herded like cattle. Foods will be made of algae. Yeast will produce protein from sawdust and bacteria will make it from crude oil.

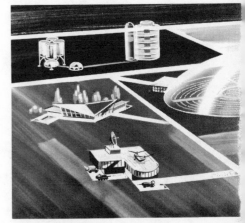

All these developments are now already fact at least on an experimental or pilot scale.

The human race took a million or more years to number 3 billion. It will reach 6 billion in 30 years. While famine is predicted to be the major fact of 21st-Century life, it need not be, according to the Ford study. Said John A. Banning, Ford tractor official, "While our primary purpose was to determine which developments could affect our own plans . . . one of the side benefits of the study is the opportunity it provides us to tell the public the story of the magnificent work being done by our farmers.

"After all, it is they who will win the battle against world hunger and we are pleased to help them achieve the recognition they deserve, not only for the job they are doing now, but for the one they will do in the future."

Concludes the study, "All of the evidence shows there is no need for hunger in the world of tomorrow. But we must gear immediately for the gigantic job ahead. Zero hour is now!"

Dr. LaVon S. Fife, agricultural economist, International Harvester Co., says computers will become one of the most significant new farm tools. They will impact upon farming, perhaps, similarly to Cyrus McCormick's first reaper. Among the computers' farm jobs, he foresaw cost projections in choosing crops or equipment, setting programs for robot field machines and programming automatic feeding schedules.

The Old Home Place may look like this in 30 years. In the right background is a high-rise climate-controlled cowbarn. Left background is a warehouse complex and refinery where wastes are purified and recirculated. At right is a huge plastic dome covering 10 acres or more under which crops are grown in a computer-controlled environment. Left of the dome is the old farmhouse with its rustic heated pool and old moss-covered computer. Foreground is the control center from which the farmer will direct an array of equipment and personnel by electronic machines now being developed.—Ford

"The potent crops of the year 2000 will require powerful new farm equipment now in planning," says a Ford study. Tractors will run on 4- or 6-wheel drive or pneumatic tracks, with electric final drive powered by fuel cells or storage batteries. This model positions the driver up front in a swingin' cab for maximum visibility. He can swivel the cab to the rear for a closer look to see how his bottom's scouring.—Ford

Future planters probably will have systems for planting, fertilizing, insect and weed control. They will have a radio or light-beam guidance system to keep rows straight and accurately spaced, and an air-conditioned cab with electronic control panel. But what about contour curves?—IHC

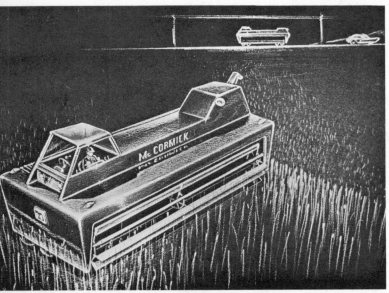

The 1984 combine will harvest at 12 MPH, then pivot its wheels 90 degrees and run on the highway at truck speeds. Centrifugal whirling chambers or electrostatic devices may separate grain from chaff.—IHC

Harvesting in 2000 will be a simple operation requiring complex equipment with electronic eyes, computerized fingers and ultrasonic sound waves, predicts the Ford Motor Co. tractor division. Sketch shows how a farmer, sitting in his control bubble atop a Buck Rodgers cherry-picker, moves down an orchard to strip trees of fruit. Fruit moves into trailer which a helicopter picks up and hauls to market.—Ford

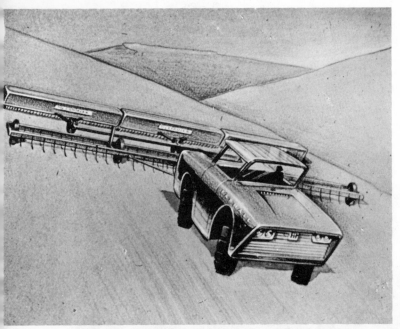

IHC is working on this giant 4-wheel-drive, 4-wheel-steer 8–10 plow tractor capable of pulling 42 feet of chisel plow and 42 feet of grain drill or 40 feet of stubble-mulching tool.—IHC

Gas turbines are the tractor power plant of the future, some believe. This experimental model generates 1 HP per pound.—IHC

450

The combine wrecked the old-time threshing rings. With the destruction of the old sense of community went neighborliness. "Be independent of your neighbors!" shrieked the ads for one-man family-size combines and balers. Thus the farmer became the rugged individualist he'd always fancied himself.

With rugged individualism came ragged individualism and the fragmentation of agriculture, making it easier than ever——one by one——for interests inimical to family farming to pick the families off. This overvaunted independence today prevents farmers from agreeing on farm

policy, bargaining power or anything else——a socio-economic disintegration as suicidal as a bomb-blast.

Now comes the salvage of classic steam power on the farm, the rebirth of arm-on-shoulder neighborin'. Once again neighbor joins neighbor in frolic and work and mutual helpfulness instead of just glaring at the boob tube and sucking beer.

Maybe there is hope for Rural America yet—— thanks to half-century-old engines that recall when steam was glory.

Dearest Readers :

This volume does not pretend to be a complete roster of all farm steam engine shows in the U. S. and Canada. There is no central list and we had to work with rumors and tips and those we stumbled onto while driving across the continent. Many steam organizations don't answer their mail; we couldn't include them when they didn't provide any information.

So — we'll welcome names and addresses of farm steam groups which you feel should be included in the next edition. Address Book Manager, North Plains Press, Aberdeen, South Dakota 57401.

INFORMATION

Those desiring more information about machines or organizations, please DO NOT write to the author or the publisher but directly to the club or owner concerned.

Photographs have been returned to the subject clubs or owners, except those taken by the author. (Photo credits accompany each picture. Photos without credits are the author's; requests for use of same should be directed to the publisher, North Plains Press, Box 910, Aberdeen, S. D. 57401.)

Additional copies of this book may be obtained through your bookseller or direct from the publisher (address above); single copies $15.00 cash with order. Attractive wholesale rates are available for organizations who wish to order in quantity for resale at a handsome profit. Inquire of Book Manager, address above.

Explore an

A few minutes later and this engine would have been marching in the Big Parade, thousands of people — a big share of them children — pressing close on either side. Note the crushed smokebox, with white gravel marks on it similar to those on the steel front tires. I believe the blast of steam out the bottom of the firebox — so powerful it carried away the cast-iron grates and bowled the steel box wall outward — cartwheeled the engine right up onto her nose and over onto her back. — Thomas Graff photos

explosion

a picture study

from inside the fire box of an engine that blew up

A big parade was making up. One of my photography students, Thomas Graff, was driving through the downtown area, his fine 35-mm camera at the ready on the seat. As he passed a parking lot, he saw this 1907 Case 20-HP steam engine steaming up for the parade. Knowing my interest, he thought to get some pix. But the crowded Main Street offered no empty spaces. He rounded the corner and parked a quarter-block away.

She blew.

"There was this big PUFF! like a lot of pressure being released all at once. It wasn't a sharp bang like an explosion. There was a little smoke and a lot of soot and this big cloud of steam came rolling down Main Street, fogging the windshields of all the cars."

Graff was on the scene within the minute. Some of his pictures show the bodies where they fell. "There was soot and ashes all over everything but no smoke and no water." The steam had put the fire out and the super-heated water had exploded into vapor the instant that tearing steel released the pressure.

Six people were injured. Engineer and fireman were scalded and slammed to the pavement. The fireman was hospitalized nine weeks, blinded by the concussion. At this writing, five months after the explosion, he is up and around at home, partial sight returning to one eye. The engineer, after three or four months in a coma, can now hold a conversation. Surgeons are battling to save a shattered leg.

A boy was standing with his bicycle on the near side of the flatbed truck that had just unloaded the engine, according to one of those curbstone stories you always hear after any disaster. He was found, it is said, badly injured, with his totaled-out bicycle on the far side of the truck.

A friend of mine, a practical steam engineer of long experience, and I examined the engine five months after the explosion. No work had been done on it other than to pick up the fragments and to move them into storage. By the waverings of a tired flashlight we crawled in and out and under and over, slithering on the freezing concrete floor in the subfreezing, unlighted warehouse. My engineer friend pointed out some interesting features:

The crown sheet—the firebox roof, in normal operation covered with water—had been red-hot, evidenced by discoloration, warping, other signs of excessive heat. The quarter-inch-thick steel, supported every few inches by 13/16-inch steel staybolts hung from the boiler shell, had torn away from the firebox wall front, rear and left, folding down like a door hinged on the right. As nearly as we could tell, the steel was in good condition.

All the staybolts held to the boiler shell. The crown sheet stripped off the riveted heads.

A pipe nipple and cap had been welded into the crown sheet where the soft plug should have been.

The fireman told me the gauge registered 75 lb. steam pressure just before the blast and that "water was moving in the water glass." He said they were not injecting feed water, nor had the engineer attempted to move the engine.

Looking up from the ground through the area where the ash pan and grates used to be into the firebox and boiler: round-cornered oblong at left is the firebox door. If the camera were still in position to take picture on opposite page, we'd see the camera in the upper corner of the firebox door. Rod-like stubs are the staybolts, still securely fastened into top of boiler. Note long tear in firebox wall, center, opening the water leg and showing accumulation of scale, rust, mud, etc. in bottom. Note how crown sheet stripped heads from staybolts. Inspection hole is in upper right corner. –dcj

I've been knocked out a few times. I know the last few seconds or minutes before the blow are often blanked out, and that minutes, hours, even weeks preceding may be remembered with blanks and confusion. The fireman's memory of those last moments may be flawed.

My engineer friend and I worked out the following hypothesis: the water level fell below the crown sheet, which heated red. If there was water in the glass, it was trapped there by lime, mud or a stuck check valve. My engineer advisor says steam can come over the top and condense enough in the glass to give a false reading. The pressure could have been only 75 lb. (this engine was designed to work at 140 lb. with a boiler safety factor of 2) and the safety valve may have been properly set and functioning.

We think the engineer either injected boiler feed water or started the engine. As the machine moved, it sloshed water over the red-hot crown sheet, softened and warped by heat. This water instantly vaporized, zooming the boiler pressure. "You can't control flash steam," my friend says. He has operated a Case steamer in the field, was a steam engineer aboard a U.S. Navy warship in WWII, and has seen the terrifying glow of a hot crown sheet reflected from his shovel.

The flash steam skyrocketed the boiler pressure. The best safety valve in creation cannot discharge flash steam. "The boys around Prairie Village [the steam show described elsewhere in this book] figure there must have been between 600 and a thousand pounds pressure in that boiler when she let go," he says.

He bought a big old Reeves. The previous owner, intending to junk it, tried to burst the boiler. He gave up at 600 lb.

The slosh of water on the red-hot crown sheet must have contracted, warped and cracked it, perhaps pulling it away from the firebox wall, opening the rent that in a fraction of an instant ripped out the crown sheet and part of the firebox wall (note how the quarter-inch-thick steel tore like paper), taking grates and all.

Like the propulsive blast of a rocket (see P. 386 for the 1910 lecture showing how a boiler contains enough energy to put a projectile into solar orbit), the steam squirting out of the firebox bottom lifted the rear end of the 14,000-pound engine: the engine must have cartwheeled over onto its nose (note the caved-in smokebox top with gravel marks on it) and landed upside down.

One person in a building across the street, out of sight of the engine, told the fireman he saw the engine in the air 30 feet above the intervening buildings. We credit him with an over-enthused post-facto imagination.

The soft plug would have melted long before the crown sheet reddened, letting steam into the firebox, thus putting out the fire and safely relieving the lethal pressure.

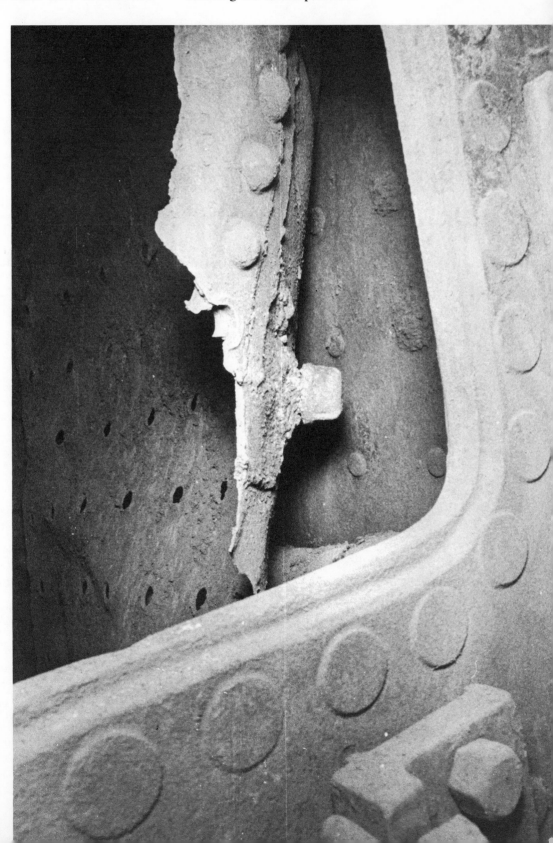

Looking into firebox door, slightly downward and to the right. Perforated sheet is the crown sheet, torn loose front, left and rear, and folded down like a sheet of paper from its attachment at right. Holes are where the staybolts were riveted into it. Jagged piece hanging down in center is the torn left rear corner of crown sheet, with part of water leg wall torn away and still riveted to crown sheet. Knob in center of picture is pipe nipple and cap where soft plug should have been.—dcj

Index

Minneapolis engine on bonanza farm pulls 14 plows.--From "The Day of the Bonanza," by H. M. Drache, courtesy the author and his publisher, N. Dak. Institute for Regional Studies.